Instrumental Analysis

JOHN H. HARLEY

U. S. Atomic Energy Commission

STEPHEN E. WIBERLEY

Rensselaer Polytechnic Institute

Instrumental
Analysis

JOHN WILEY & SONS, INC., NEW YORK
CHAPMAN & HALL, LIMITED, LONDON

Preface

This book has been written as a text for a course in instrumental analysis given to senior and graduate chemistry students at Rensselaer Polytechnic Institute. The course is designed to familiarize the students with the operation of the major analytical instruments and the possible applications of these instruments to their research problems and their future work in the field of chemistry.

A great deal of instrumentation is used in the modern courses in physics and physical chemistry, but this equipment is usually constructed or assembled in the laboratory and the emphasis is on the system being measured rather than on the instruments themselves. The present course recognizes that, in general, the analytical chemist uses commercial instruments for the determination of various elements or compounds. Therefore, the emphasis is less on the particular system being measured than on the utility of the several types of instruments and on a broad picture of the field of commercial instruments. The student who has this training will be in a position to select instruments for a particular problem with some idea of the advantages and disadvantages of the types that are available.

The selection of the equipment to be included in the text has been decided by the actual units available at Rensselaer. The simple instruments whose analytical uses are considered in the usual undergraduate courses in physical and organic chemistry have not been discussed again. An attempt has been made to describe the principles that are basic to the various types of instrumental analysis and to describe some of the commercial models of instruments that are presently available. Although the rapid changes and improvements being made in commercial instruments may make some of the descriptions obsolete, the principles learned should carry over to new equipment as it appears on the market.

The theoretical discussions in the body of the text are limited to the needs of the analytical chemist. A knowledge of physical and general analytical chemistry is assumed as a prerequisite, so that, unless some particular analytical viewpoint is to be emphasized, much elementary material has been omitted. The applications of instrumental analysis are presented only generally, since the literature, particularly *Analytical Chemistry,* contains a large number of articles on the applications of instrumental methods of analysis. The experienced analytical chemist, therefore, will not find new or unpublished techniques in this book. Instead we have striven for clarity in explaining the common techniques. If the material presented is completely understood by the student, the objective of preparing an introductory text will have been fulfilled.

Since it is realized that the instructors will devise their own or modify the suggested experiments, the instructions for laboratory work in Chapter 22 are purposely kept brief. Wherever possible, a minimum amount of chemical manipulation is required so as to make more time available for working with the equipment. Since the average laboratory does not have all types of the more expensive pieces of equipment, such as spectrographs, spectrometers and X-ray diffraction units, actual operating instructions have been given for only a few instruments which are likely to be available in all academic laboratories. We have used mimeographed instruction sheets for operation of the instruments in the laboratory. These are merely adapted from the operating instructions written by the manufacturer. Sample instructions are given in the chapter on laboratory experiments. Such a system is flexible in that it may be added to as new equipment becomes available.

We have received excellent co-operation from instrument manufacturers and suppliers in the presentation of particular instruments. We should like to express our appreciation to Professor Lewis G. Bassett of Rensselaer for his continued encouragement to us in the setting up of the course, obtaining of equipment, and the writing of the text. We are indebted to Miss Rose D'Alessandro and Mrs. Anne Wagner for their time and effort in the preparation of the text.

JOHN H. HARLEY
STEPHEN E. WIBERLEY

January 1954

Contents

CHAPTER 1

Introduction

In instrumental analysis, a physical property of a substance is measured to determine its chemical composition. Instrumental methods may be used by the analytical chemist to save time, to avoid chemical separations, or to obtain increased accuracy. Other reasons may indicate their use in particular cases.

The time-saving features of instrumental analysis are most fully realized in routine analysis, or where a considerable number of determinations are to be made. These methods usually require a standardization or calibration procedure to determine the relationship between the measured value of the physical property and the chemical composition. In some cases this relationship may be found in books of tables or in the literature, but in others the relationship must be determined in the laboratory. Therefore, for a few samples the use of a standard gravimetric or volumetric procedure is less time-consuming, whereas for routine work the time required for the initial calibration is negligible.

It must be emphasized that the accuracy of some instrumental methods is dependent upon the accuracy with which the classical or "wet" chemical analysis can be made. Therefore, improvement in classical methods of analysis will mean further improvement in the accuracy of instrumental analysis. For example, a reliable direct spectrographic method is not available for the determination of very low concentrations of aluminum in steel because existing "wet" methods of analysis do not yield results reliable enough to establish accurate values for spectrographic standards.

Physical properties may be classified as specific (emission spectra for example) or nonspecific (specific gravity, refractive index, etc.), just as chemical reagents or tests are classified. If the measured property is specific for the substance being determined, a direct measurement is possible. If no specific property is available, the

1

measurement of two or more nonspecific properties may allow correction for interfering substances. A specific reagent may be employed to form a new system allowing direct measurement, or a specific chemical reaction may be combined with an instrumental endpoint measurement to give a specific volumetric method. In other cases, a chemical separation of interfering substances must precede the measurement.

It is a common fallacy that in instrumental analysis the analytical chemist pushes a button and the machine does the rest. It is true that technicians may run routine analyses instrumentally and that our instrument makers are trying to eliminate the human element. However, in most instrumental work, a higher order of technique is required than in conventional methods, and considerable skill is needed to interpret the results.

The accuracy of instrumental methods of analysis is usually less than that of sound "wet" methods for concentrations above 1%. However, the fact that a physical measurement may maintain a constant relative rather than absolute error allows increased accuracy in determining low percentages.

The considerable interest in instrumental methods at the present time may be best observed in the current journals on analytical chemistry. The proportion of determinations using physical methods of analysis is increasing every year.

A bibliography of a general nature is appended, the articles by R. H. Müller being specially recommended for a general picture of the field.

Bibliography

W. G. Berl (editor), *Physical Methods in Chemical Analysis,* Vols. I and II, Academic Press, New York (1950).

D. Boltz, *Selected Topics in Modern Instrumental Analysis,* Prentice-Hall, New York (1952).

R. H. Müller, *Ind. Eng. Chem., Anal. Ed., 12,* 571 (1940); *13,* 667 (1941). Dr. Müller at the present time is conducting a monthly column on instrumental analysis in *Analytical Chemistry.*

J. Reilly and W. N. Rae, *Physico Chemical Methods,* Vol. I, 3rd ed. (1939); Vol. II (1939); Vol. III (1948); D. Van Nostrand, New York.

A. Weissberger (editor), *Physical Methods of Organic Chemistry,* 2nd ed., Interscience, New York (1949).

H. H. Willard, L. L. Merritt, and J. A. Dean, *Instrumental Methods of Analysis,* 2nd ed., D. Van Nostrand, New York (1951).

CHAPTER 2

Spectral Theory

The following discussion of spectral theory is intended to give the student analyst a concept of the production of spectra. The treatment is not rigorous or complete but should be sufficient for the purpose. A list of references at the end of the chapter will point out possible further study.

2.1 The electromagnetic spectrum. The electromagnetic spectrum is the complete system of radiant energy, that is, of energy propagated in wave form. An electromagnetic wave consists of an oscillating electric field and a similar magnetic field so completely connected that each depends upon the other for its existence. The two fields oscillate at right angles to one another and to the direction of propagation of the wave. Each component vibrates with the same frequency and is in equal phase with the other in free space. Electromagnetic waves travel in free space with a constant velocity, c, where c equals 3.0×10^{10} cm per second. The velocity of electromagnetic waves in a given medium, such as glass, is not necessarily c, but may vary with the frequency, and this variation is termed dispersion. Hence, a glass prism disperses the electromagnetic waves of visible light into a series of different frequencies which are seen by the human eye as different colors. Such a series of different wavelengths is termed a spectrum.

Electromagnetic waves are usually described in terms of (a) the length of the cycle or wave (wavelength, λ), (b) the number of cycles or waves in a unit distance (wave number, ν'), and (c) the number of cycles or waves passing a point in space in a unit time (frequency, ν). These units are related by the equation

$$c = \lambda \nu$$

where c is the speed of light, equal to 3.0×10^{10} cm per second. Figure 2.1 shows a graphical illustration of these terms.

3

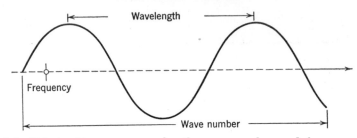

Fig. 2.1   Relationship among wavelength, wave number, and frequency (Reproduced by permission of W. R. Brode, *Chemical Spectroscopy*, 2nd ed., John Wiley, New York, 1947)

The approximate limits of wavelength and frequency for the various types of radiation, including the frequency range of sound waves, are shown in Table 2.1. The table demonstrates that the funda-

TABLE 2.1

Radiation	Wavelength, cm	Frequency, cycles/sec
Sound		1.6×10^1 –2.0×10^4
Hertzian	3.0×10^6 –1.0×10^{-2}	1.0×10^4 –3.0×10^{12}
Infrared	6.0×10^{-1}–7.5×10^{-5}	5.0×10^{10}–4.0×10^{14}
Visible	7.5×10^{-5}–4.0×10^{-5}	4.0×10^{14}–7.5×10^{14}
Ultraviolet	4.0×10^{-5}–1.0×10^{-6}	7.5×10^{14}–3.0×10^{16}
X rays	1.0×10^{-6}–1.0×10^{-9}	3.0×10^{16}–3.0×10^{19}
Gamma rays	1.0×10^{-8}–1.0×10^{-11}	3.0×10^{18}–3.0×10^{21}
Cosmic rays	$<1.0 \times 10^{-11}$	$>3.0 \times 10^{21}$

mental units would have very awkward values for some of the ranges indicated. Therefore, other, more convenient, units are used as illustrated in Fig. 2.2, which shows the complete electromagnetic spectrum. The units given in this figure will be described in the sections where they are applicable.

The purely wave theory of light has been modified to admit the existence of corpuscular units of radiant energy. These corpuscular units, or quanta, are propagated in wave form, and the energy involved may be expressed as

$$\epsilon = h\nu$$

where ϵ = energy content of the quantum in ergs, h = Planck's constant, 6.6×10^{-27} erg-second, ν = frequency in vibrations per second.

This formula implies that radiant energy is made up of discrete units of definite energy content (quanta) and states that their magnitude is dependent on the frequency of the radiation.

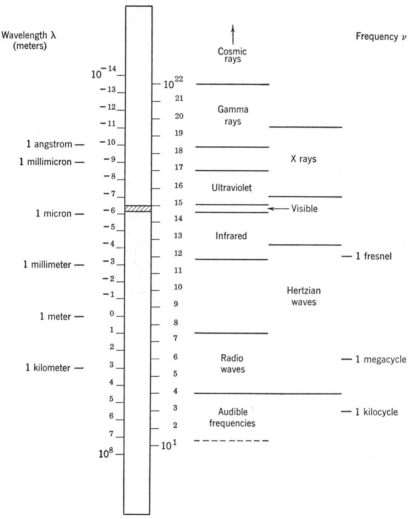

Fig. 2.2   The electromagnetic spectrum

2.2   Principles of spectral analysis.   Spectral analysis is based on the measurement of the radiant energy absorbed or emitted by atoms or molecules. The frequency of this radiation is determined by the formula

$$\Delta E = h\nu$$

where ΔE is the change in internal energy of the atom or molecule. Thus it appears that the radiant energy is quantized; that is, the absorption or emission is in discrete units of definite frequency.

An atom or molecule may be excited by the addition of sufficient energy in any form and thus raised to a higher energy state. If this state is unstable, the excess energy may be released in the form of radiation. The various frequencies of this radiation make up the emission spectrum of the substance.

If the added energy is radiant, and the higher energy state is stable, certain frequencies of the added radiant energy may be absorbed. These frequencies make up the absorption spectrum of the substance.

2.3   Spectral energy changes. The modern theory of wave mechanics precludes any physical picture of the energy changes occurring within an atom or molecule. Therefore in an elementary treatment no loss in intelligibility occurs if we speak simply of the energy levels in an atom or molecule. The concept of energy levels is necessary to explain the quantized energy changes mentioned above. It is reasonable to assume that, for certain definite energy changes to occur within a substance, there must be definite possible levels of internal energy, and that a shift from one level to another would produce a corresponding energy change and an equivalent spectral frequency absorbed or emitted.

Three types of energy level exist within a molecule, electronic, vibrational, and rotational. The shifts in these energy levels have different causes and different energy values and appear in different spectral regions.

Electronic energy levels are due to the variable energy content of an extranuclear electron. One or more of these electrons may be excited to a higher energy level than the normal state by absorbing energy, and, if the higher state is unstable, the electron may shift to a lower stable energy level and, in doing so, emit radiant energy.

From the quantum theory, there are a finite number of possible energy levels for an electron in a particular atom. Since the changes from one level to another need not occur stepwise, the number of possible energy changes for a particular electron is the mathematical combination of levels for the electron,* and the number of possible energy changes for an atom is the sum of the numbers for each electron in the atom. Each possible energy change will give rise to a spectral frequency.

---

* Certain transitions do not occur, but they may be neglected in this discussion.

In an atom with several extranuclear electrons, it is more difficult to shift an electron whose sphere of action lies nearer to the nucleus than one farther from the nucleus. (These will be spoken of as "inner" and "outer" electrons.) The energy involved is of a different order of magnitude, and the radiation is in a different portion of the spectrum, as shown in Table 2.2.

TABLE 2.2

Process	Typical Energy, ergs	Frequency, vib/sec	Region
"Inner" electron shift	4.0×10^{-9}	6×10^{17}	X ray
Ionization	4.0×10^{-11}	6×10^{15}	Far ultraviolet
"Outer" electron shift	6.6×10^{-12}	1×10^{15}	Near ultraviolet
	3.3×10^{-12}	5×10^{14}	Visible
Vibration	4.0×10^{-13}	6×10^{13}	Near infrared
Rotation	2.0×10^{-14}	3×10^{12}	Far infrared

It is possible to remove an electron from an atom completely, and, although this is really just another energy level for the electron, the nature of the change is ionization, and is treated as a special case.

The atoms in a molecule are held together by attractive forces or bonds. There is a certain average equilibrium position of the atoms, but their actual position at any instant may vary considerably from the average. These positional or vibrational energy levels may be changed by quantized absorption or emission. The energy involved in the vibrational shifts is determined by the mass of the atoms and the nature and magnitude of the bonding forces; therefore spectra are produced that are characteristic of these factors.

The molecule as a whole may rotate about its center of gravity or any axis. The modes and rates of rotation are quantized, any energy change corresponding to a change in angular momentum and producing a spectral frequency.

Finally, the atom or molecule may have energy of translation. A change in the energy of translation will result in a change in temperature of the substance. This latter change is not ordinarily considered to be quantized, but is continuously variable.

Table 2.2 shows the approximate magnitude of the energies involved and the spectral region in which the corresponding fundamental radiation occurs.

2.4 Continuous, line, and band spectra. If a solid is heated to incandescence, it produces a continuous spectrum, that is, light con-

taining all the visible wavelengths. Similar effects may be obtained
by other means in various regions of the electromagnetic spectrum.
Any instrument designed to measure radiation frequencies would
show that radiation was occurring at all frequencies over a considerable range. The relative amount of energy may vary in this range,
but all frequencies are present.

On the other hand, the emission spectrum of the vapor produced
and excited by an electric arc between two electrodes is discontinuous; that is, the radiation is confined to discrete wavelengths. Our
measuring instrument would distinguish radiant energy at particular frequencies, with large gaps where no radiation appears. These
particular frequencies are usually spoken of as lines, due to their
appearance when registered on a photographic plate by a spectrograph. They are due to excited atoms or ions emitting energy by
electronic energy-level shifts and are found in the visible and ultraviolet regions.

The emission spectrum of a molecular substance may be complicated by vibrational and rotational changes being superimposed on
the electronic energy-level shifts of the atoms involved. This results
in slight changes in the quantity of energy involved, and a consequent
slight shift in the wavelength of the line. On a photographic plate,
a fine structure of closely spaced lines would appear.

It should be noted that it is difficult to excite a substance sufficiently to produce an electronic-emission spectrum without disrupt-
ing the molecular structure, as well as vaporizing the substance.
Therefore most emission spectra used for analytical purposes are
those of atoms or ions in the vapor state.

If a molecular substance is not excited sufficiently to produce an
electronic spectrum, the vibrational spectrum may still appear. As
the total energy is small, the radiation appears in the infrared only.
The rotational energy changes may be superimposed on the vibrational, giving the spectrum a fine structure. If the excitation is still
less, only the rotational energy may be involved, and the rotational
spectrum appears alone in the far infrared.

Though the above discussion has been devoted to emission spectra,
similar considerations apply to the absorption of radiant energy.
Also, we have considered only the vapor state, and, as we generally
measure the absorption spectra of substances in their state at normal
temperatures, we must extend our ideas to liquids and solids.

When light from a continuous source passes through a substance in
the vapor state, absorption may occur. This absorption is the exact

reverse of the emission described above, is bound by the same possible energy changes, and occurs in the same spectral regions. The added restriction is that the higher energy state must be stable. As an example, the Fraunhofer lines in the spectrum of the sun are dark lines caused by absorption of certain frequencies by the vapor atmosphere of the sun. These frequencies may also be found in the emission spectra of the same elements when excited under normal conditions.

In pure liquids or solutions and in solids, the relatively close packing and resultant intermolecular or interionic forces cause a broadening of the lines. These broad lines or bands appear in the portion of the spectrum corresponding to the fundamental energy change involved.

2.5 Molecular bonds and absorption spectra. Ionic compounds are held together by the electrostatic forces on the charged particles. No one ion is permanently bound to another, but rather each ion may be considered to be in an electric field, due to the charges and positions of all the other ions in the system. There is no molecular structure or molecular spectrum; the only effect of this community interaction is the broadening of the electronic-absorption bands.

The spectral range in which the absorption occurs depends on the magnitude of the energy change. Colored ions (absorption in the visible range) are characteristic of the transition and rare-earth elements, as their electronic configuration allows electron shifts of moderate energy content. It should be noted that the absorption bands for the rare-earth ions are comparatively narrow, as the electron shifts occur in inner levels protected from interionic forces.

In its simplest case, the covalent or electron-sharing bond links together two atoms so that they have an equilibrium position with respect to each other. Unless disruption of the molecule occurs, the two atoms remain together as a unit, with the ability to absorb energy of vibration or rotation.

The bonding may consist in sharing two, four, or six electrons, corresponding to the single, double, or triple bond. Single bonds show absorption only in the infrared if the two atoms are the same, for example C—C, and in some cases where dissimilar atoms are joined, as C—OH and C—O—C. Other singly bonded groups like C—Cl, C—Br, C—I and C—NH_2 as well as doubly and triply bonded groups absorb in the visible or ultraviolet as well as in the infrared. This means that an electronic shift is occurring, and this shift is due to the phenomenon of resonance.

If the electrons forming a bond can exist in two or more configurations of approximately equal energy content, a state of rapid interchange, or resonance, between the two configurations may exist. If the energy change is relatively small, the absorption occurs in the near ultraviolet or visible regions. The unsaturated groups that exhibit resonance, such as C=C, C≡C, C=O, C≡N, or N=O, have been given the name chromophores (color-bearing), for, though they themselves absorb in the near ultraviolet, the substitution of certain other groups in the molecule, such as NH_2, OH, and the halogens, may shift their absorption to the visible range. Two or more chromophoric groups in the same molecule, particularly when conjugated, may absorb in the visible.

2.6   Spectral frequency and intensity. Although a knowledge of the available energy levels of a substance allows us to calculate the spectral frequencies that will appear, it is not possible to predict intensities, that is, exactly how the excitation energy will be divided among these frequencies. Nor is it possible to predict the energy content of a particular molecule or atom at any time. However, since we are dealing with large numbers of particles, statistical theory may be used to predict that the average behavior of the molecules or atoms will be reproducible.

The magnitude of the quanta absorbed or emitted by a substance (frequency) is governed by the possible energy levels and the average amount of energy supplied to each particle in a unit time. The number of quanta of each type (intensity) is a probability function, dependent on the likelihood of each energy change and again on the average energy supplied to each particle in a unit time. The significance of this to analytical work is that, if our excitation is maintained at a constant value for a given interval of time, we may expect the same spectral frequencies to appear and that they will have the same intensities.

As in any probability distribution, the true statistical function is approached more closely as the number of transitions is increased. Although in our seemingly instantaneous measurements we are actually averaging many transitions, it is necessary in some cases to average over a finite period of time to obtain a reliable statistical picture.

Bibliography

W. R. Brode, *Chemical Spectroscopy*, 2nd ed., John Wiley, New York (1947).
S. Glasstone, *Textbook of Physical Chemistry*, D. Van Nostrand, New York (1946).

G. Herzberg, *Atomic Spectra and Atomic Structure*, 2nd ed., Prentice-Hall, New York (1944).

L. Pauling, *The Nature of the Chemical Bond*, 2nd ed., Cornell University Press, Ithaca, N. Y. (1948).

H. S. Taylor and S. Glasstone, *Treatise on Physical Chemistry*, D. Van Nostrand, New York (1951).

CHAPTER 3

Absorption in the Visible Region

The absorption of visible light is based on stable increases in electron energy levels. The most common measurements are those made on liquids or solutions, so that the absorption is in relatively broad bands of frequencies, due to interionic and intermolecular forces. The instruments used are typical of those used for all regions of the spectrum, and the fundamental principles of measurement will carry over into further work.

3.1 Color. The visual perception of color arises from the selective absorption of certain frequencies of incident light by the colored object. The other frequencies of the incident light are either reflected or transmitted, according to the nature of the object, and are perceived by the eye as the color of the object.

It may be seen that the apparent color of an object depends on three things: (a) the frequencies present in the incident light, (b) the frequencies absorbed by the object, (c) the frequencies perceived by the eye. Assuming normal vision, we may consider white light (the entire visible spectrum) incident on solid opaque bodies. If the object appears white, all frequencies are reflected equally; if the object appears black, very little light of any frequency is reflected; if the object appears green, the frequencies that give the green stimulus are reflected, the red and blue ends of the spectrum being absorbed. If the same objects are illuminated by green light, the white and green objects appear green and the black object black. If purple (red plus blue) light is used, the white object appears purple, and the green and black objects appear black.

In chemical analysis we are chiefly concerned with measuring the amount of light transmitted by a solution and relating this to the concentration of some particular ion or compound in the solution. The major portion of the light incident on the solution that is not

TABLE 3.1

Approximate Wavelength Range of Colors

$1 \ m\mu = 10^{-7} \ cm$

Ultraviolet	400 mμ
Violet	400–450
Blue	450–500
Green	500–570
Yellow	570–590
Orange	590–620
Red	620–750
Infrared	750–

transmitted is absorbed, and we shall speak of our measurements as absorption spectroscopy.

3.2 Absorption-spectroscopy nomenclature and presentation of data. The present status of nomenclature or terminology used in the field of absorption spectroscopy is very confusing, not only to the novice in the field, but also to the more experienced worker. This is a result of the large number of different systems used in textbooks and journals over a period of many years. In order to standardize, several new systems have been proposed.[1-4] Since no one of these has been universally adopted by either the current chemical journals or by textbook writers, the result has been to add further confusion to the situation.

Some system must be adopted in every text. The authors have chosen the one recommended by Hughes et al.[*,2] since it seems to be a sensible compromise between the present-day proposed systems and previous usage. However, for comparison purposes, the other terminology recently recommended, and the nomenclature and symbols accumulated from the past have also been tabulated. This will enable the student to understand any system that may be encountered in current journals and textbooks. Table 3.2 contains this material and Fig. 3.1 depicts a graphical indication of the transmission terms [1] used in Table 3.2.

[1] W. R. Brode, *J. Optical Soc. Am.*, 39, 1022 (1949).
[2] H. K. Hughes et al., *Anal. Chem.*, 24, 1349 (1952).
[3] *Natl. Bur. Standards Letter Circ. LC* 857 (May 19, 1947).
[4] M. G. Mellon, *J. Optical Soc. Am.*, 31, 648 (1941).

[*] Hughes et al. use the italic A for absorbance and the roman A for the abbreviation for angstrom. (As the italic A cannot be shown in handwritten material, the simple roman A is often used for absorbance and the symbol Å for angstrom unit.)

TABLE 3.2

Spectral Transmission and Absorption—Definition of Terms

Terminology Used in Text	Equivalent Terms
Transmission	
P = transmitted radiant power	I = intensity of transmitted radiant energy
P_0 = incident radiant power	I_0 = intensity of incident radiant energy
T = transmittance = P/P_0	T = transmittance = I/I_0
Absorption	
$P = P_0 10^{-abc}$	$I = I_0 10^{-kcd}$
A = absorbance $A = \log_{10} P_0/P = abc$	D, d = density O.D. = optical density E = extinction A_i = absorbance * A_s = absorbancy *
a = absorptivity (a constant, characteristic of the material and the frequency) = A/bc	k, E, K = specific extinction, absorption coefficient, specific absorption
ϵ = molar absorptivity = $a \cdot M$	E = molar extinction, molar extinction coefficient, molar absorption coefficient a_M = molar absorbancy index
b = thickness of cell in centimeters	d, l, X = thickness of cell in centimeters
M = molecular weight c = concentration in grams per liter	

* Absorbance [*Natl. Bur. Standards Letter Circ. LC 857* (May 19, 1947)] indicated measurement referred to air while absorbancy indicated measurement referred to solvent.

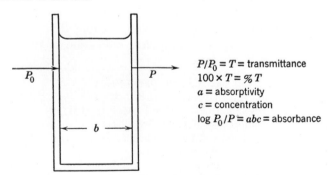

$P/P_0 = T$ = transmittance
$100 \times T = \% T$
a = absorptivity
c = concentration
$\log P_0/P = abc$ = absorbance

Fig. 3.1   Graphical illustration of transmission terms

Similar variation exists in the graphical presentation of absorption-spectra data. Figure 3.2 illustrates the many systems used.[5]

There has been general agreement in the literature that the abscissa represents the wavelength, λ, of absorption, where wavelength is expressed in millimicrons, $m\mu$ ($1\ m\mu = 10^{-7}$ cm), or in angstrom units, A ($1\ A = 10^{-8}$ cm), or less commonly in some frequency function, wave number, cm^{-1} or fresnels, $f = $ (frequency, $\nu/10^{12}$).

On the abscissa scale the direction of plotting increasing wavelength or frequency is inconsistent, but present majority usage favors wavelength values increasing to the right, i.e., frequency values decreasing to the right.†

In regard to plotting the ordinate, which represents the intensity of the absorption, the lack of agreement is more serious. The plot of ϵ or log ϵ versus wavelength is generally preferred by organic and physical chemists, whereas absorbance versus wavelength is used more by analytical chemists. The compilation of ultraviolet spectra of the American Petroleum Institute uses the latter method. A plot of $E^{1\%}_{1\ cm}$, where $E^{1\%}_{1\ cm}$ is the specific absorbance of a 1% solution (1 gram per 100 ml) measured in a 1-cm cell, is extensively used in description and assay of biological preparations or vitamins.

Since the authors of this text are primarily analytical chemists, the figures in this text are plotted as absorbance versus the wavelength, $m\mu$, in millimicrons. However, use of Table 3.3 will enable the reader to readily translate such data to any other system.

TABLE 3.3

Conversion Formulas for Absorption Terms

A	$=$	(A)	$-1(\log T)$	$(bc/M)(\epsilon)$	$bc(a)$
$\log T$	$=$	$-1(A)$	$(\log T)$	$-(bc/M)(\epsilon)$	$-bc(a)$
ϵ	$=$	$(M/bc)(A)$	$-(M/bc)(\log T)$	(ϵ)	$M(a)$
a	$=$	$(1/bc)(A)$	$-(1/bc)(\log T)$	$(1/M)(\epsilon)$	(a)

3.3 The theory of absorption. Fundamentally, the general theory is based on the Bunsen equation for the absorption of radiant energy

[5] R. A. Friedel and M. Orchin, *Ultraviolet Spectra of Aromatic Compounds*, John Wiley, New York (1951).

† A survey of *Analytical Chemistry* and the *Journal of the American Chemical Society* for the period September 1951 to February 1952 showed that, of 140 articles dealing with ultraviolet and visible spectra, 117 were plotted with increasing wavelength values to the right.

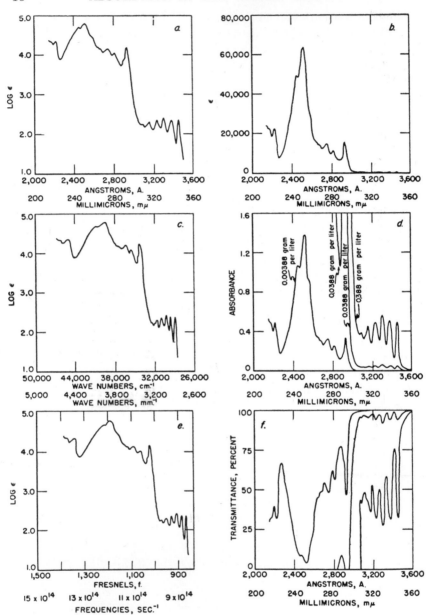

Fig. 3.2   Systems used in the graphical presentation of data for absorption spectroscopy (Reproduced by permission of R. A. Friedel and M. Orchin, *Ultraviolet Spectra of Aromatic Compounds,* John Wiley, New York, 1951)

$$P = P_0 10^{-abc}$$

where the terms expressed are defined in Table 3.2. The study of the variables in this equation has yielded Beer's law, denoting conformation with respect to changes in concentration, c, and Bouger's or Lambert's law, denoting conformation with respect to changes in thickness, b. The expression written as

$$\log_{10}(P_0/P) = abc \quad \text{or} \quad A = abc$$

has now been defined as Beer's law [2] rather than the Beer-Lambert or Bouger-Beer law. Thus absorbance, A, is a function of three factors: a constant specific for the substance, the concentration, and the thickness. The product of concentration and thickness expresses the relative number of colored ions or molecules in the light path.

A condition implied in this equation is that the light used must be monochromatic, that is, of a single discrete wavelength. This limit is hard to obtain in practice, but is approached sufficiently so that Beer's law holds. It should be noted that the definitions and thus the form of the law given apply to the solution only, and do not account for losses by reflection and absorption by parts of the measuring system.

If the absorbance of a colored solution is measured at various wavelengths, and the results plotted, a curve of the type shown in Fig. 3.3 is obtained. This curve is the absorption spectrum of uranium in alkaline solution containing hydrogen peroxide. The color of this complex is yellow to the eye. The dependence of a on wavelength is clearly noted since A varies with wavelength, and b and c are constant for the series of measurements.

If we plot the absorbances of two concentrations of the same solute (Fig. 3.3) we can show the necessity of using monochromatic light for analytical measurements. Without monochromation, the light absorbed by each solution would be measured by the area under the corresponding curves. The light transmitted in the sections where no absorption occurs is the same for both solutions, the actual absorbance of the colored ion or molecule is not being measured, and the sensitivity of measurement is reduced. If the Section XX is selected by a monochromator, the area under the curves in this section is more truly representative of the concentration. Monochromatic light, represented by the line Y, gives a direct proportion between absorbance and concentration.

To apply Beer's law to any system, the values of A or log T determined for several concentrations of the colored substance are plotted against the concentration. Figure 3.4 shows the linear variation of absorbance with wavelength for the uranium peroxide complex at different wavelengths. It should be noted that any wavelength could

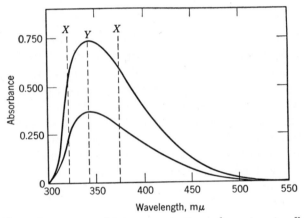

Fig. 3.3   Absorption spectra of two concentrations of uranium in alkaline solution containing hydrogen peroxide

be selected at which the complex absorbs (see Fig. 3.3). Obviously, in this case the best wavelength to select is one that will yield a line with the greatest slope, for this results in a measurement that is both more sensitive and less subject to error. The wavelength selected from Fig. 3.3 would be 340 mμ. However, a choice of wavelength is often tempered by other factors such as the absorption spectra of interfering substances. The wavelengths that are actually usable are shown in Fig. 3.4, and from these 360 mμ would be selected as the line with the greatest slope.

A deviation from linearity indicates that the light used is not sufficiently monochromatic, or that the actual concentration of the desired colored ions or molecules differs from the prepared concentration because of association, dissociation, complex formation, or a similar process.

3.4   The measurement of absorption.   For the purpose of discussion we shall confine ourselves to the absorption of liquid samples.

From Beer's law, it is apparent that, since a is a constant for any substance, we may determine concentration by measuring P_0, P, A, %T, or b while holding the other factors constant. Our instruments are therefore designed to measure one of these quantities.

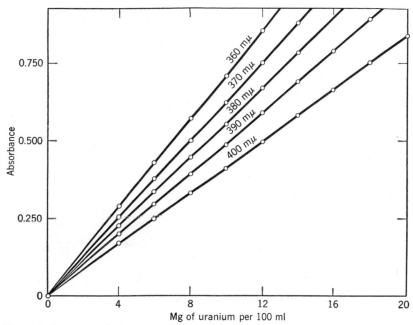

Fig. 3.4 Linearity of absorbance-concentration curve (Reprinted with permission from *Analytical Chemistry of the Manhattan Project*, McGraw-Hill, New York, p. 568, 1950)

The physical parts of an instrument for absorption spectroscopy may be summarized as:

Source (to produce a continuous visible spectrum).

Monochromator.

Optics (to give the desired light path).

Cells and cell holder (for the solution to be measured).

Receptor (for measuring the transmitted light), including scale and associated circuits.

3.5 Source. The source most commonly used for absorption spectroscopy in the visible region is the tungsten-filament lamp. The important characteristics of a tungsten lamp are the constancy of its over-all energy output, and its energy output at various wavelengths.

The over-all energy output varies as the fourth power of the applied voltage, and so, if constant output is to be maintained long enough to make a series of measurements, the voltage must be controlled very closely. This may be done by using a constant-voltage transformer or regulator or a wet battery for operation of the lamp. The latter method requires constant recharging of the battery or the use of a low-power lamp and consequently a more sensitive receptor. Fluctuations in line voltage and lamp output may also be compensated for in the design of the instrument.

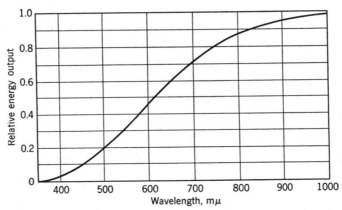

Fig. 3.5   Energy output of tungsten lamp at various wavelengths

The relative energy output of a tungsten lamp at various wavelengths is shown in Fig. 3.5. It may be seen that some system of compensation is necessary to allow for the varying output. This is done by measuring the light transmitted by a solution relative to the incident light or to the light transmitted by a reference liquid.

3.6 Monochromators. Monochromatic light is not strictly attainable, but suitable bands may be obtained in three ways: (*a*) color filters, (*b*) prism and slit, (*c*) diffraction grating and slit. Filter instruments are generally called filter photometers whereas grating or prism instruments are called spectrophotometers.

Simple color filters are usually polished plates of colored glass prepared to have definite spectral characteristics (see Fig. 3.6). They pass a broad band of frequencies, 30 to 50 mμ wide at least, and therefore are a poor approach to monochromatic light. However, if the absorption band of the solution is also broad, a filter may be very satisfactory.

To obtain narrower bands, combinations of filters may be used. The disadvantage is that the transmittance of the combination is

lowered and the system for measuring the transmitted light must be
more sensitive (see Fig. 3.7).

When two or more absorbing substances are in the light path together, a value for their transmittance may be obtained by multiplying the T values together. The product is the T value for the com-

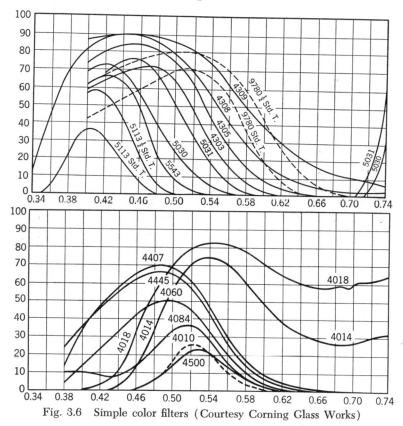

Fig. 3.6   Simple color filters (Courtesy Corning Glass Works)

bination. Of course this requires that there be no interaction. This
property is of particular value in designing glass filters for various
applications. The curves for stated thicknesses of colored glasses
are to be found in manufacturers' catalogs and chemical handbooks.
By the use of the absorption law and the above property a response
curve for glass-filter combinations can be calculated.

Recently, transmission-type interference filters ‡ have been de-

‡ These filters are available commercially from Bausch and Lomb Optical
Company and from Baird Associates, Inc.

veloped. Two highly reflecting but partially transmitting films of silver are separated by a spacer film of nonabsorbing material. This combination is deposited on a glass plate by high-vacuum methods, and a protection cover plate is then cemented on. The amount of separation of the silver films (or the thickness of the spacer film) governs the wavelength position of the pass band, and hence, the

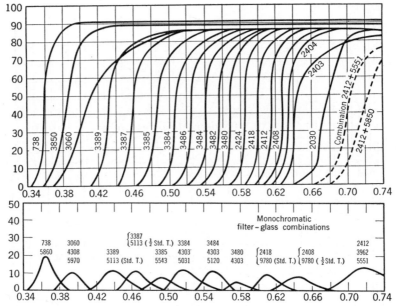

Fig. 3.7   Combination of filters to obtain narrow bands (Courtesy Corning Glass Works)

light that the filter will transmit. This is the result of an optical-interference effect which produces a high transmission of light when the optical separation of the silver films is effectively a half wave-length or a multiple thereof. Light that is not transmitted is, for the most part, reflected. Interference filters are characterized optically by the wavelength position of the peak of the pass band, by the trans-mittance at this peak, and by the half width. The half width is defined as the spectral width of the pass band in millimicrons at the level where the transmittance is one-half the peak transmittance. Transmission-type interference filters are better monochromators than ordinary glass filters because they have a narrower pass band. How-ever, they transmit less light at a given wavelength than ordinary glass filters.

A prism or diffraction grating § may be used to disperse hetero-chromatic light into its components. A slit may then be used to pick out the desired wavelength from the dispersed system. If the slit is held in a fixed position, the rotation of the prism or grating may be used to bring the proper wavelength onto the slit, and the rotation control may be calibrated directly in wavelength.

The wavelength band passed may vary from 1 to 35 mμ, depend-ing on the instrument. Therefore, the energy passed on to the re-ceptor is low, requiring a sensitive receptor to determine the intensity of the transmitted light.

3.7 Receptors. The important characteristics of a receptor are its wavelength response, its fatigue effect, and the conversion of its response to a numerical scale. The wavelength response curves for the three receptors, the eye, photovoltaic cell, and two phototubes are shown in Fig. 3.8. The other characteristics are given with the de-scription of the individual receptor.

The eye is highly sensitive to gradations in light and dark (shade), but less so to gradations in wavelength. It fatigues rapidly, and, owing to personal differences and poor color-shade memory, a nu-merical scale is impossible. Therefore the eye is used as a matching rather than a measuring receptor.

The photovoltaic cell consists of a transparent layer of metal cover-ing (and insulated from) a layer of selenium on a steel backing. Light passing through the metal releases electrons from the selenium and sets up an electric current that is proportional to the illumina-tion. This current is large enough so that it may be measured with a sensitive microammeter, but, since the internal resistance of the photocell is low, electronic amplification of the current is difficult. The photovoltaic cell suffers from fatigue; that is, the current output falls off with increasing time of exposure to light. This may be partially compensated for in the design of the instrument.

The phototube consists of a sensitized cathode surface which emits electrons when light strikes its surface and an anode held at a posi-tive potential with respect to the cathode by an external battery or power supply. The electrodes are contained in an evacuated bulb, and the electrons emitted by the cathode are attracted to the anode and set up an electric current in the external circuit. This current is small, but, as the internal resistance of the tube is high, electronic

§ A more complete discussion of prism and grating dispersion will be given in Chapter 6.

amplification is possible. The phototube does not suffer from fatigue and is available with cathodes sensitive to various spectral regions. Owing to the potential difference across the electrodes, stray elec-

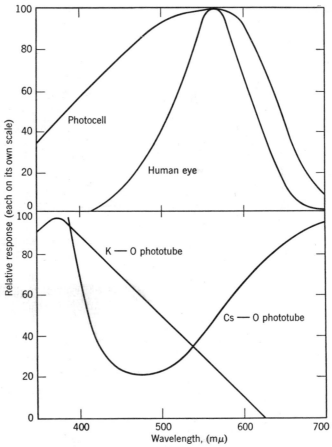

Fig. 3.8 Wavelength response curves for the three receptors, human eye, photovoltaic cell, and phototubes

trons cause a "dark current" when the tube is not illuminated. This must be compensated for in the design of the instrument.

3.8 Visual instruments. The five common types of visual instruments are the Duboscq colorimeter, Hehner cylinders, Nessler tubes, color-titration type, and the fixed standard type exemplified by the Hellige comparator.

The Duboscq and Hehner types operate on the principle of match-

ing the sample against a standard by varying the thickness of the solutions. For the two solutions we have the following equations:

$$A_1 = ab_1c_1$$

$$A_2 = ab_2c_2$$

Since the standard and sample are the same substance, the constant a is the same for both, and, if we match the absorbances, we obtain the reduced form of Beer's law,

$$b_1c_1 = b_2c_2$$

The Duboscq colorimeter (Fig. 3.9) uses glass plungers whose depth of immersion in the solution cups varies the solution thickness.

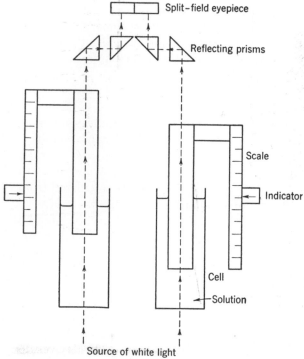

Fig. 3.9 Diagram of Duboscq colorimeter (Dotted line indicates optica

An attached scale reads directly in solution thickness. Variou fications are available, all of which are precision-made optic

ment. Their limitations are the limitations of the eye, such as fatigue, and its lack of sensitivity to low levels of illumination which prohibits use of filters in most cases.

Hehner cylinders resemble standard graduated cylinders fitted with a stopcock drain at the bottom, so that the vertical depth of the solution may be varied. A standard and a sample are matched vertically in two cylinders, and the thickness is read from the calibration marks on the glass. This type is less accurate than the Duboscq and suffers from the same limitations.

Nessler tubes are flat-bottomed cylinders with capacities of 50 or 100 ml. For measurement, equal volumes of the sample and of a standard solution are placed in separate tubes. The darker solution is diluted until the colors match when the tubes are viewed horizontally. Since the concentrations are equal, the percentage in the sample solution may be calculated from the two volumes.

Another method of using Nessler tubes is the comparison of several standards and the sample at equal volumes, the percentage being taken as that of the standard giving the closest match. This method does not depend on Beer's law but requires a large number of standards.

Color titrations may be carried out in any suitable vessels such as beakers or Nessler tubes. A convenient volume of the colored sample solution is placed in one vessel and a slightly smaller volume of the solvent or reagent solution in another. Then a standard solution of the desired constituent is added to the solvent or reagent solution until the colors match. The concentrations are then equal, and the percentage in the sample solution may be calculated from the volume and concentration of standard solution used.

The preceding methods all require that suitable standards be available at the time of analysis. To eliminate this difficulty, colored glass standards are used in the Hellige comparator (Fig. 3.10). These glasses are prepared to have the same color as a fixed thickness of a solution prepared according to a standard chemical procedure. A series of 8 to 10 fixed standards of varying percentages of the substance sought may be compared with the sample and interpolation used to estimate between the standards. This system requires absolute reproducibility of the chemical procedure for good results and is chiefly used for soil and water testing and for colorimetric pH determinations.

3.9   Filter photometers.   By using a photovoltaic cell to convert light energy into an electric current, it is possible to measure the

amount of light transmitted by a solution. By this procedure we eliminate the necessity of preparing standards with each sample but

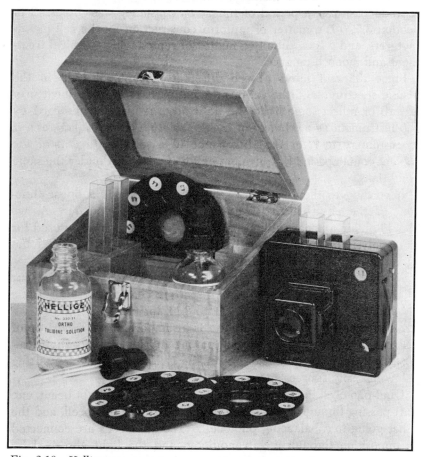

Fig. 3.10   Hellige comparator shown with standards for the *o*-tolidine method for dissolved oxygen (Courtesy Hellige, Inc.)

introduce some complicating factors into the measurements. From Beer's law,

$$\log (P_0/P) = abc$$

it is seen that the quantities P_0, a, and b must be held constant if we are to obtain c as a function of P. This was also true in the case of some visual instruments, but now we are no longer matching against a standard solution prepared simultaneously, but against standards run at some previous time. That is, we are requiring that the instrument have a color memory. Therefore, P_0, a, and b must be reproducible over a period of time. P_0 constancy was discussed in Section 3.5, b is a matter of uniform construction by the cell manufacturers, and a is essentially a matter of reproducing chemical treatment and monochromation.

Since different filters absorb different amounts of light in the visible spectrum, and the various optical parts of an instrument may absorb or reflect some light, the light absorbed is that absorbed by the instrument as a whole, not by the solution alone. Therefore, it is customary to refer the absorbance of a solution to that of the solvent contained in an equivalent cell and measured under the same conditions.

According to the Beer's law, the concentration is a linear function of the absorbance. Therefore, if we plot c against A, we should obtain a linear calibration curve. This curve may be used for the analysis of an unknown solution at any time, as long as the quantities P_0, a, and b remain constant.

Many different filter photometers are available commercially. Four of these are compared as to their important characteristics in Table 3.4 and are illustrated in Figs. 3.11 to 3.14, inclusive.

As previously mentioned, fatigue is an important characteristic of photocells and is particularly apparent in single-photocell instruments. It may be minimized, as in the Evelyn instrument by using a low-intensity source, and a high-sensitivity meter.

Dual-photocell instruments operate by splitting the light beam, one part passing through the solution to the measuring photocell, and the other going to a balancing photocell. The photocells are connected in opposition through a galvanometer, and the light absorbed by the solution causes an unbalance in the circuit. This arrangement compensates for source fluctuations, but only partially eliminates fatigue, as the two photocells are at different illumination levels. The two photocells must be matched for output and frequency response.

3.10   Spectrophotometers. Several manually operated photoelectric spectrophotometers are available. The characteristics of the Beckman model B (shown with flame attachment in Fig. 11.3), the Beckman model DU (Fig. 3.15), and the Coleman (Fig. 3.16) are shown in Table 3.5.

TABLE 3.4

Classification of Filter Photometers

	Source Regulation	No. Cells in Rack	Cells Available	100% Setting	Reading	Photo-cells	Other Features
Evelyn photometer	Battery	1	Test-tube type	Lamp voltage	Galvanometer scale	1	Low drain to minimize recharging
Photovolt Lumetron	Compensated	1	5, 10, 20, 50, 100, 150 mm and test-tube type	Rotation of compensating photocell	Calibrated slide-wire galvanometer balance	2	Light source rheostat to set lamp output
Klett-Summerson	Compensated	1	1, 2, 4 cm and test-tube type	Diaphragm	Calibrated slide-wire galvanometer balance	2	
Fisher electrophotometer	Compensated	2	Test-tube type and 5 cm	Potentiometer	Calibrated slide-wire galvanometer balance	2	

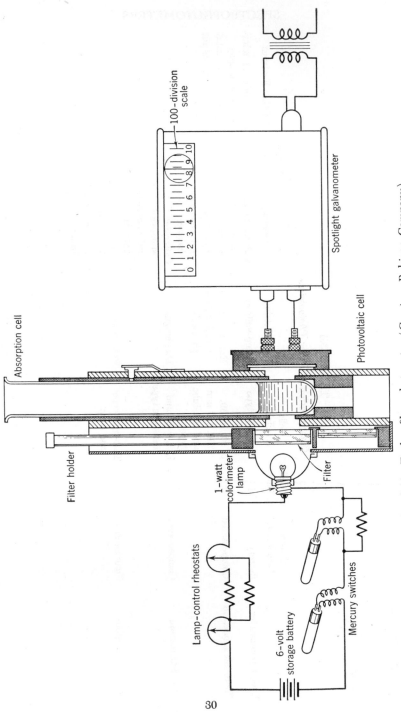

Fig. 3.11 Evelyn filter photometer (Courtesy Rubicon Company)

100-division scale

Spotlight galvanometer

Absorption cell

Photovoltaic cell

Filter holder

1-watt colorimeter lamp

Filter

Lamp-control rheostats

6-volt storage battery

Mercury switches

TABLE 3.5

Classification of Manual Spectrophotometers

	Beckman B	Beckman DU	Coleman Model 14
Dispersion	Glass prism	Quartz prism	Grating
Range	325–1000 mμ	200–1200 mμ	350–800 mμ
Slit width	Variable *	Variable,* 2 mμ max.	35 mμ
Cells in rack	4	4	2
Receptor	Interchangeable phototubes	Interchangeable phototubes	Phototube
100% setting	Slit-width dial	Slit-width dial and potentiometer	Potentiometer
Reading	Meter scale	Potentiometer scale	Meter scale
Lamp operation	Constant-voltage transformer or storage battery	Storage battery	Storage battery or a-c line
Phototube and amplifier operation	A-c line	Dry cells	A-c line

* Not a completely independent variable.

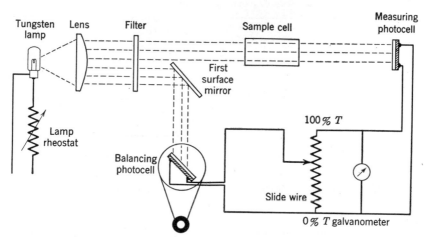

Fig. 3.12 Photovolt Lumetron filter photometer (Courtesy Photovolt Corporation)

The Hardy–General Electric recording spectrophotometer operates over the range of 400 to 750 mμ with a band width of 5 or 10 mμ.

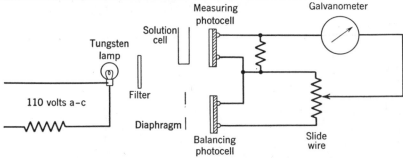

Fig. 3.13   Klett-Summerson filter photometer (Courtesy Klett Instrument Company)

The light beams transmitted by the sample and a reference solution alternately illuminate a photocell. Any unbalance causes a photocurrent which operates a polarizing prism in the reference beam. The rotation of this prism balances the illumination and records the sample transmission. A complete recording takes as little as 3 minutes, but an experienced operator is necessary if good results are to be obtained.

Since the Cary recording quartz spectrophotometer is mainly used in the ultraviolet region of the spectrum, it will be discussed in the

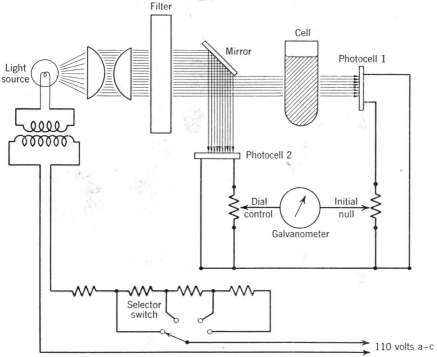

Fig. 3.14   Fisher Electrophotometer (Courtesy Fisher Scientific Company)

following chapter. However, this instrument is equally useful for obtaining spectra in the visible region.

3.11   Selection and maintenance of equipment. Once the basic type of instrument has been decided upon, certain important points should be considered.

(*a*) *Ruggedness.* Do the parts and their mountings appear sufficiently sturdy to withstand normal usage?

(*b*) *Ease of Servicing.* Can the parts that may deteriorate be easily repaired, and can the others be reached for maintenance and cleaning?

(*c*) *Reproducibility.* Do repeated readings on the same solution check within the desired limits of error?

(*d*) *Versatility.* Does the instrument allow the use of several cell sizes to vary the depth of solution? (This point may be unimportant for routine work.)

(*e*) *Simplicity.* Is the operating procedure easy to follow and perform?

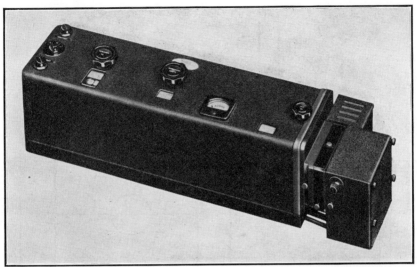

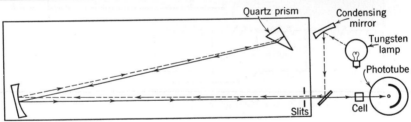

Fig. 3.15 Beckman model-DU spectrophotometer (Courtesy Beckman Instrument Company)

(*f*) Is the instrument complicated by unnecessary gadgets?

These points may be checked before the instrument is purchased, but one important feature, dependability, may only be determined by experience. However, all the instruments mentioned at least fulfill this minimum requirement.

Solution cells are an extremely vital part of the instrument, and their effect is not always considered. It is frequently stated that cylindrical cells are to be avoided, because of their lens action. If the cell holder is not perfectly rigid, this lens action may cause the illumination to strike different portions of the photocell, causing varying response and an error in the measurement. Also, if the 100% T setting is made with distilled water, the sample solution may differ

Fig. 3.16a Coleman Universal spectrophotometer (Courtesy Coleman Instrument Company)

in refractive index sufficiently so that a different area of the cell is illuminated. The final practical test, of course, is the over-all reproducibility of the instrument, and, if this is good, the effect of the cells is negligible.

Rectangular cells should have optically flat entrance and exit windows that are parallel. The cells should be fused, rather than cemented, and should be marked so that they are always inserted in the holder the same way. If more than one cell is to be used in a determination, they should be checked with the same solution in each cell to test their equality.

Cleanliness of the cells is of prime importance. They should be cleaned by swabbing with cotton swabs, using distilled water. One method of keeping the cells is to leave them immersed in distilled

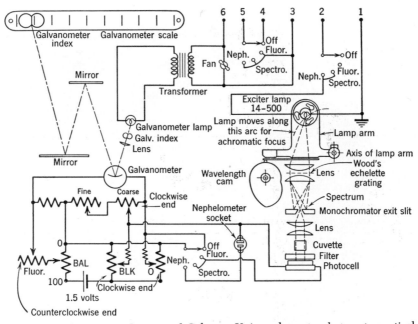

Fig. 3.16b   Schematic diagram of Coleman Universal spectrophotometer optical and electric systems (Courtesy Coleman Instrument Company)

water in a covered beaker. If necessary, they may be cleaned with nitric acid or aqua regia. Thorough rinsing with distilled water after cleaning is required. Dichromate cleaning solution should be used sparingly on absorption cells as it is very difficult to remove completely.

The selection of cells for use in an analysis is dependent on several factors: (a) cells available that fit the instrument, (b) amount of solution available, (c) absorbance of the solution.

In all cases, an attempt should be made to stay within the range of from 10 to 90% T. The range of 20 to 70% T has been found to give the greatest reproducibility and accuracy with most instruments (the optimum transmittance is usually quoted as 37%). This limiting range may be attained by varying the dilution of the solution or varying the cell length.

Color filters should be firmly mounted and marked to insure that they are always inserted in the instrument the same way. They should be perfectly clean, and combination filters should be checked for interference patterns. It must be remembered that in two-cell instruments generally the two photocells are illuminated by light from different portions of the filter. Photovoltaic cells and first-surface mirrors should only be dusted with a soft brush. Other optical parts may be cleaned with lens paper, a soft brush, or a cotton swab dipped in alcohol.

Switch contacts, wire-wound potentiometers and similar parts may be cleaned with carbon tetrachloride and given a thin coat of petrolatum. Other repairs should generally be handled by the makers of the instrument.

Battery-operated instruments should be checked periodically, and dry batteries having less than 80% of their rated voltage under load should be discarded. Wet batteries should be kept fully charged at all times.

Perhaps the chief point in maintenance is that prevention is better than cure. Instruments should be kept in a room free from chemical fumes and protected from dust. Careful operation will be repaid by comparative freedom from breakdowns.

As a means of checking the wavelength scale of a new instrument, didymium glass filters are available. By running a transmittance-wavelength curve for the glass, and checking against positions of the known minima in the curve, the wavelength scale can be accepted as correct, adjusted, or a calibration curve made. A more tedious but more accurate method is to use the known emission lines of a mercury lamp. This method is described in detail in the following chapter. Under ordinary circumstances, this calibration is not necessary, but, if the data are to be published, or if two instruments are to be compared, it will insure the accuracy of the wavelength selected.

3.12 Developing a colorimetric method. In the development of a new method, there are many factors that must be examined, if the full value of the method is to be realized. The following list gives the most important ones:

(a) Proper wavelength or filter.

(b) Interferences, preferably with means of removing them.

(c) Effect of pH.

(*d*) Linearity of absorbance-concentration curve.

(*e*) Effect of varying the amount of reagents.

(*f*) Effect of changes in procedure.

(*g*) Effect of time of standing before measurement.

(*h*) Factors that may cause fading (light, heat, etc.).

(*i*) Concentration range of the method.

(*j*) A reasonable estimate of the precision and accuracy of the method.

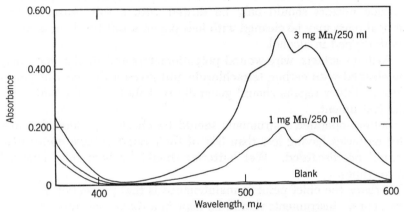

Fig. 3.17   Absorbance of MnO₄ ion in acid solution

Let us now consider some of these factors in more detail.

(*a*) *Proper Wavelength or Filter.* The spectrophotometer is a necessity for the optimum development of new methods. The first step in establishing a method is to obtain the absorption spectrum of the reagent blank, i.e., containing only the reagents used, and the spectrum of the solution containing a known amount of the compound of interest and the color-developing reagents. If an aqueous system is employed, distilled water should be used to set the zero absorbance reading, but if an organic solvent is involved, then the zero absorbance setting should be made on the organic solvent. Figure 3.17 illustrates the type of data that is obtained for the acid permanganate system. It should be noted in obtaining such a spectrum that closely spaced readings are necessary only at wavelengths where the absorbance values are large and changing rapidly. For example, in the wavelength intervals 400 to 460 mμ and 600 to 700 mμ readings need be taken only every 10 or 20 mμ, whereas in the interval 500 to 560 mμ readings should be taken at least every 5 mμ and even every 2 mμ at the maxima in order to obtain the fine structure shown.

It is wise to remeasure both solutions after known time intervals at the wavelength where maximum absorbance occurs (in this case 525 mμ) to see if the absorbance is changing with time. If the color is fading rapidly, this will be noticed visually, but slow or slight changes, which cannot be seen visually, will be evident in such data.

The ideal situation is one similar to that illustrated in Fig. 3.17 where the blank solution has no absorption in the wavelength region in which the compound absorbs. If the blank does not show zero absorbance, either the reagents contain some of the desired constituent or they absorb at the same wavelength. The reason may be determined by some other method of analysis, or, if the deviation is small, it is usually ignored. A simple test is to run three blanks with different concentrations of reagents to see if the deviation is real and then vary the separate reagents to determine the one responsible.

The use of a reagent blank for setting the zero absorbance automatically corrects the sample for the content of the blank, if the calibration curve is prepared on the same basis. This, of course, means that the value obtained depends on the validity of the blank. If the blank is checked against the pure solvent each time, gross errors may be eliminated, but the practice of using the solvent itself for the zero absorbance setting is to be recommended.

In some methods where solutions of high absorbance are to be measured, it has been recommended that the zero absorbance setting be made on a standard solution containing a moderate amount of the colored substance. For example, manganese determinations in the range of 1 to 2% could be carried out by setting the zero absorbance with a 1% manganese standard. This practice gives a greater spread for the absorbance values for the given range. Hiskey and Young [6] have described techniques for selecting the reference standard concentration so that maximum precision may be obtained in any given range.

If the solution contains other colored substances than the one being determined, a similar procedure to the one mentioned above may be employed. Two aliquots of the sample are used, the color being developed in one, and the other serving for the zero absorbance setting. A corollary method is to develop the color in the entire sample and then destroy this color in an aliquot to be used for the zero absorbance setting.

[6] C. F. Hiskey and I. G. Young, *Anal. Chem.*, 23, 1196 (1951).

Occasionally serious and unavoidable interference of the reagent is encountered in practice. An extreme case of such interference is the dithizone–mercury dithizonate system, where the organic reagent, dithizone, absorbs at the same wavelengths as the mercury dithizonate. The spectrum of mercury dithizonate in the presence of excess mercury (to insure the absence of free dithizone) and the spectrum of the reagent are shown in Fig. 3.18. The minimum absorption of dithizone is at 518 mμ, and this wavelength is selected for measurement of the mercury complex plus excess reagent. The absorption of the excess reagent is corrected for by measurement at 630 mμ. A correction curve (Fig. 3.19) is used to determine the reagent absorbance at 518 mμ.[7]

The mercury calibration curve is prepared by measuring known concentrations of mercury with excess dithizone at 518 and 630 mμ. The absorbance of the reagent at 518 mμ is found from the correction curve and subtracted from the total absorbance at 518 mμ. The net absorbance is then plotted against concentration of mercury to obtain the calibration curve. Unknown solutions are then measured in the same manner.

(b) *Interferences.* Interferences may be classified as chemical, where a reaction with the desired constituent occurs, and optical, where an interfering substance absorbs in the same wavelength region as the desired constituent. Chemical interferences must be removed by one of the separation methods available such as precipitation, extraction, electrolysis or volatilization, or by the formation of a suitable complex. Optical interferences may be treated by separation, complexing, or by the optical methods described below.

At times, because of optical interference by materials other than the one under observation, it may be necessary to use a different wavelength from the one that normally would be selected. The wavelength selected should be a compromise between maximum spread for the desired constituent and minimum effect of the interference. A good rule of thumb is that the absorption by the interference must be less than 10%, and then only if the concentration of the interference is constant in all the samples.

It is possible to determine two or more substances simultaneously by spectrophotometric methods, the simplest example being where two substances absorb at two well-separated wavelengths and do not

[7] J. U. Shepardson, Ph.D. thesis, Rensselaer Polytechnic Institute (1950).

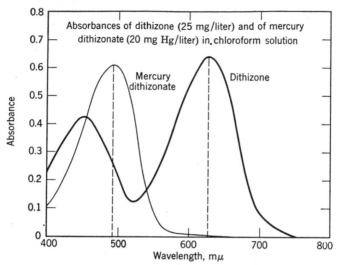

Fig. 3.18 Spectrum of mercury dithizonate in the presence of excess mercury and the spectrum of the reagent (J. U. Shepardson Ph.D. Thesis, Rensselaer Polytechnic Institute)

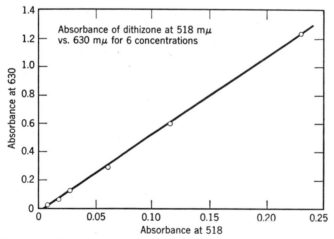

Fig. 3.19 Correction curve of absorption of excess reagent for the mercury–dithizone system (J. U. Shepardson Ph.D. Thesis, Rensselaer Polytechnic Institute)

interfere. Figure 3.20 is a plot of the absorption spectra of two rare-earth oxides, neodymium and dysprosium, dissolved in hydrochloric acid, and illustrates the example under consideration.

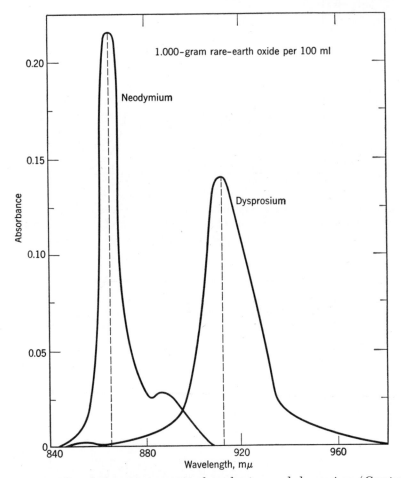

Fig. 3.20   Plot of absorption spectra of neodymium and dysprosium (Courtesy Lindsay Light & Chemical Company)

If one substance absorbs weakly at the absorption maximum of the other (Fig. 3.21), a correction curve may be used. This technique was used by Silverthorn and Curtis [8] to determine manganese and chromium simultaneously. First the absorbance values for

[8] R. W. Silverthorn and J. A. Curtis, *Metals & Alloys*, **15**, 245 (1942).

several concentrations of permanganate ion alone at 575 and 450 mμ, and the absorbance for dichromate ion alone at 450 mμ, are determined. From the curves for dichromate and permanganate at 450 mμ, the per cent chromium corresponding to each concentration of manganese is determined, and these values are plotted against the absorbance values for permanganate at 575 mμ (see Fig. 3.22). The per cent chromium is then determined by subtraction, and the per cent manganese by the usual method. Alternatively, the method below may be used.

If two substances interfere mutually (Fig. 3.23), the above process does not work, but a calculation based on simultaneous equations is possible. Assuming that no chemical interaction occurs, the absorbance at each wavelength is the sum of the absorbances of the components; thus the absorbance A_1, measured at 575 mμ,

$$A_1 = a_{Nd(575)}c_{Nd}b + a_{Pr(575)}c_{Pr}b$$

and the absorbance A_2, measured at 590 mμ,

$$A_2 = a_{Nd(590)}c_{Nd}b + a_{Pr(590)}c_{Pr}b$$

Since b is known and the a values may be obtained by measurement of pure solutions at 575 and 590 mμ, the measurement of A_1 and A_2 at 2 wavelengths allows the concentrations c of neodymium and praseodymium to be calculated. This process is used for five or more substances in infrared spectroscopy, the calculations being performed by IBM punch-card calculators [9] or by an electronic calculator.

(c) *Effect of pH.* In almost every colorimetric system the pH of the solution is a critical variable. An acid-base indicator is a simple illustration of the dependency of color upon the pH of the solution. However, indicators are a rather special example; normally in colorimetric analysis the absorption spectrum does not change its pattern with pH, but only decreases or increases in intensity as the pH of the solution changes. This is true of both aqueous systems and systems involving the extraction of an organic complex with an organic solvent. For example, in the colorimetric determination of the uranium peroxide complex in alkaline medium, the absorbance continually increases from pH 7 until at pH 12.0 it reaches a constant, maximum value from 12.0 to 12.6. Hence, in this system the colorimetric measurement is made at pH 12.3 which is midpoint in

[9] W. H. King and W. Priestley, *Anal. Chem.,* 23, 1418 (1951).

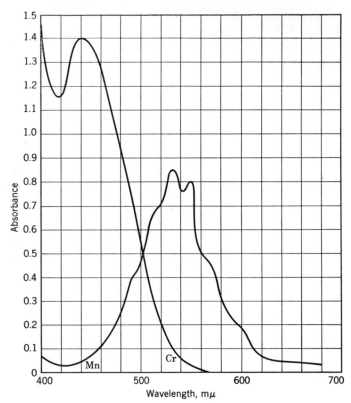

Fig. 3.21   Absorption curves for permanganate and chromate ions in acid solution

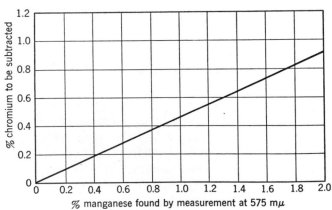

Fig. 3.22   Correction curve for determination of chromium in the presence of manganese

this range.   Figure 3.24 illustrates the effect of pH on the extraction of metal derivatives of sodium diethyl–dithiocarbamate.[10]   The pH is very critical for the uranium and chromium derivatives, but not

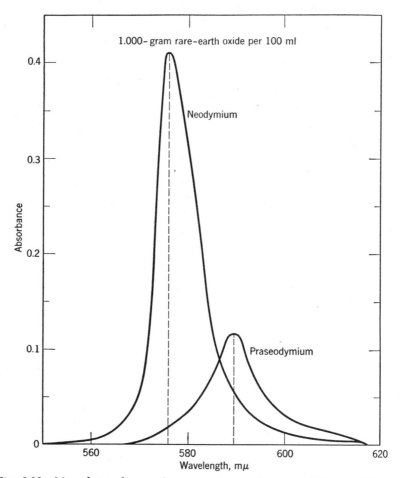

Fig. 3.23   Mutual interference by two colored substances (Courtesy Lindsay Light & Chemical Company)

for the other elements studied.   It should be clear from this example that control of pH is often a useful means of eliminating interferences.

In establishing a colorimetric method, it is desirable that the pH range be broad, so that small errors in the adjustment of the pH do

[10] R. LaCoste, M. H. Earing, and S. E. Wiberley, *ibid.*, *23*, 871 (1951).

not lead to large errors in the absorbance value measured. Generally, a pH range of 0.2 unit, i.e., from 4.5 to 4.7, is the minimum acceptable for a useful method. In evaluating new color-forming reagents the qualitative observations and quantitative measurements should be

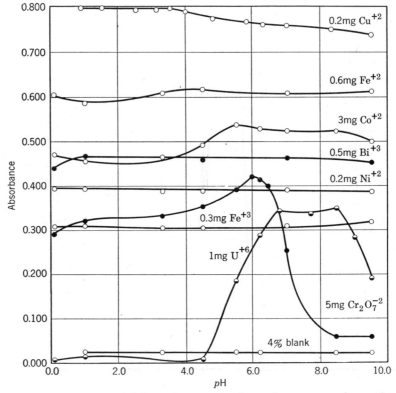

Fig. 3.24   Absorbance of dithiocarbamate complexes of various metals as a function of pH (Courtesy *Analytical Chemistry*)

made in acidic, neutral, and basic media. In this way a new specific reagent will not be lost to analytical chemists, simply because the investigator neglected to consider the important variable, pH.

(*d*) *Linearity of Absorbance-Concentration Curve.* It is not necessary that a system show a linear relationship to be useful in colorimetric analysis, for an empirical curve of absorbance versus concentration can be used provided it is reproducible. Systems that yield a linear plot of absorbance versus concentration when measured with a spectrophotometer often do not yield a linear relationship with filter photometers but show a tapering off at higher concentrations.

This is caused by the broad pass band of the filters as previously discussed.

The other factors listed (*e* through *j*) will not be discussed in detail, since it should be evident how these factors can affect a colorimetric method. Besides these, if a method is being considered for publication, the account should contain (*a*) a clear description of the method, (*b*) the name of the instrument used, (*c*) any details not defined by *b*, such as cells, source, slit width, or any modification of the original instrument, (*d*) a reproduction of the calibration curve, or a statement that it is linear.

For a more comprehensive treatment, the references at the end of the chapter may be consulted, particularly the pamphlet by Mellon.

3.13   Applications. In the analysis of metals, absorption spectroscopy has resulted in considerable saving of time and in many cases an increase in accuracy. Steels, copper-base alloys, white-metal and light alloys, as well as several high-purity metals, may be analyzed for many constituents, using absorption methods. In practically all instances a color-forming reagent is added to produce the color, and the measurement is made without previous chemical separations.

In the determinations of inorganic ions, organic reagents offer the advantage of great sensitivity, because of the highly colored complexes that are formed, and the advantage of the relatively specific action of many of the reagents. A method coming into prominence at the present time is the extraction of organic complexes into an organic solvent and measurement of the color in the solvent or re-extraction of the complex into aqueous solution before measurement. This procedure allows separation of the desired constituent from interfering elements without the necessity for the precipitation, filtration, and washing necessary in wet-method separations. Another possibility is the measurement of colored complexes which are insoluble in aqueous solution but which may be extracted into a suitable organic solvent.

The high sensitivity of colorimetric methods has extended their use to the determination of trace elements in biological materials and in high-purity materials, such as chemical reagents. Many elements may be determined in the range of a few parts per million, where ordinary methods are unreliable. In this range, however, constant vigilance in respect to purity of reagents, cleanliness of apparatus, and careful technique must be maintained.

The application of absorption methods to organic compounds has not been covered extensively in the visible region. The development of apparatus and methods for the infrared and ultraviolet regions has caused the visible region to be by-passed in many cases. A fruitful field for research is the use of inorganic reagents to develop colors with organic compounds.

The application of the spectrophotometer to the control of dye baths and the classification and grading of dyes has been extensive. A complete wavelength-transmittance curve shows not only the concentration of the dye but also its purity.

3.14 Turbidimetry and nephelometry. Other methods to which the principles of absorption spectroscopy apply are turbidimetry, where the absorption due to suspended solid particles is measured, and nephelometry, where the scattering of light by suspensions is measured.

The accuracy of turbidimetric and nephelometric methods is inherently low, because the absorption or scattering is a function of the number of particles and their size. These particles are not molecular but are aggregates, and the preparation of reproducible aggregates is practically impossible because of the large number of variable factors. Any instrument designed for absorption spectroscopy may be used for turbidimetry. Nephelometry requires a receptor at right angles to the light path, and some filter photometers may be adapted for this type of measurement.

Bibliography

General

W. R. Brode, *Chemical Spectroscopy*, 2nd ed., John Wiley, New York (1947).
T. R. P. Gibb, *Optical Methods of Chemical Analysis*, McGraw-Hill, New York (1942).
M. G. Mellon, Colorimetry for Chemists, G. F. Smith Chemical Co. (1945).
ASTM, *Chemical Analysis of Metals*, Am. Soc. Testing Materials, Philadelphia (1951).
M. H. Odeen, Bibliography of Applications for Beckman Model B and DU Spectrophotometers, Beckman Instruments, South Pasadena, Calif. (1952).

Applications

E. B. Sandell, *Colorimetric Determination of Traces of Metals*, 2nd ed., Interscience, New York (1950).
J. H. Yoe, *Photometric Chemical Analysis*, Vol. I (1928); J. H. Yoe and H. Kleinman, Vol. II (1929), John Wiley, New York.
F. D. Snell and C. T. Snell, *Colorimetric Methods of Analysis*, 2 vols., 3rd ed., D. Van Nostrand, New York (1948).
E. S. Miller, *Quantitative Biological Spectroscopy*, Burgess Publishing Co., Minneapolis (1939).

CHAPTER 4

Absorption in the Ultraviolet Region

The principles and methods utilized in absorption measurements in the visible region carry over into the ultraviolet. Certain modifications of the instruments are necessary to insure transmission of ultraviolet radiation; usually the optical parts are made of quartz. The source and receptor must be capable of radiating and measuring radiant energy to 200 mμ.

The cause of absorption is an electronic energy-level shift with an energy value in the proper range. For organic compounds, the molecule must include a resonant structure, usually of the type C=C, C=O, N=N, C=N or other doubly bonded groups. These absorbing groups are called resonators or more commonly chromophores. The chief inorganic materials absorbing in this region are the rare earths and certain radicals.

As in the visible, the spectra of most materials are very simple. Since the measurements are made at room temperature, the majority of the electrons are in the ground state, and the number of possible transitions is necessarily limited. This limitation in number of possible transitions does not apply to the rare earths, and their spectra are more complex. Organic compounds may show a marked vibrational fine structure in conjugated and particularly aromatic compounds, but the electronic spectra in themselves are still simple.

The major applications of ultraviolet-absorption analysis have been to vitamins and other biochemical materials and to aromatic compounds. The recent introduction of better instrumentation should result in a larger number of applications.

In the ultraviolet, the common unit of wavelength is the millimicron (mμ) and the unit of frequency is the Fresnel (f), which is the number of vibrations per second times 10^{-12}. Thus the visible limit at 400 mμ equals 750 f, and the ultraviolet limit at 200 mμ equals 1500 f.

4.1   Apparatus.   There is no simple source of continuous radiation for the range 200 to 400 mμ which would correspond to the tungsten lamp used in the visible region.   For many years a high-voltage spark between high-alloy steel or uranium electrodes was used.   This produces a line spectrum with many discontinuities and of variable intensity.   By operating the spark under water, a more regular spectrum is produced, but the experimental difficulties are numerous.[1]

The most satisfactory source yet developed is the hydrogen-discharge lamp.   Commercial units with quartz bulbs or windows have emission down to 160 mμ.   The limitation in spectrophotometer wavelength range is the absorption limit of the quartz optics (180 mμ) and air (200 mμ).   A moderately high lamp voltage and regulation of the voltage are necessary for stable operation.

The optical parts, such as cells, lenses, and prisms, may be made of quartz for the full range, or of Corex glass made by the Corning Glass Works if only the region above 250 mμ is to be studied.   It is possible that certain plastic materials may be useful for optical parts in the future.

The photographic plate as a receptor was quite common in the older instruments.   The gelatin of the emulsion absorbs strongly below 240 mμ, but the plate may be sensitized down to 200 mμ by a thin coating of a fluorescent mineral oil.   The light activating the plate is thus visible light which penetrates the gelatin readily.

Phototubes with cathode surfaces sensitive to ultraviolet radiation are readily available, and, if a quartz or thin Corex window is used, the absorption by the bulb is minimized.   The barrier-layer photocell has low sensitivity in the ultraviolet and is not found in commercial instruments.

4.2   Photographic instruments.   Only one example of this type is given, as these instruments are being replaced by the photoelectric spectrophotometers.   Figure 4.1 shows the spectrum obtained from benzene with the Hilger-Spekker photometer.

The optical system of the photometer splits the radiation from an alloy-steel spark and directs it through a sample and a blank or solvent cell.   The transmitted radiation is collimated and brought onto the slit of a medium quartz spectrograph and produces two

[1] J. Strong, *Procedures in Experimental Physics*, Chap. IX, Prentice-Hall, New York (1945).

adjacent spectra of the electrodes on the photographic plate, one having been transmitted through the sample and the other through

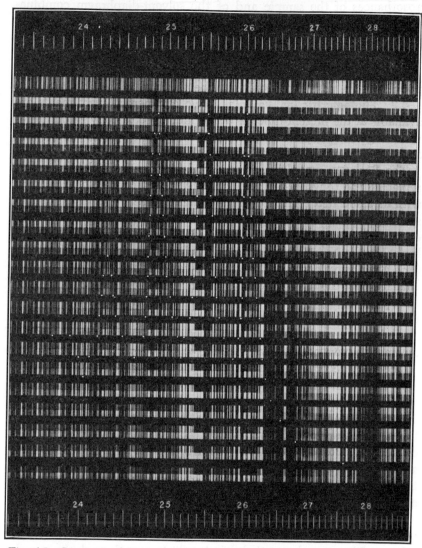

Fig. 4.1   Spectrum of benzene taken on Hilger-Spekker photometer (Courtesy Jarrel-Ash Company)

the solvent. A variable diaphragm in the solvent beam allows its absorbance to be varied in known steps.

The measurement of the ultraviolet spectrum consists in taking a series of these dual exposures with various absorbance settings of the diaphragm. The developed plate appears as in Fig. 4.1. Where the absorbances of the sample and of the solvent-diaphragm combination are equal, the spectral lines at that wavelength will be of equal intensity. These lines are spotted (as shown on the plate), and a graph of absorbance versus wavelength may be prepared.

Several other methods of altering the absorbance values have been popular in the past, and details may be obtained in the literature.

4.3 Photoelectric instruments. Two commercial instruments are available at the present time for absorption spectroscopy in the ultraviolet region. They are the Beckman model DU spectrophotometer, and the Cary recording quartz spectrophotometer.

The Beckman model DU is modified for the ultraviolet region by replacing the tungsten-filament lamp by a hydrogen-discharge lamp with its associated regulated high-voltage source. The instrument is so designed that this change can be made in a few minutes. However, with newly acquired instruments, it is necessary to focus the hydrogen-discharge lamp correctly to obtain the minimum slit width for a given wavelength.[2] Once this adjustment has been made, interchanges with the tungsten-filament lamp offer no problems. Quartz-absorption cells are available as well as Corex glass cells. Kaye, Canon and Devaney [3] have described the modification of this instrument for automatic operation at 210 to 270 mμ, and a recording attachment is now commercially available.

The Cary recording quartz spectrophotometer (Fig. 4.2) is available in two models, one recording per cent transmittance and the other absorbance. The ranges covered with both instruments are 200 to 350 mμ and 300 to 800 mμ with suitable sources and photo-tubes. Cells up to 10.0 cm may be accommodated, with two sample cells in the slide carrier. The visible spectrum may be recorded in approximately 2 to 17 minutes and the ultraviolet in 1 to 12 minutes, the accuracy and reproducibility at slower speeds being about 0.01 absorbance.

The double-monochromator system (designed to reduce stray light) with two quartz prisms, gives a band pass that varies from 0.1 to 2.0 mμ. The monochromatic beam is split to pass through the sample cell and the solvent or blank cell, and is registered by two multiplier phototubes. The electric output of the system to the recorder is in

[2] Beckman Bull. 89-A, Beckman Instruments, South Pasadena, Calif.

[3] W. Kaye, C. Canon, and R. G. Devaney, *J. Optical Soc. Am.*, *41*, 658, 1951.

proportion to the intensity ratio of the two beams. The light beam is chopped at a rate of 60 cps by a rotating shutter between the source and the entrance slit. The chopped beam gives a pulsating signal which may be amplified by a stable a-c amplifier. Spectral recording, including the required continuous variation in slit width is completely automatic.

The optical system of the spectrophotometer is shown schematically in Fig. 4.2. Radiation from the source, A, is focused by a quartz

Fig. 4.2a   Cary recording spectrophotometer (Courtesy Applied Physics Corporation)

lens, B, and is chopped at 60 cps by a cylindrical shutter, C. It passes through the entrance slit, D, to the collimating mirror, E. The collimated radiation falls on the quartz prism, F, which is aluminized, on its back surface. The dispersed radiation returns to the collimating mirror and is focused on the fixed intermediate slit, H, by the diagonal mirror, G. In the second half of the monochromator, the same optical elements are traversed in the reverse order.

After leaving the exit slit, L, the radiation falls on the beam splitter, M. This splits the light into two beams of one-half the height of the original. The split beams fall on the off-axis spherical mirrors,

N and N', which approximately collimate the beams with respect to the exit slit and direct the radiation through the cell compartment.

The radiation leaving the absorption-cell compartment passes through the quartz lenses, Q and Q', which form an image of the slit approximately in the plane of the phototubes, R and R'.

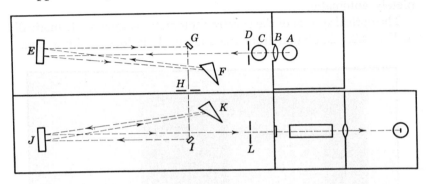

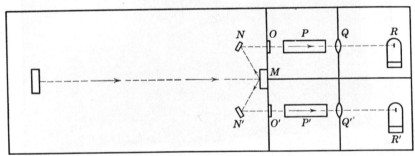

Fig. 4.2b Optical system of Cary recording spectrophotometer (Courtesy Applied Physics Corporation)

Figure 4.3 shows the ultraviolet spectrum of the same solution measured on both instruments for comparison purposes.

4.4. Calibration. Ewing and Parsons [4] have shown the necessity for calibrating a spectrophotometer, particularly in the ultraviolet region. A simple and accurate method of calibration is to replace the hydrogen lamp source with a mercury-vapor lamp such as a Beckman 2260 or a General Electric A-H-4. Since a mercury-vapor source is intense, it need not be carefully focused, but it should be shielded to prevent damage to the retina of the eye. Calibration data can be obtained by varying the slit width over the wavelength

[4] G. W. Ewing and T. Parsons, Jr., *Anal. Chem.*, 20, 423 (1948).

interval of interest; for each strong mercury-emission line the slit width will approach a minimum value. Or with the slit almost closed (0.02 mm or less) one can note the wavelengths at which maximum intensities are obtained as the wavelength dial is slowly rotated. A comparison of the known wavelengths of the mercury-emission lines (see Appendix A) with the wavelengths as measured on the spectrophotometer dial will enable one to prepare a correction graph.

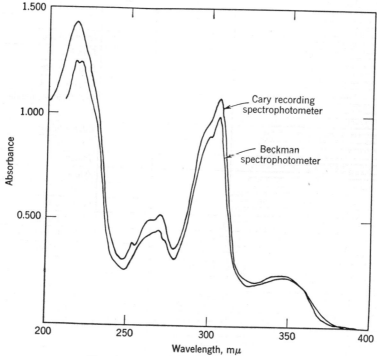

Fig. 4.3 Typical ultraviolet spectrum

Another simple method of calibration is to measure benzene vapor or a dilute solution of benzene in isoöctane and compare the wavelengths of the maximum peaks with the known values.

4.5 Ultraviolet analysis. The chief differences between ultraviolet- and visible-absorption measurements are in the apparatus, sensitivity, and solvents used. Water is a suitable solvent as far as freedom from absorption is concerned, but, as most of the materials analyzed are organic, it is necessary to find suitable organic solvents. Since the ultraviolet absorption of aromatic compounds is so intense, 1-cm cells do not yield useful spectra for the pure materials. Al-

TABLE 4.1

Ultraviolet Absorption of Chromophoric Groups

Group	Absorption, $m\mu$	Conjugation	Absorption, $m\mu$
$C{-}C$	<153		
$C{=}C$	$175{-}185$	$C{-}C{-}C{=}C$ (cyclopropane ring with apex C)	>175
		$C{-}C{-}C{=}C$ (cyclopropane ring with apex O)	<210
		$C{=}C{-}C{=}C$	220
$C{\equiv}N$	180	$C{-}C{-}C{\equiv}N$ (cyclopropane ring with apex C)	210
		$C{=}C{-}C{\equiv}N$	$214{-}217$
$C{=}S$	208		
$\underset{C{-}OH}{\overset{O}{\parallel}}$	208	$HO{-}\underset{\parallel}{\overset{O}{C}}{-}\underset{\parallel}{\overset{O}{C}}{-}OH$	250
$S{-}H$	228		
$C{=}O$	$270{-}280$	$C{-}C{-}\underset{\parallel}{\overset{O}{C}}$ (cyclopropane ring with apex C)	290
		$\underset{\parallel}{\overset{O}{C}}{-}\underset{\parallel}{\overset{O}{C}}$	286
		$C{=}C{-}\underset{\parallel}{\overset{O}{C}}$	$310{-}330$
		$\underset{\parallel}{\overset{O}{C}}{-}\underset{\parallel}{\overset{O}{C}}{-}OH$	331
		$C{=}C{-}\underset{\parallel}{\overset{O}{C}}{-}C{=}C$	340
$N{=}O$	302	$O{=}\underset{\parallel}{\overset{O}{N}}{-}$	366
$N{=}N$	350	$N{-}N{-}N$ (three-membered ring)	288
(benzene ring)$-R$	259	(benzene ring)$-\underset{C}{\overset{O}{\diagup\diagdown}}C$	260
		(benzene ring)$-C{-}C$ (cyclopropane with apex C)	274
		(benzene ring)$-C{=}C$	290
(naphthalene)	311		
(anthracene)	475		

structure of the bands of the parent compound. In general, saturated groups with oxygen or nitrogen atoms containing electron pairs which can react with the chromophoric group will cause the greatest change in intensity and usually a bathochromic shift. Examples are the amino and methoxy groups.

For aromatic compounds, the substituents alkyl, halogen, hydroxyl, and alkoxyl (arranged in ascending order of their effectiveness) increase the absorption of the benzene ring. In disubstituted aromatic compounds the effect of the substituent is also dependent on the position occupied, ortho and para substituents being more effective than meta in causing shifts to longer wavelengths. Substitution in the para position also produces more pronounced fine structure.

Jones [14, 15] has further classified the effects of substituents on the ultraviolet spectra of aromatic compounds according to bathochromic (B) effect, conjugation (C) effect, steric hindrance (S) effect, and fine structure (F_s) effect. These terms are in the literature and are mentioned here for that reason. The references listed should be consulted for a detailed explanation of these terms.[7, 14, 15]

The usual effect of substitution next to a chromophore is to cause a shift to longer wavelength. In the case of the aliphatic groups shown in Table 4.1 maximum shift toward longer wavelength is caused by R—C=O while hydrogen has little effect, and negative groups cause a shift toward shorter wavelengths, so that compounds containing a carbonyl group and two negative groups do not absorb in the quartz ultraviolet.

Large numbers of ultraviolet spectra are appearing in the current literature, particularly in conjunction with organic synthetic and theoretical studies. A recent paper contains 135 such spectra.[16] The largest compilations are those of the American Petroleum Institute [17] and a recent text on aromatic compounds.[7] Two typical spectra from these two references are reproduced in Fig. 4.5. The different ways of plotting spectra, discussed previously in Chapter 3, are further emphasized by this figure.

The application of ultraviolet-absorption spectra to qualitative identification of organic compounds is limited by the relative simplicity of the spectra and the fact that many compounds do not

[14] R. N. Jones, Chem. Revs., 32, 1 (1943).

[15] R. N. Jones, J. Am. Chem. Soc., 67, 2127 (1945).

[16] W. A. Schroeder, P. E. Wilcox, K. N. Trueblood, and A. O. Dekker, Anal. Chem., 23, 1740 (1951).

[17] Am. Petroleum Inst. Research Project 44, Carnegie Institute of Technology.

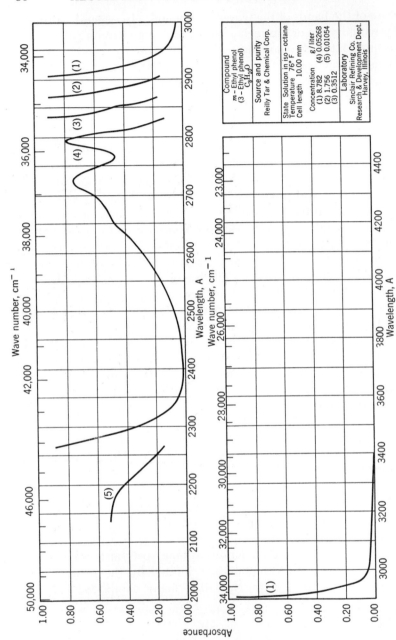

Fig. 4.5a   Typical ultraviolet spectrum as distributed by the American Petroleum Institute (Courtesy American Petroleum Institute)

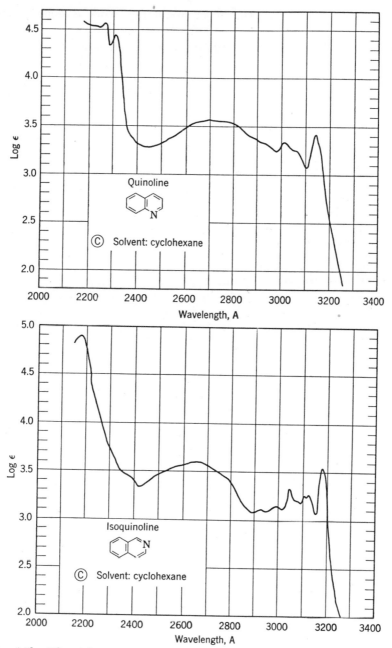

Fig. 4.5b Ultraviolet spectra of quinoline and isoquinoline (Reproduced by permission of R. A. Friedel and M. Orchin, *Ultraviolet Spectra of Aromatic Compounds,* John Wiley, New York, 1951)

absorb in this region. The major qualitative work is done in the infrared.

Outside of standard quantitative analysis of suitable mixtures, ultraviolet spectra are valuable for certain structural determinations in the organic field. Examples of materials showing recognizable differences in spectra are *cis-trans* compounds, *keto-enol* forms, and *o-m-p*-benzene derivatives.

Bibliography

W. R. Brode, *Chemical Spectroscopy*, 2nd ed., John Wiley, New York (1947).

L. F. Fieser and M. P. Fieser, *Natural Compounds Related to Phenanthrene*, 3rd ed., Reinhold, New York (1949).

G. R. Harrison, R.C. Lord, and J. R. Loofbourow, *Practical Spectroscopy*, Prentice-Hall, New York (1948).

E. S. Miller, *Quantitative Biological Spectroscopy*, Burgess Publishing Co., Minneapolis (1939).

R. A. Morton, *Application of Absorption Spectra to Vitamins, Hormones, and Co-enzymes*, 2nd ed., Adam Hilger, London (1942).

CHAPTER 5

Absorption in the Infrared Region

The development of infrared-absorption spectroscopy is progressing more rapidly at this time than any other field of analysis. The materials determined by means of their infrared spectra have been very difficult to handle by ordinary methods. Not only increased speed of analysis but also higher accuracy is possible with this new technique.

The infrared region may be divided into four sections, the photographic (visible to 1.2 microns), overtone (visible to 3 microns), near infrared (2.5 to 25 microns) and far infrared (25 to 300 microns). Beyond the far infrared, considerable work is being done in the microwave region (high-frequency radio waves), but at the present time the analytical applications are rather limited.

The region of the spectrum of interest for analysis is from 2.5 to 25 microns (1 micron, or 1 μ equals 10^{-4} cm) or, expressed in frequency units, 4000 to 400 wave numbers (waves per centimeter, cm^{-1}). Because the usual optical materials absorb strongly in the infrared, the apparatus is considerably different from that for the visible and ultraviolet regions.

Absorption in the near infrared is caused by the vibration of atoms about an equilibrium position in the molecule and the combination of these vibrations with rotation of the atoms to produce vibrational-rotational spectra. The vibrational energy absorbed induces an instantaneous dipole moment in the molecule and produces an absorption band. The bands are characteristic of the linkages or bonds in the molecule and also to a lesser degree of the size and structure of the rest of the molecule.

Infrared spectra are applied to both qualitative and quantitative analysis of organic compounds. While the organic molecule must be capable of resonance to show absorption in the visible and ultraviolet, all organic compounds absorb in the infrared region. The types of problems attacked and the apparatus used will be discussed in detail in later sections.

5.1 Vibrational-rotational spectra. A molecule with n atoms may be shown to have a certain number of fundamental modes of vibration. If the molecule is linear, the number is $3n - 5$, and, if the molecule is nonlinear, the number is $3n - 6$. The criteria for a fundamental mode are that the center of gravity of the molecule remain fixed and that the atoms maintain the same phase and frequency of vibration. For molecules with increasing symmetry, some of these modes become degenerate, that is, equivalent, and the actual modes appearing may be fewer than the number given by the formula. In most cases it is possible to assign the cause of a particular infrared frequency as to the bond involved and whether the motion is one of stretching or bending of the bond.

While two atoms are changing in their vibrational energy, a simultaneous change in rotational energy may occur. The energy of these quanta are low and would appear as absorption in the far infrared, but the combinations of vibrational and rotational energy changes appear as a series of closely spaced absorption bands centered about the fundamental vibration frequency. If the pass band of the instrument is narrow enough, they may be resolved, or separated into distinct bands; otherwise they will coalesce and appear to the instrument as a single broad band.

The fine structure mentioned is particularly apparent in gaseous samples where molecular interaction is minimized. Pure liquids and solutions frequently show none of the rotational structure, because of association in the liquid or solvent-solute interaction.

The fundamental vibrations and the vibration-rotation combinations are not the only absorption bands that appear. Overtones or integral multiples of the fundamental frequency are possible, as well as combinations equal to the sum or difference of two fundamentals. The molecule as a whole may rotate, and energy changes may occur which cause absorption at the low-frequency end of the region considered. The probability of these particular quantized energy changes and therefore the absorption intensity of the bands that they produce is ordinarily low.

As a first-order approximation, we may consider that an absorption band is caused by a quantized change in the vibrational energy of 2 atoms. The energy change and thus the absorption frequency will be a function chiefly of the strength of the bond and the masses of the atoms.

As an approximation we can apply Hooke's law for simple harmonic motion to two atoms so that the equation for the frequency of vibration between them is

$$\nu = (1/2\pi c)\ \sqrt{k/u}$$

where ν = the frequency of the vibration in cm^{-1}, k = the force constant (i.e., the stretching or restoring force between the two atoms) in dynes per centimeter, c = the velocity of light in centimeters per second, u = the reduced mass of the vibrating atoms, that is, $1/m_1 + 1/m_2$, where m_1 and m_2 are the relative masses of the vibrating atoms.

The equation may be evaluated numerically, using the reduced mass in atomic mass units and k as a pure number. This yields

$$\nu = 1307\sqrt{k/u}\ \text{cm}^{-1}$$

If we consider a typical example such as the C-H bond, where $k = 5$, the reduced mass is approximately unity, and

$$\nu = 1307\sqrt{\tfrac{5}{1}} = 2920\ \text{cm}^{-1}$$

The experimentally observed region for the aliphatic carbon-hydrogen stretching vibration is 2800 to 3000 cm^{-1}. Hence, if the force constant is known, the approximate frequency of a bond can be calculated. Or, conversely, the observed frequency being known, the force constant can be calculated. Barnes et al.[1] have calculated the force constants for the more important atomic linkages in this manner. Thus, any given functional group in a molecule should absorb at characteristic frequencies, and the infrared spectrum should enable the analyst to assign the proper functional groups to the molecule. This is the idealized case for structure analysis, as no allowance has been made for the influence of the rest of the molecule.

As the structure of the rest of the molecule which is attached to a particular group is changed, the absorption frequencies may shift within a rather narrow range and changes in the shape of the band may occur. Although this is a disadvantage for simple structure analysis, it means that the complete absorption spectrum of a compound is highly characteristic and thus very useful for qualitative analysis by comparison with known pure compounds. In a homologous series, as might be expected, the frequency shifts in comparing

[1] R. B. Barnes, R. C. Gore, U. Liddel, and V. Z. Williams, *Infrared Spectroscopy, Industrial Applications and Bibliography*, Reinhold, New York (1944).

butyric acid, a C_4 compound, to caproic acid, a C_6 compound, are considerably greater than in comparing myristic acid, a C_{14} compound to palmitic acid, a C_{16} compound.[2]

The shape of a particular band is often a more characteristic property than the frequency of maximum absorption for members of a homologous series. It is possible that a plot of log absorbance against frequency would be of value for distinguishing nearby members, as this plot is very sensitive to changes in shape.

With present prism instruments, the spectral slit widths are of the same order of magnitude as the widths of the absorption bands of liquids or solids. For this reason, the experimentally determined band intensities are not true physical constants of the compound, but depend upon the instrumental conditions employed, and little effort has been devoted to the measurement of true band intensities. Ramsay[3] has shown that integrated absorption intensities are reproducible to approximately 5% and are of considerable value because they show correlations with molecular structure.[4]

5.2 Optical materials. The transmittance of several optical materials for infrared radiation is shown in Table 5.1. For efficient

TABLE 5.1

Approximate Low-Frequency Limits for Optical Materials

Glass	4500 cm^{-1}
Quartz	2500
Mica	2000
LiF	1500
CaF_2	1200
NaCl	650
KBr	350
AgCl	350
KRS-5 (TlBr + TlI)	250
CsBr	250

These substances, with the exception of mica and AgCl, are considered as prism materials. For windows in thin sections, their range may be slightly extended.

operation, all parts of the instrument that are required to transmit the radiation should have as high a transmittance as possible.

[2] W. W. Harple, S. E. Wiberley, and W. H. Bauer, *Anal. Chem.*, 24, 635 (1952).

[3] D. A. Ramsay, *J. Am. Chem. Soc.*, 74, 72 (1952).

[4] R. N. Jones, D. A. Ramsay, D. S. Keir, and K. Dobriner, *ibid.*, 74, 80 (1952).

To overcome the absorption losses in lenses, the focusing of infra-red radiation is done with aluminized first-surface mirrors which show very little absorption. The prism, absorption cells, and any desired windows must be of transmitting material. For the prism the optical property of dispersion must be considered, and for the cells possible attack by the sample must be considered.

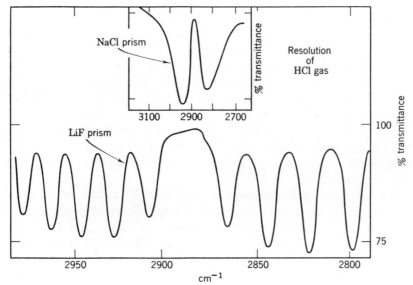

Fig. 5.1   Spectrum of HCl on NaCl and LiF prisms

The dispersion * of a prism is a measure of the angle over which the prism spreads a given spectral range. Other things being equal, a greater dispersion means that the instrument will resolve bands that are closer together as distinct absorption peaks. For the mate-rials given in Table 5.1, a prism that cuts off at a higher frequency will have a higher dispersion in the region where it transmits than any of the materials that follow it. For this reason it is common practice to use one prism out to the cutoff wavelength and then switch to the next prism.

Figure 5.1 shows the spectrum of anhydrous hydrogen chloride measured under identical conditions with a sodium chloride and a lithium fluoride prism. Sodium chloride (rocksalt) is the most widely used prism material as its range is wide enough to cover the most useful bands.

* A more detailed discussion of dispersion and gratings is given in Chapter 8.

High-dispersion grating instruments are needed in the far infrared to measure rotational bands accurately. Grating instruments also require a prism prior to the grating in the optical path to eliminate higher orders † so that a narrow frequency range falls on the entrance slit of the spectrometer proper. The wide spectral range necessary requires several gratings to cover the complete region, and, except in special instruments, the cost would be excessive. For this reason, coupled with the fact that prisms offer sufficient dispersion for the majority of infrared investigations, all of the commercial instruments available at this time have a prism as a monochromator.

The material for absorption cells depends upon its spectral characteristics, but it must not be attacked by the sample. Cells with windows of rocksalt are commonly used with rocksalt prisms, but all samples must be carefully dried to prevent their attacking the windows. If drying is impossible, or the sample reacts chemically with the rocksalt, cell windows can be made of silver chloride. If the sample is to be examined in the shorter wavelength region, quartz or mica are suitable.

5.3 Apparatus for infrared absorption. The parts of an infrared-absorption apparatus may be listed as follows: (1) source, (2) monochromator and optics, (3) receptor, (4) scale and associated circuits, (5) sample holder. These parts will be fully described in later sections. Accessory equipment needed depends on the particular instrument.

In any instrument it is desirable to have some means of eliminating or minimizing the absorption bands of atmospheric water vapor and carbon dioxide. The chief water vapor bands in the rocksalt region are in the neighborhood of 6 microns, whereas carbon dioxide absorbs at about 4.3 and 15 microns. Methods of reducing the effect include filling the light path with dry nitrogen or other nonabsorber, evacuation of the system, or building a compensating system into the instrument.

5.4 Source of radiation. The source of infrared radiation is ordinarily either a Globar or a Nernst glower. Other sources are not available commercially at the present time, but several types have been reported in the literature.

The Globar (trade name of the Carborundum Company) is a silicon carbide rod which is heated to a temperature of 1200 to 2000° C by passage of an electric current. It may be operated from the 110-

---

† A more detailed discussion of dispersion and gratings is given in Chapter 8.

volt a-c line with a variable transformer to give the 40 to 60 volts required for operation. The resistance of the Globar increases slowly with time, and the voltage may be increased with the variable transformer to maintain the output. The source may be stabilized against line voltage fluctuations with a constant-voltage transformer.

The Nernst glower is a tubular filament of rare-earth oxides which operates at a temperature of 1800 to 2000° C, using about 75 alternating volts to supply the heating current. The glower has a negative temperature coefficient of resistance, and so it is necessary to preheat for starting and to include a stabilizing device to prevent a surge of current and burning out of the filament.

Neither source described has ideal characteristics. The radiant energy output falls off rapidly at lower frequencies, and so in order to obtain sufficient radiation to operate the receptor system the pass band of the instrument must be increased at the low frequencies. This results in a loss in resolution of the instrument as a whole.

Another disadvantage of the low radiant-energy output at lower frequencies is the possibility of stray high-frequency light reaching the measuring system. This is possible because the relative energy output of the source at 5000 cm^{-1} may be 50 to 60 times as great as that at 1000 cm^{-1} (see Fig. 5.2), and a relatively small fraction of

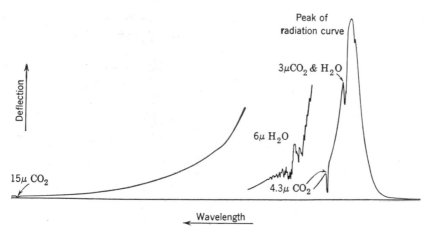

Fig. 5.2   Globar output (Courtesy Perkin-Elmer Corporation)

this high-frequency radiation appearing as stray light when measuring at low frequencies is extremely serious. The modern commercial instruments have been designed to compensate for a major portion of the stray light.

5.5 Monochromator and optics. The usual optical system of an infrared spectrometer consists of a collimating-mirror system at the source, a variable entrance slit to regulate the amount of light, a spherical or parabolic mirror to produce parallel light, the prism and Littrow mirror, an exit slit to select the desired radiation, and a spherical mirror to focus the radiation on the receptor.

A new "double-pass" principle suggested by Walsh [5] involves the passage of radiation through the prism of a Littrow-type monochromator four times instead of twice as in the conventional system. Thus, the dispersion and the energy per spectral slit width is doubled (multiplied by the efficiency factor of the instrument), and scattered radiation is reduced to a negligible amount. This principle is illustrated in Fig. 5.6.

Because of the necessity of focusing with mirrors, the light path is more complex than that of spectrophotometers for the ultraviolet and visible regions. The diagrams in Figs. 5.4 to 5.8 will clarify the typical systems better than any description. In these cases the wavelength focused on the exit slit is varied by rotation of the Littrow mirror.

The dispersion and frequency range of several prism materials were discussed in Section 5.2. This text does not cover the actual operation or design of the optics, and for further treatment, the original journal articles on the design of the instruments are recommended.

Filters for infrared monochromation are being studied for quantitative analysis and for industrial process control. Since the cost of the monochromator is relatively low in infrared installations, it seems unlikely that instruments resembling filter photometers will ever be popular for general exploratory use. They have distinct possibilities, however, for the two fields mentioned.

5.6 Receptor. The receptors or detectors of infrared radiation are designed as black-body absorbers and convert the heat produced into an electric current or mechanical motion for measurement. The energy content of the radiation is small, and every precaution must be taken to reduce losses of energy and insure high conversion. The illuminated area is kept small, and the detector is usually run in a vacuum of 10^{-4} or 10^{-5} mm of mercury to reduce reradiation and conduction and convection losses.

[5] A. Walsh, *Nature, 167,* 810 (1951).

The thermocouple and bolometer are the only detectors in commercial instruments. The thermocouple is similar to the one used for temperature measurement, where a bimetallic junction produces an emf which is proportional to the temperature of the junction. By blackening the junction itself or an attached shield, the radiation is converted to an electric current. The bolometer in its simplest form consists of a thin blackened platinum strip connected as one arm of a Wheatstone bridge. Any radiation absorbed raises the temperature of the strip and changes its resistance. Ambient temperature changes cause a drift in the zero setting of d-c (continuous-radiation) thermocouples and bolometers.

Both receptors may be compensated for changes in ambient temperature by connecting a second junction or strip in opposition to the measuring unit. This compensating junction is not illuminated and subtracts any temperature change of the surroundings from the measured quantity. Since it is difficult to make compensating junctions with identical characteristics, present infrared detectors have been made to respond rapidly to changes in radiant energy so that an interrupted beam can act as a source of radiation with a-c characteristics.

If the thermocouple or bolometer is a true black-body absorber, the sensitivity should be independent of the radiation frequency. In the region of 2.5 to 25 microns (4000 to 400 cm^{-1}), the ideal condition is approached very closely, and the sensitivity, though low, is uniform. The present trend is toward development of a-c thermocouples and bolometers with a high sensitivity, low noise level, and rapid and uniform response.

5.7 Scale and associated circuits. Both of the receptors mentioned in the preceding section give a direct current of small magnitude which may operate a sensitive galvanometer, or else may be amplified to drive a pen recorder. Because of the labor of point-by-point measurement and plotting, the amplifier-recorder system is preferred in commercial instruments.

In addition to the advantage mentioned with regard to the receptor, the chopped beam is now being used for commercial instruments, since it is much easier to build a stable high-gain amplifier for alternating current than for direct current. The beam of radiation coming from the source is interrupted by a rotating disk which is sectored to alternately pass and block the beam. The pulses of electric current produced by the receptor may be amplified by an a-c amplifier, rectified, and fed into a pen recorder. The success of this system required the development of receptors with a sufficiently rapid response time.

The final record of the spectrum is a plot of the amplified voltage values against time, the time function being the speed of travel of the recorder chart. By proper initial settings, the amplified voltage scale may be converted to a per cent transmittance scale. By synchronizing the chart motor and a motor drive on the wavelength adjustment of the monochromator system, the time scale may be converted to a wavelength or frequency scale. The chart will then represent the desired transmittance-wavelength curve.

5.8   Sample holders. The absorption bands of most materials in the near infrared are very strong, and the sample thickness needed for studying liquids or solids is usually in the range of 0.01 to 0.25 mm. This factor and the nature of cell-window materials make sample handling difficult. Cells for gaseous samples may vary from 5 cm to 1 meter in length, depending on the gas pressure and the strength of the absorption bands, so that they are less troublesome.

The small spacing and attackable nature of the cell windows mean that reproducible sample thickness is difficult to obtain. For most quantitative work, the standards and samples must be measured in the same cell, and any calibration curve is valuable only as long as the cell remains constant. It is possible to measure the thickness and calculate to a standard basis, such as 0.1 mm, but this is very laborious.

In qualitative work where the complete spectrum is to be obtained the cell thickness is not critical. It is desirable to use a sample thickness so that the strongest absorption band will show a transmittance of about 5 to 10%. Thicker sections may cause loss of detail by showing complete absorption over a range of wavelengths.

Typical cells are shown in Fig. 5.3. In *a* the spacing is achieved with a lead-foil washer, the windows being clamped in place. The spacing of this type of cell is only approximate, and volatile liquids are hard to retain. In *b* the assembly is spaced, clamped, and measured by the manufacturer. It is filled, emptied, and cleaned through the hypodermic-syringe needles mounted on the cell. Type *c* is a 1-meter gas cell for weakly absorbing gases. Type *d* is a variable-space cell. In the infrared region solute concentrations often range from 5 to 30%. Hence, matched cells will not generally give compensation since it is difficult to predict the net solvent thickness in a given sample because of volume changes on solute mixing. The purpose of this variable cell is to obtain true solvent compensation for a given sample.[6]

The effect of atmospheric water vapor on window materials such as sodium chloride and potassium bromide is very serious. Rocksalt must be handled at relative humidities of 45% or less, whereas for

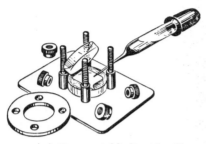

(a) Demountable liquid cell

(b) Sealed liquid cell

(c) One-meter gas cell

(d) Variable-space cell

Fig. 5.3   Infrared cells for Perkin-Elmer instruments (Courtesy Perkin-Elmer Corporation)

potassium bromide 30% or less is recommended. An air-conditioned laboratory is recommended as well as a temperature-control system.

Even with care, optical parts of sodium chloride and potassium bromide will show fogging after a time. Visually opaque windows may show partial infrared transmission. They may be tested by comparison with a clear window. Fogged windows may be polished by hand with fine rouge moistened with alcohol, since the optical flatness is not extremely critical.

It should be noted that in commercial instruments, the cell is placed before the monochromator, rather than after. This allows

[6] J. U. White, *Rev. Sci. Instruments*, 21, 629 (1950).

sharp focusing of the beam on the small receptor and reduces scattered or stray radiation effects.

5.9 Commercial instruments. The more important instruments for the recording of infrared spectra made in the United States today are the Beckman IR-2 and IR-3, the Perkin-Elmer 12-C, 21, and 112, and the Baird. The data given are taken from the manufacturers' literature. The variation in design and construction makes comparison difficult, and, as many changes are constantly being made, critical comparisons would also have little value. The descriptions, however, show the present state of infrared instrumentation.

The Beckman IR-2 infrared spectrophotometer has a Globar source whose radiation is chopped at 10 cps. The output of the bolometer receptor is amplified by a tuned amplifier and may be read on a potentiometer scale or fed into a pen recorder. The temperature is maintained constant by water circulating through coils embedded in the case, and the source output is held constant by a phototube regulator.

The entrance and exit slits are variable and are operated by a calibrated drum. The rocksalt prism covers the range of 0.546 to 15 microns, and the wavelength is read directly from a dial. The wavelength scale may be set manually, or scanned over the complete range by a motor drive synchronized with the pen recorder. The rocksalt region may be scanned in 12, 18, or 43 minutes, depending on the speed and the chart resolution desired.

The Beckman IR-3 infrared recording spectrometer shown in Fig. 5.4 is a single-beam double monochromator instrument employing "memory standardization" to obtain direct-transmittance recordings. A Nernst glower is the source with a monitoring phototube to maintain its emission constant. The beam is chopped at 10 cps. A double monochromator with interchangeable prisms and Littrow mirrors is employed. The 100% reference level for direct-transmittance recording is automatically determined by making a standardizing run against an empty or solvent filled cell. The automatic slit-control system maintains the amplified signal constant and is so arranged that the slit width versus wavelength function is recorded on a wire recorder. On subsequent playback the wire recorder controls the slit and wavelength servomotors, reproducing the standardizing conditions so that absorption spectra from a sample are recorded directly in transmittance.

In Fig. 5.4, A is the Nernst glower source while Z is the phototube which monitors the source to maintain its emission constant. B is the condensing mirror. *C* is the 10-cycle motor-driven beam chopper. *E* is a negative lens which collimates the radiation beam in the liquid-cell region *G*. This feature permits the use of long liquid cells and allows the liquid-cell compartment to be lengthened to

Fig. 5.4*a*   Beckman IR-3 spectrometer (Courtesy Beckman Instrument Company)

accommodate still longer cells or other special equipment without refocusing. The lens *H* brings the beam to a focus on the entrance slit *K*. Lens *J* together with *H* produce an image of the front face of the first prism in the plane of the external aperture *P* in order to permit the use of a narrow external beam and to avoid the introduction of radiation into the monochromator at angles wider than can be usefully employed. In the exit-beam system, lens *Q* confines the beam, producing an image of the front face of the prism in the plane of the thermocouple condensing mirror *V*. The thermocouple window is in the form of a hemispherical lens of potassium bromide which, together with spherical mirror V, forms a condensing system which minifies the image of the exit slit tenfold and has a numerical aperture of 0.65.

Y and Y' are locations for photomultiplier tubes for the visible and ultraviolet spectrum while X is the off-axis condensing mirror which can be swung into place by an external control to deflect the beam

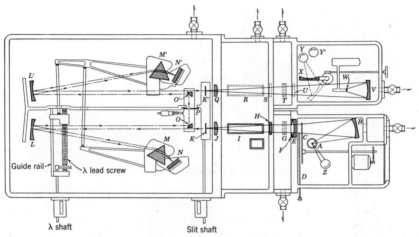

Fig. 5.4b Optical path of Beckman IR-3 spectrometer (Courtesy Beckman Instrument Company)

onto the desired phototube cathode. This control also is coupled to the switch which makes the required electric connections for operating with a phototube in place of the thermocouple.

The valves and arrows show the location of connections for evacuating the instrument, while windows S and U can be inserted if it is desired to isolate the exit beam liquid cell compartment T.

The scanning time per spectral slit width can be varied from 1 to 128 seconds by factors of two. Using the 2-second period, with rocksalt optics, the range of 2 to 15 microns can be scanned at constant time per spectral slit width in 14 minutes. At maximum recording speed, this range can be traversed in 7 minutes.

The Perkin-Elmer model-12-C recording infrared spectrometer is shown in Fig. 5.5, including a diagram of the optical path. The Globar source S_0 has a power consumption of about 200 watts at 40 to 50 volts alternating current. Its radiation is chopped ‡ at approxi-

‡ The chopper is not shown in the diagram.

mately 13 cps, and a collimated beam is formed by the mirrors M_2 and M_3 and the entrance slit S_1. The slits S_1 and S_2 are bilateral and

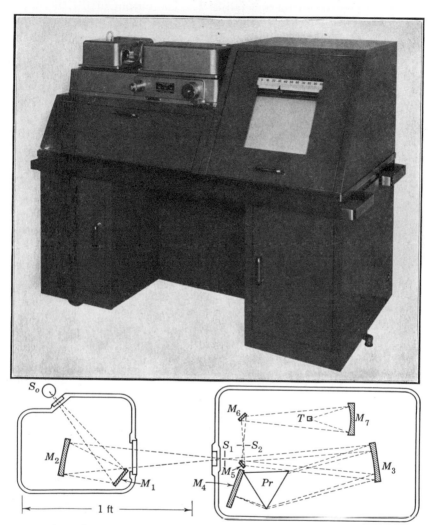

Fig. 5.5 Perkin-Elmer model-12-C recording infrared spectrometer (Courtesy Perkin-Elmer Corporation)

simultaneously operated. The entrance slit jaws are curved to compensate for image curvature introduced by the prism Pr.

The wavelength setting is made by rotation of the Littrow mirror M_4. The manual drive is a 2000-division micrometer drum which rotates the Littrow mirror through 9°. M_3 focuses the image of the entrance slit on the exit slit S_2, and M_7 focuses the image of the exit slit on the high-speed thermocouple T. The output of the thermocouple is amplified, rectified, and fed into a pen recorder. Several interchangeable prisms are available: glass, quartz, calcium fluoride, lithium fluoride, sodium chloride, and potassium bromide for the appropriate spectral regions, and so the wavelength mechanism is marked in arbitrary units and must be calibrated for each prism.

The entrance and exit slits may be coupled to the wavelength drive for continuous recordings. The continuous slit drive corrects for the variation in source output with wavelength. The wavelength drive is synchronized with the pen recorder for running the complete spectrum, or may be set manually to any desired position. The rocksalt region may be scanned in 15, 30, 60, or 120 minutes.

Savitzky and Halford[7] have described a method for the conversion of a Perkin-Elmer model-12-B instrument with a minimum of changes to a ratio-recording double-beam spectrophotometer using phase discrimination and a single detector.

The Perkin-Elmer model-112 infrared spectrometer consists of the model-99 "double-pass" monochromator combined with the source unit and recording system of the model-12-C spectrometer discussed previously. As shown in the optical diagram in Fig. 5.6, light entering the entrance slits is collimated by the off-axis paraboloid onto the prism. After one refraction, the beam is reflected by the Littrow mirror for a second refraction by the prism. The returning beam is brought to a focus by the paraboloid between the two halves of the corner mirror. The corner mirror sends the beam back through the system, slightly displaced so that after the second traversal through the paraboloid, prism, and Littrow portion it is brought to a focus on the exit slit. From the geometry of the system, for any given wavelength of second-pass radiation, a wavelength (always longer) of first-pass radiation also passes through the exit slit. A radiation chopper is inserted after the corner mirror so that the signals produced in the detector may be separated.

The entrance and exit slits are bilateral and controlled simultaneously and equally by a micrometer graduated in microns from 0 to 2 mm. The Littrow mirror angle is varied by means of a second micrometer which is graduated in 2000 divisions. The rocksalt prism can be readily replaced by other prisms.

[7] A. Savitzky and R. S. Halford, *ibid.*, *21*, 203 (1950).

The Perkin-Elmer model-21 double-beam recording infrared spectrometer [8,9] has a single 60° Littrow-mounted rocksalt prism, which can be replaced by other prisms. Unique features include grating filters to remove scattered light, an etched foil compensator to trim the reference beam to match the beam through the sample, and an electric cam to maintain constant energy through the spectrum. This

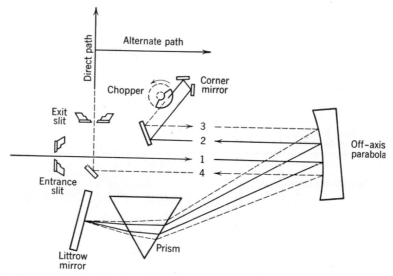

Fig. 5.6 Optical path of Perkin-Elmer model-112 double-pass infrared spectrometer (Courtesy Perkin-Elmer Corporation)

cam is a potentiometer tapped and shunted at several intervals about its circumference to yield a voltage distribution nearly proportional to the slit widths required for uniform energy distribution as the spectrum is traversed. By balancing the voltage from a potentiometer coupled to the slits, against the cam voltage, a servomotor maintains the slits at the proper value. The beam from a Globar source is chopped at 13 cps and the thermocouple signal amplified, rectified, and filtered and remodulated at 60 cycles to drive the two-phase rebalancing servomotor. The spectrum is recorded directly in transmittance on 11 x 32-inch charts. The wavelength scanning speed can be varied from about 5 minutes to 16 hours for the rocksalt region.

A diagram of Baird Associates infrared recording spectrophotom-

[8] J. U. White and M. D. Liston, *J. Optical Soc. Am.*, *40*, 29, 93 (1950).
[9] M. D. Liston and J. U. White, *ibid.*, *40*, 36 (1950).

eter[10] is shown in Fig. 5.7. The Globar source radiation passes through a sample and a compensation cell, and the two beams are

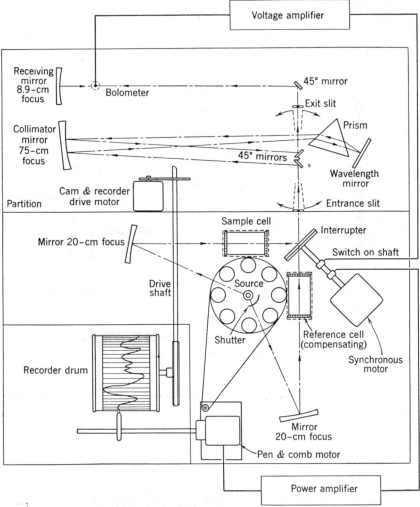

Fig. 5.7   Baird infrared spectrometer (Courtesy Baird Associates, Inc.)

combined at the rotating interrupter. The bolometer is illuminated alternately by the beams from the two cells. Thus the a-c component of the bolometer output represents the transmittance ratio

[10] W. S. Baird, H. M. O'Bryan, G. Ogden, and D. Lee, *ibid.*, *37*, 754 (1947).

of the sample and the reference material in the compensation cell. In this way, the absorption of atmospheric water or carbon dioxide or of the solvent used for a sample solution is mostly removed.

The alternating voltage component is amplified, rectified, and passed through a power amplifier. The resulting d-c power is used to operate an equalizing shutter to balance the two beams, and also to operate the recorder pen.

The entrance and exit slits, the wavelength drive, and the pen recorder are synchronized by a cam system. The chart is linear with respect to wavelength and is directly calibrated. The rocksalt range is scanned in approximately 12 minutes.

5.10 Prism calibration. It is often necessary to calibrate a single-beam instrument or to check the calibration of a double-beam instrument. This is usually done by measuring the spectra of gases whose absorption bands are accurately known. Table 5.2 lists the gases

TABLE 5.2

Compounds for Prism Calibration

Compound	Approximate Frequency Range, cm^{-1}	Prisms
Mercury arc [*]	5400–9900	Quartz
Methane [†]	2800–3200	Quartz, LiF
Ammonia [‡]	700–1300, 3100–3700	Quartz, LiF, NaCl
Hydrogen chloride [§]	2700–3100	LiF
Hydrogen bromide [‖]	2400–2700	LiF
Carbon monoxide [¶]	2000–2300	LiF
Water vapor [**]	1300–2000, 3700–3900	LiF, NaCl
Carbon dioxide [††]	650–725, 2300–2400	LiF, NaCl
Methanol [‡‡]	400–800	KBr

[*] See Appendix A.
[†] A. H. Nielsen et al., *Phys. Rev.*, *48*, 864 (1935).
[‡] G. A. Stinchcomb et al., *ibid.*, *33*, 305 (1929).
[§] E. S. Imes, *Astrophys. J.*, *50*, 251 (1919).
[‖] E. F. Barker, *Phys. Rev.*, *44*, 984 (1933).
[¶] R. T. Lagemann et al., *ibid.*, *72*, 284 (1947).
[**] K. A. Oetjen et al., *Rev. Sci. Instruments*, *13*, 515 (1942).
[††] E. F. Barker, *Astrophys. J.*, *55*, 391 (1922).
[‡‡] A. Borden et al., *J. Chem. Phys.*, *6*, 553 (1938).

most often used for the more common prisms and the references where the absorption bands are tabulated.

Care must be used in matching the spectrum of a gas such as ammonia against a known spectrum by having the ammonia at the same pressure as the reference spectrum. Errors in matching spectra are apparent when the data are plotted on a large-scale graph, for the curve will not be perfectly smooth.

Anhydrous hydrogen chloride and hydrogen bromide are particularly helpful in the calibration of a lithium fluoride prism since they yield simple, symmetrical patterns which are very easy to match (see Fig. 5.1). However, they are corrosive gases and should be removed from the gas cell immediately after the measurement. Liquids, such as 1,4-dioxane,[11] can also be used, provided the absorption bands are sharp. Occasionally, a rough check in the rocksalt region is made with a plastic film such as polystyrene.

5.11   Sample handling.   The cells for holding gaseous and liquid samples have been shown and discussed, but the treatment of solutions and solids in the infrared region is specialized and requires further discussion.

Water is a poor solvent in the infrared region because it absorbs so strongly. Although the region from 2 to 15 microns can be covered [12] using H_2O and D_2O, the resolution is not so good as with organic solvents. The selection of a suitable solvent is governed by three factors. The solvent should have high solvent power for the compound under consideration, should not show absorption in the wavelength region under consideration, and should not react chemically with the solute (complex formation, hydrogen bonding, etc.). Simple, nonpolar liquids such as carbon tetrachloride and carbon disulfide are the best for the two factors mentioned but are not good solvents for all compounds. Ard and Fontaine [13] have suggested the addition of 0.5 to 2.5% triethylamine to these solvents as a means of increasing the solubility of acidic solutes. Torkington and Thompson [14] have discussed various possible solvents, such as benzene, cyclohexane, dioxane, and halogenated hydrocarbons, and have shown that by working with different solvents in different spectral regions it is possible to avoid absorption bands of the solvent.

In many instances it is desirable to use solutions of liquid samples, either to enable the analyst to use a greater sample thickness or to allow the splitting up of associated liquids by dilution. Dilution

[11] D. S. McKinney, C. B. Leberknight, and J. C. Warner, *J. Am. Chem. Soc.*, 59, 481 (1937).

[12] R. C. Gore, R. B. Barnes, and E. Petersen, *Anal. Chem.*, 21, 382 (1949).

[13] J. S. Ard and T. D. Fontaine, *ibid.*, 23, 133 (1951).

[14] P. Torkington and H. W. Thompson, *Trans. Faraday Soc.*, 41, 184 (1945).

reduces the interaction of solute molecules among themselves, but caution must be observed in selection of the solvent.

Solid samples may be dissolved in a suitable solvent, or mulled to a paste with a small amount of Nujol and placed in cells such as shown in Fig. 5.3*a*. Low-melting substances may be melted or sublimed on a cell window and then clamped in a holder. Other techniques of preparing thin layers include sheeting of plastic materials, evaporation of a volatile solvent from a solution placed on a window

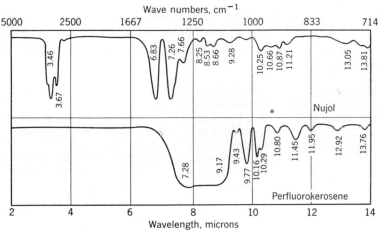

Fig. 5.8   Infrared spectra of Nujol and perfluorokerosene

or forming a colloidal suspension in a suitable solvent. Dolinsky [15] has obtained quantitative infrared spectra of such widely differing materials as sugars, sulfonated coal-tar colors, sulfa drugs, and amino acids by dispersing the materials in the presence of aluminum stearate in nonpolar solvents. Since Nujol (mineral oil) absorbs strongly in the carbon hydrogen region, perfluorokerosene, a completely fluorinated kerosene, is often used as a mulling agent for this region. Figure 5.8 shows the infrared spectra of these two materials.

A recently developed technique promises to be the most satisfactory for obtaining the infrared spectra of solid materials. [16-18] Solid potassium bromide sample disks are prepared by mixing 2 to 4 mg of the samples with 1 gram of pure potassium bromide powder. The

[15] M. Dolinsky, *J. Assoc. Offic. Agr. Chemists*, *34*, 748 (1951).

[16] M. M. Stimson, *J. Am. Chem. Soc.*, *74*, 1805 (1952).

[17] U. Schiedt, *Z. Naturforsch.*, *76*, 270 (1952).

[18] *Instrument News* (Perkin-Elmer Corp., Norwalk, Conn.), *4*, no. 3 (1953).

powders are intimately mixed in a ball mill or with a vibrator and then pressed in a hydraulic molding press at a pressure of 10 tons for approximately 1 minute. The resulting disks are visually clear and of a known weight concentration, and so they make excellent permanent standards for quantitative analysis. The disks can be readily placed in the conventional sample holder. The usual difficulties and interferences resulting from solvents or Nujol mulls are avoided, and the spectra obtained show considerably better detail and resolution.

5.12 Structural analysis. In Fig. 5.9, a chart by N. B. Colthup, Stamford Research Laboratories, American Cyanamid Company, is reproduced. The text [19] accompanying this chart is reproduced here in its entirety.

A chart is presented summarizing our knowledge concerning the probable positions of the characteristic infrared absorption bands of specific groups from 4000 to 400 wave numbers. Especial attention has been given to the region below 1400 wave numbers where specific group vibrations are complicated by their interaction with the rest of the molecule. This difficulty is particularly noticeable for assignments in the single bond region for such groups as ethyl, propyl, aldehyde, ketone, etc., where the bands are relatively weak and quite sensitive to the manner in which these groups are attached to the rest of the molecule.

Some of the data were taken from the literature, and most of these have been rechecked and extended in the course of routine work. The rest of the correlations are made from unpublished work done in these laboratories.

As some of the correlations are tentative and much overlapping of band positions occurs, this chart should be used with discretion mainly as an aid in extrapolating from known compounds to unknown samples.

The indicated regions on the chart are the regions within which the band is normally expected to fall. The abbreviations *s*, *m*, and *w* under the region markers indicate that the band is generally strong, medium, or weak.

The alkane groups are characterized by the well-known carbon–hydrogen stretching [1,20] (3000–2800 cm^{-1}) and carbon–hydrogen bending [1] (1475–1300 cm^{-1}) bands. When the methyl group is attached to a nitrogen atom the 2900-cm^{-1} bands generally shift to higher wave numbers, and when it is on an oxygen atom the bands are lower. When the methyl is adjacent to a carbonyl as in acetates and methyl ketones all the bands are shifted somewhat and the 1370-cm^{-1} band is intensified. A similar intensification occurs for the 1420-cm^{-1} band when a methylene is adjacent to a carbonyl or nitrile group. The C–H bending band at

[19] N. B. Colthup, *J. Optical Soc. Am.*, **40**, 397 (1950).

[20] E. L. Saier and N. D. Coggeshall, *Anal. Chem.*, **20**, 812 (1948).

1340 cm^{-1} is weak in hydrocarbons but is intensified when this group is adjacent to an oxygen or nitrogen atom.

A branched methyl grouping such as isopropyl and tertiary butyl generally results in a splitting of the 1370-cm^{-1} band [1] and gives rise to the branched single bond vibrations [21] around 1200 cm^{-1}. The correlations of the single-bond stretching bands of ethyl and n-propyl [22] between 1100 and 800 cm^{-1} are less reliable as the bands are sometimes weak. In addition these particular correlations apply only when the groups are attached to a carbon, nitrogen, or oxygen atom. Attachment to heavier atoms such as sulfur shifts these bands to lower wave numbers.

When four or more methylene groups are adjacent in a chain, they give rise to a fairly reliable medium-strong rocking band [23] at 730 cm^{-1}. When there are less than four, this band shifts to a higher wave number.

The alkene and alkyne groups have been well covered in the literature.[24-28] The out-of-plane hydrogen bending vibrations give rise to strong bands from 1000 to 600 cm^{-1} and the in-plane hydrogen bending vibrations from 1450 to 1250 cm^{-1}. These are quite sensitive to the type of alkene present. The medium-strong double- and triple-bond bands are lowered by conjugation and weakened if they are centrally located in the molecule. The hydrogen stretching bands are higher than for the alkane groups, centering around 3000 cm^{-1} for alkenes and 3250 cm^{-1} for alkynes.

Aromatic groups [29] are characterized below 1400 cm^{-1} by a series of sharp bands between 1200 and 1000 cm^{-1} and by the strong out-of-plane hydrogen bending bands between 900 and 675 cm^{-1}. These latter are the most useful in substitution studies. Five adjacent hydrogen atoms on the ring as in monosubstituted benzene generally give rise to bands at 700 cm^{-1} and 740 cm^{-1}, 4 adjacent hydrogen atoms as in ortho disubstitution give rise to a band at 750 cm^{-1}, 3 as in meta and vicinal trisubstitution at 780 cm^{-1}, 2 as in para and unsymmetrical trisubstitution at 820 cm^{-1}, and 1 isolated hydrogen atom on the ring as in meta unsymmetrical and symmetrical trisubstitution at 860 cm^{-1}. This empirical method of classification can be extended to fit nonbenzene aromatic molecules (with slightly greater deviations) such as α-naphthalenes (4 adjacent and 3 adjacent hydrogen atoms), β-naphthalenes (4 adjacent, 2 adjacent, and

[21] G. B. B. M. Sutherland and D. M. Simpson, *J. Chem. Phys.*, 15, 153 (1947).

[22] K. W. F. Kohlrausch, *Ramanspektren*, Akademische Verlagsgellschaft Becker und Erler, Leipzig; Edwards Brothers, Ann Arbor, Mich. (1943).

[23] N. Sheppard and G. B. B. M. Sutherland, *Nature*, 159, 739 (1947).

[24] H. W. Thompson and P. Torkington, *Trans. Faraday Soc.*, 61, 246 (1945).

[25] R. C. Gore and J. L. Johnson, *Phys. Rev.*, 68, 283A (1945).

[26] J. E. Kilpatrick and K. S. Pitzer, *J. Research Natl. Bur. Standards*, 38, 191 (1947).

[27] J. H. Wotiz and F. A. Miller, *J. Am. Chem. Soc.*, 71, 3441 (1949).

[28] F. Halverson, R. F. Stamm, and J. J. Whalen, *J. Chem. Phys.*, 16, 808 (1948).

[29] G. Herzberg, *Infrared and Raman Spectra of Polyatomic Molecules*, D. Van Nostrand, New York (1945).

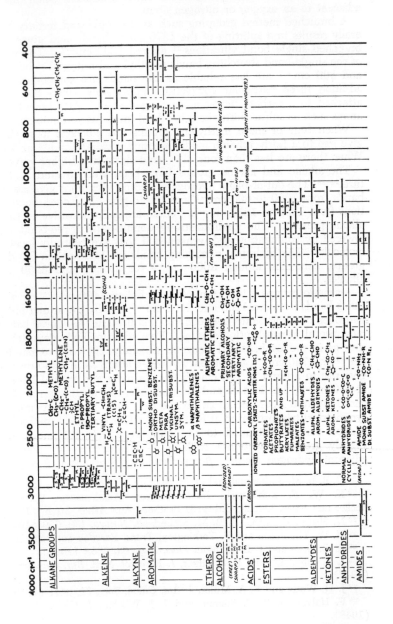

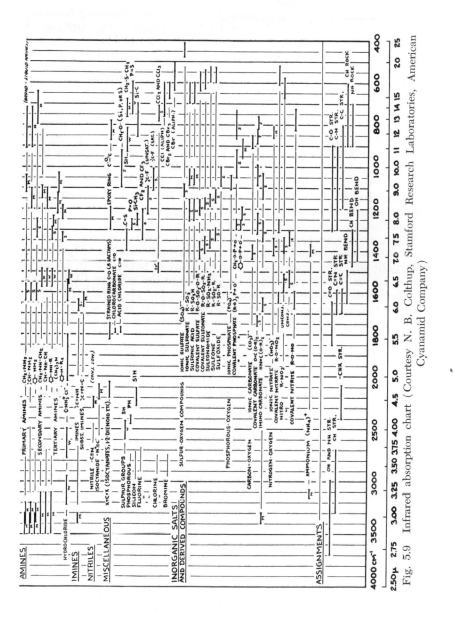

Fig. 5.9 Infrared absorption chart (Courtesy N. B. Colthup, Stamford Research Laboratories, American Cyanamid Company)

on 1 isolated), substituted anthracenes, substituted pyridines, tetrasubstituted benzenes and steroids.

The well-known 1500- and 1600-cm^{-1} bands of substituted benzenes are probably caused by in-plane skeletal vibrations.[29] The 1620-cm^{-1} band shown by para disubstitution is generally variable in intensity but is strongest when one of the substituents is ortho-para directing and the other meta directing.

The position of the strong C—O band as in ethers, alcohols, and esters is dependent on the manner of the substitution of the hydrogens on the carbon atom.[30-32] Generally, the greater the degree of substitution, the higher will be the wave number of the band. The OH bending in primary alcohols[32] interacts with the adjacent methylene vibrations, giving rise to several weak bands from 1450 to 1300 cm^{-1}. A single stronger band appears here in tertiary alcohols and phenols. The C—O band in alcohols is sensitive to hydrogen bonding, just as is the well-known OH stretching band. Both the OH bending and the C—O stretching bands shift to lower wave numbers when unbonding occurs as it does on dilution or vaporization.

The carboxylic acid carbonyl and the C—O (1300–1200-cm^{-1}) bands are replaced by a symmetric and asymmetric vibration of the CO_2^- group near 1420 and 1600 cm^{-1} when the carboxyl is ionized as in metal or amine salts or zwitterionization. In addition to the in-plane COH bending, there exists, in the acid dimer only, an out-of-plane OH ← O bending vibration which gives rise to a broad, medium band at 920 cm^{-1}. This band has been investigated by monomer-dimer studies of normal and deuterated acetic and formic acids.[33] This type of band also appears near here in acetylacetone which is partially enolized, giving a similar OH ← O structure. This disappears upon making the salt.

In the amines the positions of the bands caused by the single bonds vary not only with the substitution of the hydrogens on the carbon atom as do the alcohols but also with the substitution of the hydrogens on the nitrogen. In addition to the other well-known amine bands,[1,31] there is a broad strong band in primary aliphatic amines, especially the straight-chain amines, around 800 cm^{-1} which is probably caused by a rocking of the amino and methylene groups.[34,35] The band due to the NH bending vibration which is medium strong in mono-N-substituted amides (1530 cm^{-1}) is generally weak in secondary amines.

[30] J. Lecompte, *Traité de chimie organique*, Tome II, Masson, editeurs, Paris (1936).

[31] V. Z. Williams, R. Hofstadter, and R. C. Herman, *J. Chem. Phys.*, 7, 802 (1939).

[32] A. Borden and E. F. Barker, *ibid.*, 6, 553 (1938).

[33] L. G. Bonner and R. Hofstadter, *ibid.*, 6, 534 (1938).

[34] A. P. Cleaves and E. K. Plyler, *ibid.*, 7, 563 (1939).

[35] C. R. Baily, S. C. Carson, and E. F. Daly, *Proc. Roy. Soc. London*, A173, 339 (1939).

The inorganic salts [29] and halogen compounds [29, 36] have been covered in the literature. The symmetric and asymmetric sulfonyl stretching vibrations and those of related compounds have been studied by Schreiber [37] and others [38] and extended in these laboratories to complete the series. A set of general regions in which various vibrational frequencies occur is included at the bottom of the chart.

McMurry and Thornton [39] have shown that, in a study of hydrocarbons only, considerably narrower ranges are obtained for structural correlations than those shown in the preceding figure.

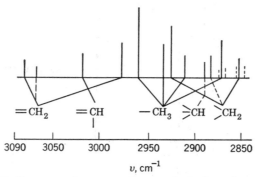

Fig. 5.10   C—H Absorption-frequency diagram for hydrocarbons (Reprinted by permission of *Analytical Chemistry*)

Articles are continually appearing in the literature, which add to the knowledge tabulated in Fig. 5.9. For example, an article [40] on phosphorus compounds lists the characteristic frequencies of such groups as P—H, P—Cl, P—C, P—O—C and P—O—H. A study [41] of the absorption patterns in the 5-to-6-micron region yields information relative to the number and positions of the substituents on the benzene ring. A fruitful field for research is the carbon–hydrogen region using a lithium fluoride prism. Figure 5.10 shows the correlations obtained in this region.[42]

Evidence of the presence of the cyclopropyl,[43] cyclobutyl, and

[36] P. Torkington and H. W. Thompson, *Trans. Faraday Soc.*, *41*, 236 (1945).

[37] V. C. Schreiber, *Anal. Chem.*, *21*, 1168 (1949).

[38] D. Barnard, J. M. Fabian, and H. P. Koch, *J. Chem. Soc.*, 2442 (1949).

[39] H. L. McMurry and V. Thornton, *Anal. Chem.*, *24*, 318 (1952).

[40] L. W. Daasch and D. C. Smith, *ibid.*, *23*, 853 (1951).

[41] C. W. Young, R. B. DuVall, and N. Wright, *ibid.*, *23*, 709 (1951).

[42] A. Pozefsky and N. D. Coggeshall, *ibid.*, *23*, 1611 (1951).

[43] S. E. Wiberley and S. C. Bunce, *ibid.*, *24*, 623 (1952).

higher saturated ring systems [44] is more conclusively established by a study of the carbon–hydrogen region under high resolution. Even in the identification of inorganic materials, infrared spectroscopy has proved to be a valuable aid.[45, 46]

Considerable information on structure has been gained with isotopes, particularly deuterium. Since the mass of the atoms affects the absorption frequency, it is apparent that the frequency differences obtained with normal and isotopic carbon, hydrogen, and nitrogen would permit the classification of bond vibrations. The observed frequency shifts are also useful in the determination of relative bond strengths (force constants).

5.13 Qualitative organic analysis. In the chemical method of qualitative organic analysis, the sample is tested for solubility class and functional groups, and a derivative is prepared. These data, along with various physical constants are compared with textbook tables and the literature, and, if the compound properties and the derivative have been previously reported, the problem is solved.

In the infrared method, the spectrum of the compound is obtained, functional groups and general class are noted, and the spectrum is compared with a library of curves for compounds of this type. If the compound has been previously measured, the two curves will match and the problem is solved.

Both methods require that the compound be previously known and reported. The infrared method is a single measurement of a multivalued property, while the classical method is a series of measurements of several single-valued properties and a series of yes–no–maybe chemical tests. The superiority of the newer system is evident; yet there are certain drawbacks.

The equipment is expensive and requires a certain amount of operator skill, particularly in interpretation of spectra rather than in operation of the equipment. The library, or compilation of spectra, is lacking. The variation in operating properties and conditions of various instruments makes it difficult to compare results among different laboratories. The exact superposition of curves which allows the choice between two members of a homologous series is often

[44] E. K. Plyler and N. J. Acquista, *J. Research Natl. Bur. Standards, 43,* 37 (1949).

[45] J. M. Hunt, M. P. Wisherd and L. C. Bonham, *Anal. Chem., 22,* 1478 (1950).

[46] F. A. Miller and C. H. Wilkins, *ibid., 24,* 1253 (1952).

difficult even on two instruments of the same make, and the filing and handling of the number of curves involved is troublesome.

Some of these problems are being attacked by workers who realize the value of the method. Standardization of all infrared equipment is impossible, but progress can be made in the other factors.

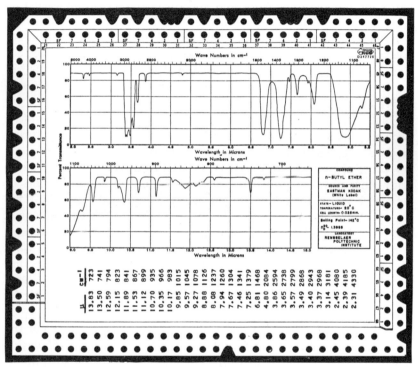

Fig. 5.11   Punch card for infrared spectra (Courtesy National Research Council)

Laboratories § doing sufficient qualitative work are compiling their own libraries of curves. The American Petroleum Institute is preparing and distributing spectra of compounds, mostly hydrocarbons. A collection of 2500 spectra measured on the Baird instrument is available from Samuel Sadtler and Sons, a consulting laboratory.

The handling of large amounts of accumulated data is being speeded with edge-punch cards. In this way, data recorded on a card can be selected from the files on the basis of absorption fre-

§ An excellent bibliography, classified by author, compound, and subject has been compiled by the Texas Company, Beacon, N. Y.

quencies, structural features, or other criteria with great speed. The punch card may contain a reproduction of the spectrum or a file number so that the actual chart may be picked out. A punch-card committee || of the Symposium on Molecular Structure and Spectroscopy of Ohio State University headed by E. C. Creitz of the National Bureau of Standards has developed standardized infrared punch cards for bibliography work and spectra characterization (see Fig. 5.11).

Even edge-punch cards become unwieldy when the number of spectra exceeds the 10,000 mark. In order to cope with such a situation, L. Kuentzel [47] has used International Business Machine (IBM) cards which are sorted by machine, and the 2500 spectra mentioned above are available on such cards.

Qualitative organic analysis by infrared spectroscopy is rapidly becoming available in many academic and industrial laboratories. In the study of an unknown, the use of infrared spectroscopy to show the proof of presence or absence of certain functional groups, along with other physical properties such as melting or boiling points or refractive index, may indicate the major component. By obtaining the spectrum of a known sample and comparing with the unknown, the proof is complete, and the library of spectra has been increased.

5.14   Quantitative analysis. Infrared spectroscopy is very valuable for the quantitative analysis of complex mixtures which are impossible to analyze accurately by other methods. Even isomers have sufficiently different spectra to permit the estimation of one in the presence of others.

In the case of ultraviolet and visible spectra, the simplicity of the spectra and the broad bands obtained limit the selection of usable wavelengths. In the case of infrared spectra, even the simplest molecules have complex enough spectra to permit the selection of many wavelengths.

In quantitative work, the first step is to obtain the spectra of all the components of a mixture. The next step is to select wavelengths at which only one of the components absorbs. Standards can then be prepared and measured at these wavelengths and a calibration curve prepared. Figure 5.12 shows the plot of absorbance versus concentration at such wavelengths for a number of alkaloids.[48]

|| The work of this committee has been taken over by a committee on infra-red absorption spectra established by the National Research Council.

[47] L. E. Kuentzel, *ibid.*, 23, 1413 (1951).

[48] G. Pleat, J. H. Harley, and S. E. Wiberley, *J. Am. Pharm. Assoc., Sci. Ed.*, 40, 107 (1951).

Generally, a linear plot is obtained for liquids unless there is intermolecular reaction with the solvent. In the case of gases of the simpler molecules, pressure-broadening effects [49] often cause a deviation from linearity.

In the measurement of absorbance, two techniques are used. In one instance the zero absorbance is set with a blank cell, and then

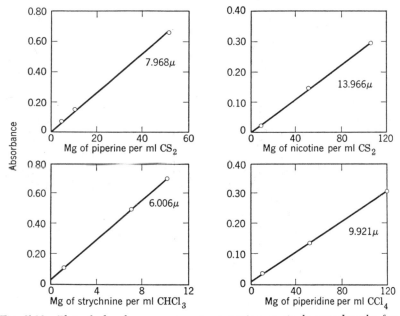

Fig. 5.12 Plot of absorbance versus concentration at single wavelengths for a number of alkaloids (Courtesy American Pharmaceutical Association)

the absorbance of the same or a matched cell containing the compound is determined. In the second method, referred to as the "baseline density" method, the spectrum is recorded through the absorption bands selected for the components, and a straight line is drawn across the base of the absorption band between two determined frequencies. The zero absorbance is measured from the zero signal point to the drawn base line, and the absorbance of the compound being determined from the zero signal to the maximum point of the absorption band itself. These two methods are equal in the accuracy obtainable, but the first method is simpler and less subject to per-

[49] M. G. Mellon, *Analytical Absorption Spectroscopy*, p. 502, John Wiley, New York (1950).

sonal judgment, and the "base-line density" method has the advantage of indicating the presence of unexpected components and serving as a calibration check.

In the quantitative analysis of multicomponent mixtures, the same principles and methods discussed in detail in Chapter 3 hold true and need not be developed further.

The continuous monitoring of gas streams is an important industrial application of infrared in the field of quantitative analysis. Commercial infrared gas analyzers, which operate on the same principles as the commercial spectrometers previously described are available from Leeds and Northrup Company and Baird Associates, Inc.

5.15 Microwave spectroscopy. As evidence of the growing interest in microwave spectroscopy, the National Bureau of Standards has published as an NBS Circular a set of molecular microwave-spectra tables tabulating 99 molecules.[50] Molecular-spectra investigations by microwave-frequency techniques involve insertion of microwave energy of known and controllable frequencies (2000 to 150,000 Mc) into a low-pressure gas cell containing the gas to be studied. The energy absorption by the gas is recorded as a function of frequency. Absorption maxima occur at the characteristic absorption frequencies of the gas, with negligible absorption at the other frequencies. The microwave spectrum obtained is an invariant characteristic of the gas and may be applied to qualitative or quantitative analysis similarly to infrared spectra. Gordy[51] and Townes[52] have written excellent reviews of this relatively new but expanding field and a text by Gordy, Smith and Trambarulo[53] is now available.

5.16 Theoretical applications. In addition to its value in structural analysis, infrared spectroscopy has been of tremendous value in the field of thermodynamics. Once the fundamental frequencies of a molecule are known from infrared and Raman spectra, it is possible to calculate the partition function of a molecule and then the related thermodynamic quantities such as heat capacity, entropy, enthalpy, and free energy.[54–57] The numerical agreement of these values cal-

[50] P. Kisliuk and C. H. Townes, Molecular Microwave Spectra Tables, *Natl. Bur. Standards Circ. 518* (June 23, 1952).

[51] W. Gordy, *Revs. Modern Phys., 20,* 668 (1948).

[52] C. H. Townes, *Am. Scientist, 40,* 270 (1952).

[53] W. Gordy, W. V. Smith and R. Trambarulo, *Microwave Spectroscopy,* John Wiley, New York (1953).

[54] H. Eyring and J. Walter, *J. Chem. Ed., 18,* 73 (1941).

[55] S. Glasstone, *Thermodynamics for Chemists,* pp. 95–120, D. Van Nostrand, New York (1947).

culated from spectroscopic data with those determined by thermal methods is a striking confirmation of the validity of the theory of statistical mechanics.

Bibliography

Books

G. Herzberg, *Spectra of Diatomic Molecules,* D. Van Nostrand, New York (1950).

J. LeCompte, *Spectrométrie infrarouge et ses applications physicochimiques,* University of Paris Press, Paris (1949).

H. M. Randall, R. G. Fowler, N. Fuson, and J. R. Dangl, *Infrared Determination of Organic Structures,* D. Van Nostrand, New York (1949).

L. N. Ferguson, *Electronic Structures of Organic Molecules,* Prentice-Hall, New York (1952).

Articles

R. B. Barnes, R. C. Gore, R. W. Stafford, and V. Z. Williams, *Anal. Chem.,* **20,** 402 (1948).

Symposium, Application of Infrared Spectra, *Trans. Faraday Soc.,* **41,** 171 (1945).

V. Z. Williams, *Rev. Sci. Instruments, 19,* 135 (1948).

[56] S. Glasstone, *Theoretical Chemistry,* Chap. VIII, D. Van Nostrand, New York (1944).

[57] G. Herzberg, *Infrared and Raman Spectra of Polyatomic Molecules,* Chap. V, D. Van Nostrand, New York (1945).

CHAPTER 6

Raman Spectroscopy

If electromagnetic radiation of energy content $h\nu$ is used to irradiate a molecule, this energy may be transmitted, absorbed, or scattered. A large percentage of the energy may be transmitted or absorbed but only a small percentage may be scattered. In absorption, the energy is directly related to the vibrational and rotational energy. In the previous chapters we have discussed the absorption of electromagnetic radiation in the various regions of the spectrum.

The energy may be scattered as in the Tyndall effect by minute, randomly distributed particles in a heterogeneous system (i.e. smoke particles) or by Rayleigh scattering, which is the result of transitory changes in the index of refraction of the medium. It was shown by Lord Rayleigh[1] that the colors of the sky are caused by scattered light and that the molecules of the air are the scattering particles. Radiation resulting from Rayleigh scattering has the same frequency as the incident radiation and is of little spectroscopic value.

In 1928 C. V. Raman[2] described another type of scattering, known as the Raman effect. Raman scattered light has a different frequency from the incident light. The Raman effect is produced by molecular vibration and rotation of the molecule and is relatively weak compared to the absorption of energy caused by molecular vibration and rotation. This effect had been theoretically predicted by Smekal[3] in 1923 and is sometimes referred to as the Smekal-Raman effect, particularly in the German literature.

Rayleigh and Raman scattering are related in that the intensity of both increases as the fourth power of the frequency of the incident radiation.

[1] J. W. S. Rayleigh, *Phil. Mag.*, 47, 375 (1899).
[2] C. V. Raman, *Indian J. Phys.*, 2, 387 (1928).
[3] A. Smekal, *Naturwiss.*, 11, 873 (1923).

6.1 The Raman effect. The Raman effect can best be illustrated by considering an actual example such as the Raman spectrum of carbon tetrachloride, which is shown in Fig. 6.1.

In this example, mercury lines of 4046.6 A (24,713 cm^{-1}) and 4358.4 A (22,945 cm^{-1}) are used as the incident radiation. Actually the mercury lines at 4077.7, 4108.0, and 4339.2 A would also appear in such a spectrum, but they have been omitted for the sake of simplicity. Raman lines appear on either side of the exciting mercury

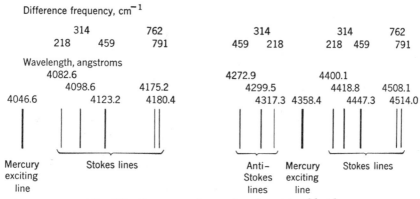

Fig. 6.1 Raman spectrum of carbon tetrachloride

lines at both higher and lower frequencies than the incident radiation. The lines, occurring at higher frequencies than the incident radiation are called anti-Stokes lines and those at lower frequencies are called Stokes lines. This terminology arises from the Stokes rule of fluorescence, which stated that scattered radiation does not have a higher frequency than the exciting radiation. Anti-Stokes lines, though of theoretical interest since, as predicted by quantum theory,[4] they have a much smaller intensity than Stokes lines, are of little practical importance since they have only been observed for the smaller frequencies of such polyatomic molecules as CCl_4, CS_2 and $CHCl_2Br$. These particular compounds have very intense Raman lines.

It should be noted that both mercury lines yield identical Raman lines. Since Raman lines are frequency differences, they are often termed Raman shifts and are designated as $\Delta \bar{\nu}$ in cm^{-1} and are calculated by means of the formula

[4] G. Herzberg, *Infrared and Raman Spectra of Polyatomic Molecules*, p. 251, D. Van Nostrand, New York (1945).

$$\Delta \bar{\nu} \; \text{cm}^{-1} = \frac{10^8}{\lambda^*} - \frac{10^8}{\lambda}$$

where $\lambda*$ is the wavelength in angstroms of the exciting line and λ is the wavelength in angstroms of the Raman line.

In addition to the frequency of the Raman lines, the intensity of the lines and their degree of polarization are also of value. In a mixture of one or more components, the intensity of the Raman line is proportional to the concentration of the molecular compound from which it originates. Line-intensity measurements are therefore of value in both qualitative and quantitative estimation. In the past, the intensities of Raman lines have been reported as strong to very weak, or on a 10-to-0 basis with 10 being the strongest intensity. A more accurate and reproducible system is to measure the ratio of the intensity of the sample's Raman line to that of $\Delta \bar{\nu} = 459 \; \text{cm}^{-1}$ line of carbon tetrachloride; such a ratio has been defined as the scattering coefficient.[5]

The intensities of Raman lines are found to vary if the scattered radiation is polarized by means of a Polaroid sheet or a Nicol prism. The degree of depolarization of a Raman line is described by its depolarization factor p where

$$p = \frac{I_{\perp}}{I_{\|}}$$

$I_{\perp}$ = the intensity of the horizontal light vibrations; $I_{\|}$ = the intensity of the vertical light vibrations.

Experimental studies of the polarization of Raman lines show that each line can have a state of polarization independent of the usual diffused scattering and independent of the other Raman lines simultaneously emitted. The depolarization factor p varies from 0 to $\frac{6}{7}$. The polarization of a given Raman line depends upon the symmetry of the molecular vibration from which the line originates. For example, vibrations symmetrical to a center of symmetry produce highly polarized Raman lines, i.e., the depolarization ratio is small or zero. Knowledge of the depolarization factors of Raman lines therefore aids in correlating observed spectral frequencies with the fundamental vibrational modes of the molecule. Although the experimental measurements of these depolarization factors are difficult as

[5] M. R. Fenske, W. G. Braun, R. V. Wiegand, D. Quiggle, R. H. McCormick, and D. H. Rank, *Anal. Chem.*, *19*, 700 (1947).

described by Cabannes and Rousset [6] as well as by Reitz,[7] somewhat simpler photographic methods have been described by Edsall and Wilson [8] and Cleveland and Murray.[9] Fenske, Rank and co-workers [5] have described photoelectric methods for these measurements.

6.2 Raman equipment. To measure the Raman effect, a high-intensity source, filtered to provide essentially monochromatic radiation, is directed on a cyclindrical Raman tube parallel to the source. Since the intensity of Raman scattering is only a few thousandths of the intensity of Rayleigh scattering, which is in turn much less than the radiation of the source, only the light scattered by the sample at right angles to the incident beam is focused on the spectrograph. Similar to absorption measurements, equipment for Raman measurements can be grouped under the following essential components: source, filter, sample holder, monochromator, and receptor.

(*a*) *Source*. Since the Raman effect is relatively weak, it is essential to have a source of high intensity. The most common source of excitation is the mercury arc, which yields strong lines at 2537, 3650, 4047, 4358, 5461 and 5770 to 5790 A. In order to reduce the time of exposure required to obtain a useful image on a photographic plate, as many as 2 to 12 lamps are placed around the sample. Four type-FL5 lamps are used in the Hilger Raman source unit. This lamp emits the characteristic line spectrum of mercury at great intensity with only a comparatively weak background in the region between 4358 and 4916 A. The heat created by a group of such lamps must be dissipated by water cooling.

A type of water-cooled low-pressure mercury lamp, referred to as the "Toronto" type because of the extensive work of Welsh and Crawford at the University of Toronto, is shown in Fig. 6.2. This lamp is produced commercially by the Applied Research Laboratories for their Raman spectrograph. The active portion of the ARL lamp is a four-turn 3½-inch inside diameter helix constructed of 25-mm Pyrex tubing. The power electrodes and the starting electrode (centered on the helix) are mercury pools. Extending through each of the mercury pools of the power electrodes is a water-cooled condenser. This lamp has a very high intensity, a low background and a very favorable ratio of unwanted mercury lines (4338 and 4349 A) to the

[6] J. Cabannes and A. Rousset, *Ann. phys.*, *19*, 229 (1933).

[7] A. W. Reitz, *Z. physik. Chem.*, *B33*, 179 (1936).

[8] J. T. Edsall and E. B. Wilson, Jr., *J. Chem. Phys.*, *6*, 124 (1938).

[9] F. F. Cleveland and M. J. Murray, *ibid.*, *7*, 396 (1939).

desired 4358 A line.[10]   A similar "Toronto"-type lamp has been described by Heigl, Dudenbostel, Black and Wilson.[11]

(*b*) *Filters.* It can be seen from Fig. 6.1 that the mercury lines at
4047 and 4358 A yield identical Raman shifts.   Since Raman lines

Fig. 6.2   Low-pressure mercury lamp (Courtesy Applied Research Laboratories)

may overlap one another and yield patterns that are difficult to interpret, it is necessary to have monochromatic radiation.   Either glass
filters, or solutions, which transmit only the desired wavelength, are
suitable for such a purpose.   Although such filters do remove the

[10] J. W. Kemp, Recent Advances in Raman Equipment, Optical Soc. America
Convention, Chicago (Oct. 1951).

[11] J. J. Heigl, B. F. Dudenbostel, J. F. Black, and J. A. Wilson, *Anal. Chem.*,
22, 154 (1950).

undesired wavelengths from the source, they also reduce the intensity of the desired wavelength. This is objectionable because the time of exposure must be increased. Table 6.1 lists the filters or solutions [12] that are commonly used for the various exciting lines.

TABLE 6.1

Filters for the Raman Effect

Hg Line	Filters
2537	Mercury vapor (or alternatively a mercury resonance lamp as a source).
3650	Corning Glass no. 5874 (a nickel oxide glass).
4047	Corning Glass Noviol 0 (no. 3060) or a sodium nitrite solution to remove Hg-3650.
	Iodine in carbon tetrachloride to remove Hg-4358, or 0.003 M potassium ferricyanide to remove Hg-4358.
4358	Saturated sodium nitrite solution for lower wavelengths.
	Praseodymium chloride.
	Rhodamine 5GDN Extra.
5461	Basic sodium chromate (pH 8.7) for lines below 5461.
	Cupric nitrate solution.
	Saturated solution of neodymium chloride.

(*c*) *Sample Holder.* For a study of the Raman effect the type of sample holder is dependent upon the intensity of the source and the nature and availability of the sample. For measuring gases and liquids, the volume of the tube may vary from 5 to 100 ml. For handling liquids, a Wood's tube, a tube with a curved and blackened neck, has been popular in the past. A simple Raman tube, which is easily cleaned and filled, is used in the Hilger Raman source unit. This tube fits inside a double-jacketed housing, which provides an outer jacket for water cooling and an inner jacket for holding a liquid filter solution, and is a straight glass tube with a plane-parallel glass window sealed to the lower end. It requires 7 ml of liquid to fill it to the required depth. A similar-type Raman tube with a ground-glass stopper has been described by Heigl et al.[11] Such a ground-glass joint has an advantage in case it is necessary to distil a sample directly into the tube. Solids are usually dissolved before the Raman spectrum is obtained. Water, which is so opaque in the infrared region, is an ideal solvent for inorganic compounds. For organic compounds the solvents suitable for ultraviolet and infrared work are equally useful. The choice of such a solvent is dependent upon

[12] R. F. Stamm, *Ind. Eng. Chem., Anal. Ed., 17,* 318 (1945).

its solvent power, its Raman spectrum, and possible chemical inter-action with the solute.

(*d*) *Monochromator.* The majority of Raman measurements have been made with wide-aperture prism spectrographs. Prism spectro-graphs are suitable for Raman measurements if they have high speed

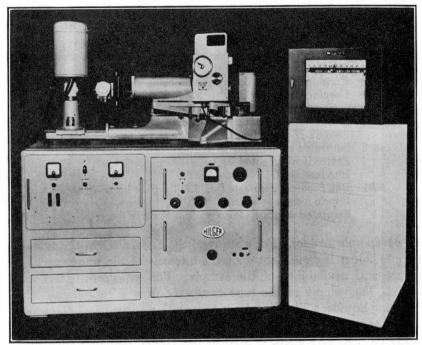

Fig. 6.3   Hilger Raman recording spectrograph (Courtesy Jarrell-Ash Company)

and moderate resolution and dispersion. A spectrograph with a lens of effective aperture of $f/4.5$ and a dispersion of 20 A per mm yields reasonable exposure times for qualitative work. Commercial instru-ments such as the Hilger medium glass or quartz spectrographs or the equivalent Bausch and Lomb type are satisfactory for Raman measurement.

The two commercial Raman spectrographs presently available are prism types. The Hilger large-aperture spectrograph can be pur-chased with two alternative and rapidly interchangeable cameras. A spectrograph camera with a relative aperture $f/1.5$ and a com-paratively small dispersion (64 A per mm at 4358 A) is convenient for a preliminary survey with a short exposure. If it is then found that the conditions of excitation and alignment are satisfactory, more detailed examination with a longer exposure time can be made with a camera of $f/5.7$ aperture and a dispersion of 16 A per mm at 4358 A. The main part of the Hilger instrument consists of a collimator, with a symmetrical slit and glass lens, a rigid metal base with two glass prisms in their mounts, and a rotatable mount upon which either or both of the alternative cameras can be fixed. This instrument is modified for direct recording (Fig. 6.3) by inserting a tilting mirror in one of the two camera positions, thus converting the spectrograph into a monochromator with double dispersion. The mirror is rotated automatically at one of four easily selected speeds and may be set to a calibrated scale. The collimator is modified by the addition of a separate, curved exit slit. The monochromatic light from this slit is interrupted by a "chopper" and then focused on a photomultiplier. The signal from this photomultiplier is amplified and used to operate a pen recorder. To compensate for variations in source intensity, a monitor is used on the light exciting the sample, and the record is made of the ratio of the main signal to the signal of the monitor.

The Applied Research Laboratories high-speed Raman spectrograph (Fig. 6.4) is a stigmatic three-prism instrument with glass optics and a reflecting camera. High speed is achieved with a fast camera (relative aperture $f/3$) and MgF_2 coatings where it is essential to reduce reflection losses. Adequate linear dispersion is secured by making the focal length approximately 1 foot, and by using three 60° prisms of highly dispersive, extra-dense flint glass. These features entail a camera-aperture diameter of approximately 4 inches and correspondingly large prisms. The spectrum is focused on a film strip 8 x 100 mm, which is curved into precise conformance to the focal surface of the camera by means of the film holder. For automatic pen recording the film holder is withdrawn, and an exit slit scans along the circularly curved focal surface. Light is conveyed from the exit slit through an exit periscope, over and downward to the stationary multiplier phototube located on the axis of rotation. The scanning rate can be varied from about 2 to 200 cm^{-1} per minute. At the highest speed, about $6\frac{1}{2}$ minutes are required to explore the 4358 A Raman region from 200 to 1500 cm^{-1}. For higher precision and detail the scanning rate can be extended down to approximately 1 cm^{-1} per minute.

The present availability of excellent echelette gratings for short wavelengths has stimulated development of grating Raman spectrographs for research purposes.[5, 11] These instruments are the auto-

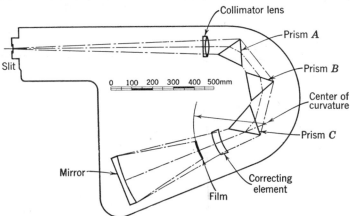

Fig. 6.4   ARL Raman spectrograph (Courtesy Applied Research Laboratories)

matic-recording type with photomultiplier tubes. Extensive Raman spectra including the polarization data of many hydrocarbons have been obtained by D. H. Rank and M. R. Fenske and their co-workers on such an instrument.[5, 13]

(e) Receptors. The photographic plate or film and the photo-multiplier tube are the receptors employed for the recording of Raman spectra. In order to keep exposure times to a minimum, high-sensitivity plates or films are selected, such as Eastman Kodak type 103 or type I or Ilford Zenith plates. The wavelength of the exciting line and the spectral region of which the plate is most responsive should coincide (see Fig. 8.18).

The photomultiplier tube is a phototube with a series of anodes, each one at a higher positive potential than the preceding one. If a quantum striking the cathode releases a single electron, this electron is accelerated to the first anode. Upon collision, it frees several electrons from the anode surface which are then accelerated to the second anode where the process is repeated. By the use of nine or more anodes, each original electron is multiplied many times to give an appreciable current in the external circuit.

The RCA 1P21 or 931A photomultiplier tubes are the types most commonly employed. These tubes are almost identical except that the 1P21 tube is hand-selected and when operated at 100 volts per stage has an amplication factor twice that of the 931A tube. For this reason the cost of the 1P21 tube is approximately five times that of the 931A tube. In recording very weak Raman lines, the total noise present in a signal is important. The photomultiplier tube dark current is not detected with the a-c system present in the commercial instruments, but thermionic noise, which is a function of tube voltage and temperature, is detected. This noise increases at about the same rate as tube sensitivity with increasing voltage up to approximately 100 volts per stage, and so there is no optimum voltage for best signal-to-noise ratio. By using a refrigerant to cool the phototube, thermionic noise can be successfully reduced. However, some of the 1P21 tubes recently produced have such slight thermionic noise at room temperature that they need not be cooled.[10] Light noise, which is a function of the square root of the light intensity, is the final part of the total noise and can be reduced by increasing the intensity of illumination at the phototube.

[13] W. G. Braun, D. F. Spooner, and M. R. Fenske, *Anal. Chem.*, 22, 1074 (1950).

6.3   Qualitative applications.   Raman spectra are valuable for qualitative analysis because each compound has a unique spectrum, and because, as shown in Table 6.2, there are characteristic Raman frequencies for many functional groups.

TABLE 6.2

Characteristic Raman Frequencies

Group	Cm^{-1}	Group	Cm^{-1}
O—H (bonded)	3400	C=O (acids)	1645–1665
C—H (aromatic)	3050	C=NOH (oximes—aliphatic)	1655–1665
H		(oximes—aromatic)	1630
C—C—C	2970	C=C	1600–1680
H		C—O—C	1270–1280
C—CH$_3$	2930	H$_2$C——CH$_2$	1265
	2862	\ /	
C—H (aliphatic)	2918	O	
S—H	2570	C—SH	590–700
C≡C	2100–2250	C—Cl	640–780
C≡N	2150	C—Br	560–630
C=O (anhydrides)	1804	C—I	490–540
	1745–1754	NO$_3^-$ (organic) 730, 1074,	
C=O (esters)	1720–1740	1391, 1659	
C=O (aldehydes—aliphatic)	1715–1725	(inorganic) 720, 1050,	
(aldehydes—aromatic)	1690	1350	
C=O (ketones—aliphatic)	1700–1710	SO$_4^=$ (inorganic) 450, 620,	
(ketones—aromatic)	1675	980, 1100	

This table is by no means complete but will serve to indicate the qualitative possibilities. It should be noted that there are many functional groups whose Raman shifts occur at the same frequency as their infrared absorption (see Fig. 5.9). However, there are differences between the infrared bands and Raman lines, which appear in the same region. For example, the 3400-cm^{-1} band attributed to the bonded OH group appears for all alcohols in infrared absorption, but appears as a characteristic Raman frequency for only the simpler members of the series, and in less than half of the alcohols, which have been studied.

The regions shown for the functional group assignments are only an indication of the limits that may be expected for a given class of compounds and may be appreciably altered by substitution. In ethylene derivatives the C=C group occurring at 1620 cm^{-1} in ethylene is increased to approximately 1640 cm^{-1} by substitution of a single hydrocarbon radical. Further hydrocarbon substitution produces a negligible effect, whereas the substitution of a halogen group has the opposite effect and diminishes the frequency.

In the case of ethers the Raman line at 1270 to 1280 cm^{-1} presumably caused by the C—O—C group only appears for the simpler straight-chain members. From this brief discussion, it should be realized that a thorough study should be made of the Raman spectra of analogous compounds before assuming proof of the presence or absence of a particular functional group.

Inorganic compounds such as H_2O, CS_2, S_2Cl_2, B_2O_3, and $TiCl_4$ containing covalent bonds also yield Raman spectra as well as gases such as HCl, HBr, H_2 and its isotopes, N_2, O_2, Cl_2, CO_2, CO, NO, N_2O, NH_3, and SO_2. As shown in Table 6.2 radicals such as $SO_4^=$ and NO_3^-, as well as NH_4^+, ClO_4^-, and $PO_4^{\equiv}$, yield Raman spectra characteristic of the radicals. Different cations cause variations in the principal shifts of the $SO_4^=$ and NO_3^- radicals shown in Table 6.2.

In addition to distinguishing between functional groups, Raman spectra are valuable in distinguishing between isomers such as the ortho, meta, and para disubstituted derivatives of benzene. In general, as the structure changes from one isomer to another, the entire symmetry of geometrical isomers also changes from the *cis* to the *trans* form, and both the Raman spectra and the polarization factors for the two forms are different. With the exception of a few compounds such as ethylene dichloride and ethylene dibromide, the frequency of the C=C linkage in the *trans* form is always higher than in the *cis* form.

For qualitative purposes, a match of the spectrum of the unknown with a known spectrum is the best proof of structure. Although thousands of Raman spectra are available in the literature and can be found by searching *Chemical Abstracts,* a great number of these spectra are not very valuable for analytical work because experimental conditions are not given or are vaguely described, the relative intensities of lines are not indicated, or materials of doubtful purity were measured.

An excellent catalog of Raman spectra is that of the American Petroleum Institute, Research Project 44 at Carnegie Institute of Technology. Recent articles by Fenske and co-workers previously referred to contain the Raman spectra of 291 pure organic compounds. The text by Hibben [14] also contains a great number of

[14] J. H. Hibben, *The Raman Effect and Its Chemical Applications,* Reinhold, New York (1939).

spectra, which are valuable not only for comparison purposes but also for an indication of the amount of work that has been done on a given class of compounds.

6.4   Quantitative applications. The application of Raman spectroscopy to quantitative analysis is based on the principle that the

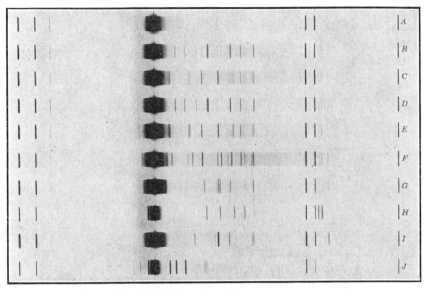

Fig. 6.5   These Raman spectra were recorded on an E612 Hilger two-prism large-aperture glass spectrograph, using an E614 camera with an aperture of $f/5.7$. Exposure time was 60 seconds (Courtesy Jarrell-Ash Company)

A. Light source only
B. o- (20%) and p- (80%) xylene mixture
C. o- (15%), m- (56%), and p- (8%) xylene, ethyl benzene (17%) toluene (1%) and styrene (2%) mixture
D. p-Xylene
E. m-Xylene
F. o-Xylene
G. Ethyl benzene
H. Cyclohexane
I. Benzene
J. Carbon tetrachloride

intensities of the Raman lines are proportional to the concentrations of the compounds present. It can be qualitatively seen from Fig. 6.5, which shows some typical Raman spectra including two mixtures, that the Raman line intensities for the components of the mixtures are proportional to the concentrations present. Therefore, in order to determine the concentration, we need to measure the line intensities. If the Raman spectra are recorded by photoelectric methods as discussed in Section 6.2, the photoelectric intensities are obtained directly. However, with the photographic method it is necessary to correlate the density or blackening of a photographic plate with the actual line intensity as emitted by the source. Since this correlation, which is a function of the light intensity, the frequency of the light, the exposure time, and the emulsion characteristics, is discussed in detail in Chapter 10 in relation to emission spectroscopy, it will not be amplified further at this point. In addition to obtaining an emulsion calibration curve to take care of these variables, it is necessary to correct for the continuous background, which is caused by Rayleigh scattering and fluorescent impurities, by subtracting the intensity of the background from the intensity of the Raman line to obtain the corrected intensity.[15] Furthermore, since the Raman lines are relatively weak, it is necessary to use fast emulsions of low contrast. It can be seen that all these factors combine to make the photographic approach a tedious one. Stamm,[12] who has employed the photographic approach successfully, suggests five general methods for quantitative analysis as follows: (a) intensity proportional to the number of molecules (no standards involved), (b) intensity proportional to the number of molecules (one standard solution involved), (c) synthetic standards, (d) internal standard method, (e) method of dilution. As two detailed examples, procedures for methods b and d as published by Stamm are as follows:

(b) 1. Take Raman spectrum of a solution containing A and B in a 1-to-1 mole ratio.
2. Pick a line of A and B uninfluenced by any other lines. Find the ratio (int. A/int. B)$_{1:1}$.
3. Take a spectrum of unknown containing A and B.
4. Find (int. A/int. B)$_x$ for the same line pair in this spectrum.
5. Assume intensity of scattering to be proportional to the number of molecules, thus:

$$(\text{moles } A/\text{moles } B)_x = \frac{(\text{int. } A/\text{int. } B)_x}{(\text{int. } A/\text{int. } B)_{1:1}}$$

(d) 1. Make standard solutions containing known amounts of A and B. Add to each solution approximately the same weight per cent of substance S, the internal standard.*

[15] W. C. Pierce and N. H. Nachtrieb, Ind. Eng. Chem., Anal. Ed., 13, 774 (1941).

* The internal standard recommended for method d is carbon disulfide or carbon tetrachloride.

2. Obtain the spectra of the standard solutions and find (int. A/int. S) as well as (int. B/int. S) for as many lines of A and B as desired.

3. Plot (int. A/int. S) versus (grams A/grams S). Do the same for B.

4. Use the graphs as working curves for analyzing unknowns, the spectra of the unknowns being obtained with approximately the same concentration of S in each unknown as was used in the standards.

Table 6.3 lists some typical quantitative results obtained by direct-recording and photographic techniques.

TABLE 6.3

Quantitative Results on Mixtures of Organic Compounds

Direct-Recording Method *			Photographic Method †		
	Percentage			Percentage	
Mixture	Known	Found	Mixture	Known	Found
1,2,3-Trimethylbenzene	28.2	28.7	o-Xylene	20.1	20.7
1-Methyl-4-isopropylbenzene	43.8	43.5	m-Xylene	55.1	54.7
Hydrindene	28.0	28.3	p-Xylene	24.8	24.7
Total	100.0	100.0	Total	100.0	100.1

* D. H. Rank and R. V. Wiegand, *J. Optical Soc. Am.*, *36*, 325 (1946).
† R. F. Stamm, *Ind. Eng. Chem.*, *Anal. Ed.*, *17*, 318 (1945).

6.5 Symmetry and fundamental frequencies of a molecule.
With the nuclei of a molecule in their equilibrium positions, a molecule may have one or more of the following symmetry elements:

Symmetry Element	Molecule Transformed into Itself
A plane of symmetry	By reflection at the plane
A center of symmetry	By reflection at the center (inversion)
A p-fold axis of symmetry	By rotation by an angle $360°/p$ about the axis
A p-fold rotation-reflection axis of symmetry	By rotation by $360°/p$ about the axis followed by reflection at a plane perpendicular to the axis.

Vibrational frequencies are classified as symmetrical, antisymmetrical, or degenerate to these symmetry elements. For a given vibration, if the molecule is inspected with the nuclei in their extreme positions, it can be determined whether or not this vibrational mode is symmetrical or antisymmetrical to the various symmetry elements possessed by the molecule at rest. Degenerate frequencies occur when there are two or more vibrational modes with the same frequency and only when the molecule has a threefold or higher rotation or rotation-reflection axis of symmetry.

A molecule usually has several of the symmetry elements listed above, but only in certain combinations, for not all combinations of symmetry elements are possible. A possible combination of symmetry operations that leaves at least one point unchanged is termed a point group. A point group is characterized by the property that the "product" of any two symmetry operations is equivalent to one that belongs to the same combination. Only a limited number of such point groups exist according to mathematical group theory, and every molecule can be assigned to one of these point groups. Wilson [16] and others have prepared tables for the different crystallographic point groups characteristic of every possible type of molecular symmetry. These tables show for each point group the number of vibrational frequencies appearing in the infrared spectrum and in the Raman spectrum and their polarization properties if they are Raman-active.

The problem, then, once the infrared and Raman spectra are obtained, is to attempt to assign the molecule to a characteristic point group. Occasionally there may be a choice between two models with similar selection rules. In such cases deuterated analogs [17] may be of considerable help in making the correct choice. Once the correct model has been assumed, a set of equations can be derived relating the frequencies to the structural factors and force constants. A set of force constants can then be found that permits the calculation of a set of vibrational frequencies for comparison with those found experimentally. This procedure is limited because of mathematical complications to comparatively simple molecules.

6.6 Theoretical applications. Raman and infrared spectra are valuable not only for qualitative and quantitative analysis, but also for the determination of thermodynamic constants. Thermodynamic constants can, of course, be determined directly by strictly thermal methods, but the calculation of these constants from spectroscopic data is in many cases less tedious and more accurate and further serves as an independent check on the thermal measurements. In

[16] E. B. Wilson, *J. Chem. Phys.*, 2, 432 (1934).
[17] F. Halverson, *Revs. Modern Phys.*, 19, 87 (1947).

addition, from spectroscopic data we can predict the heat capacity for such unstable molecules as CH, OH and others for which heat capacity cannot be measured by direct thermal methods.

Bibliography

Books

W. G. Berl (editor), *Physical Methods in Chemical Analysis,* Vol. I, pp. 405–23, Academic Press, New York (1950).

S. Bhagavantam, *Scattering of Light and the Raman Effect,* Chemical Publishing Co., Brooklyn (1952).

K. W. F. Kohlrausch, *Der Smekal-Raman Effekt,* Julius Springer, Berlin (1931); see also *Erganzungsband,* Berlin (1938).

K. W. F. Kohlrausch, *Ramanspektren,* Akademische Verlagsgesellschaft Becker und Erler, Leipzig; Edwards Brothers, Ann Arbor, Mich. (1943).

Articles

G. Glockler, The Raman Effect, *Revs. Modern Phys., 15,* 111 (1943).

G. M. Murphy, The Raman Spectra Method, *J. Optical Soc. Am., 30,* 396 (1940).

CHAPTER 7

Fluorometric Methods

Fluorescence is caused by the absorption of radiant energy and the re-emission of this energy in the form of visible light. The light emitted is almost always of lower frequency, that is, higher wavelength than that absorbed. If the wavelength of the emitted light is the same as that of the exciting light, the fluorescence is known as *resonance fluorescence*. In true fluorescence the absorption and emission take place in a short but measurable time, of the order of microseconds. If the light is emitted with a time delay, the phenomenon is known as *phosphorescence*. This time delay may range from months down to seconds, so that the difference between the two phenomena is one of degree only. *Luminescence* is the general term applied to the process of absorption and emission of radiant energy. In the German literature the terms luminescence and phosphorescence are often used interchangeably; so, although one of these terms is generally to be preferred for a given case, there is some justification for considering the three words as synonyms.

7.1 Intensity of fluorescence. In analytical work fluorescence is important because the intensity of the light emitted by a fluorescent material is dependent upon the concentration of that material.

The fluorescence of a given material in a particular instrument is also a function of other variables and is given by [1]

$$P = KP_0(1 - 10^{-abc})$$

where P = the radiant power of the fluorescent light; K = the fraction of the incident radiation that is absorbed (determined by such factors as the dimensions of the light beam, the area of solution irradiated, the transmission band of the filter before the photocell, and the spectral response of the photocell); P_0 = the radiant power of the incident radiation; a = a constant (corresponding to the absorptivity

[1] F. Kavanagh, *Ind. Eng. Chem., Anal. Ed.*, 13, 108 (1941).

in colorimetry) which is dependent upon the material, the wavelength of incident radiation, and the solvent; c = the concentration of the fluorescent material; b = the depth of the fluorescent solution.

As abc becomes small and approaches a value of 0.01 or less, as it frequently does, this expression becomes

$$P = 2.3KP_0abc \quad \text{or} \quad P = K'c$$

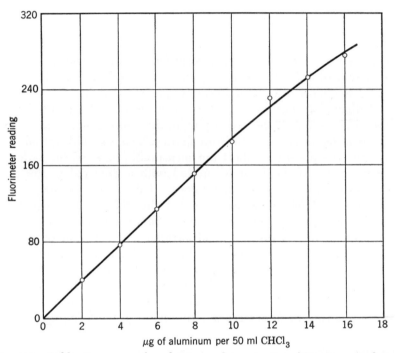

Fig. 7.1   Calibration curve for aluminum determination (Courtesy *Analytical Chemistry*)

where K' is an over-all constant for one particular substance in a given instrument.

Figure 7.1 is a plot of the fluorescence (potentiometer scale reading) versus the concentration of aluminum measured as the salt of 8-hydroxyquinoline in a chloroform solution. There is a linear relationship between the fluorescence and the concentration at low concentrations, but, at higher concentrations, the curve tapers toward the concentration axis. In general, if the measurable concentration range is large, the fluorescence-concentration curve will bend toward the concentration axis, but, if it is small, a linear plot is obtained. This is a common effect in fluorescent measurements and is caused by several factors including self-quenching. Any material that causes the intensity of the fluorescence to be less than the expected value given by the equation above is known as a quencher, and the effect is termed quenching. Quenching is normally caused by the presence of foreign ions, but in self-quenching the concentration of the fluorescent molecules is high enough to prevent all the molecules capable of fluorescing from becoming activated, thus yielding the result shown in Fig. 7.1.

It should be noted from Fig. 7.1 that the concentration range covered is only a few micrograms. In the average colorimetric method milligram quantities of material are determined, but in the average fluorometric method, the quantity of material determined is in the order of micrograms or even fractions of a microgram. As the need for determining more minute quantities becomes more urgent, fluorometric methods will show a marked increase in popularity because of this marked advantage of extreme sensitivity.

7.2   Experimental method.   Once the principle of fluorescence is known, the design of a simple fluorimeter to measure the intensity

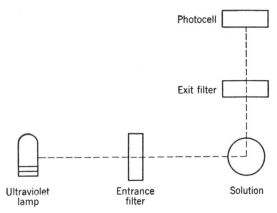

Fig. 7.2   Design of a simple fluorimeter

of the fluorescence is rather obvious. Figure 7.2 shows the basic design of such a fluorimeter.

The diagram of such an instrument shows its similarity to a simple filter photometer, the main differences being the need for a filter between the receptor and the sample, and the measurement of the light emitted by the sample at right angles to the source to avoid interference from the direct beam of the source. The cells, receptors, and filters are identical with those present in a filter photometer, and so there is no need to discuss their physical characteristics again (see Chapter 3). It is of interest, however, to consider the choice of appropriate filters. This choice is dependent upon the wavelength of the exciting mercury line or lines and the wavelength of the emitted light. Usually the band of the emitted light is very broad (of the order of 200 mμ) so that selection of a proper exit filter is not too critical. A visual observation of the color of the fluorescent solution, which may be blue, green, yellow, or red, may be sufficient for selecting a correct filter. Occasionally combination filters are more satisfactory than a single one (see Fig. 3.7).

The commonest source of radiation for fluorimetric measurements is a mercury-vapor lamp, which emits an intense line spectrum superimposed on a continuous background. These are available * in many types for both visual measurements and fluorimeters and will be briefly discussed in the following section in conjunction with specific instruments.

One major difference between a fluorimeter and a filter photometer, besides the placement of the filter and receptor, is in the settings for the high and low ends of the calibration curve. In the filter photometer, distilled water or solvent and an opaque barrier are used, respectively. For the fluorimeter, distilled water or solvent is used for setting the low end of the scale. The high end must be set with a fluorescent material. This should be a standard, reproducible operation.

7.3 Typical fluorimeters. The Klett fluorimeter model 2070 is shown in Fig. 7.3. This instrument has many of the features of the simple fluorimeter design previously discussed. However, similar to the Klett-Summerson filter photometer, the Klett fluorimeter has two matched photocells of the barrier-layer type to compensate for moderate line-voltage fluctuations and for photocell fatigue. The source is a high-pressure General Electric A-H-4 mercury-vapor lamp enclosed in a metal housing to prevent damage to the eyes. Like mercury-vapor lamps of this type, this lamp requires a minimum of 5 minutes' operation before reaching full intensity. The galvanom-

---

* Available from General Electric Co., Lamp Division, Cleveland, Ohio; Sylvania Electric Products, Boston, Mass.; Hanovia Chemical and Manufacturing Co., Newark, N. J.; Westinghouse Electric and Manufacturing Co., Pittsburgh, Pa.; Ultra-Violet Products, Inc., South Pasadena, California.

eter switch allows the selection of high or low galvanometer sensitivity. The potentiometer is a precision, linear-wound type with a 300-division scale. The scale readings obtained are proportional to the ratio of the intensity of the fluorescent light to the intensity of the

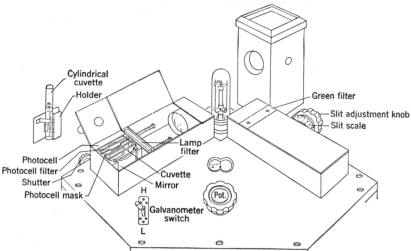

Fig. 7.3. Klett fluorimeter (Courtesy Klett Instrument Company)

light from the lamp that strikes the reference photocell. Both rectangular and cylindrical glass cells are furnished with the instrument.

The Fisher Nefluoro-Photometer shown in Fig. 7.4 has been designed for colorimetric, nephelometric, and fluorimetric measurements. As a colorimeter, the light from the source is divided by mirrors into two paths, one passing through the cell containing the absorbing solution and falling on a measuring photomultiplier tube, and the other through two Polaroid units which can be rotated with respect to each other in order to balance the amount of light falling on the reference photomultiplier tube. A vacuum-tube voltmeter acts as a null-point device for comparing the output of the two photomultipliers.

For fluorescent and nephelometric (the scattering of light by suspensions) measurements, the two mirrors are removed from cells A

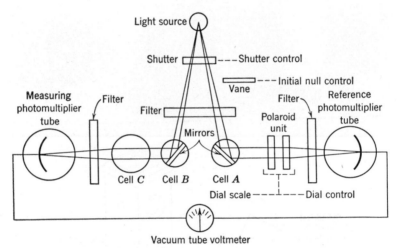

Fig. 7.4 Fisher Nefluoro-Photometer (Courtesy Fisher Scientific Company)

and B. Cell A is filled with a standard solution approximately twice as strong as any to be measured, cell B with the most concentrated solution to be measured, and cell C with distilled water. The vane in the light beam on the right is then adjusted until the meter balances at 100%. The fluorescence of less concentrated solutions can then be measured by adjusting the Polaroid unit to read the percentage of light emitted by the less concentrated solution relative to that of the most concentrated. In this manner, with several known standards, calibration curves can be obtained.

Fluorescent attachments are available for the Beckman and Coleman spectrophotometers and the Lumetron colorimeter. The Duboscq and similar-type colorimeters can also be adapted for simple visual measurements.

An unusual fluorimeter,[2] which was specifically designed for the

---

[2] C. J. Rodden, *Analytical Chemistry of the Manhattan Project*, p. 568, McGraw-Hill, New York (1950).

determination of uranium in a solid flux of sodium fluoride or sodium fluoride–sodium carbonate mixture, is shown in Fig. 7.5. This instrument adapts a standard photometer (Photovolt model 512), to measurement of solid samples. The source and receptor are located at 45° angles on opposite sides of the normal to the surface of the dish. The light from the source is filtered by an ultraviolet glass filter which passes the three mercury lines at approximately 365 mμ while a com-

Fig. 7.5 Photovolt fluorimeter (Courtesy Photovolt Corporation)

bination filter (Corning no. 3486, 9780) filters the light emitted by the sample. Standard platinum crucible covers or platinum sheet dishes can be used to melt the flux. The sample disks are brought under the photocell by means of a slide which holds five disks. Shutters are provided to shut off the ultraviolet light when necessary and to reduce the intensity of the emitted light so that samples of high concentration can be measured. The sensitivity of the method is 10^{-9} gram of uranium per dish, and this has been increased in more recent fluorimeters.

7.4 Establishment of a fluorometric method. The procedure to be followed in establishing a fluorometric method is very similar to that discussed for a colorimetric method in Chapter 3. However, there are some differences which it is well to consider. The important variables are the following:

(*a*) *Proper Filters.* For a given material there is usually an optimum wavelength band of exciting radiation. This can be determined experimentally with a simple fluorimeter by ascertaining which of a group of glass filters gives the maximum fluorescence. The correct selection of the filters for filtering the light emitted by the sample is made in a similar manner.

(*b*) *Effect of pH.* Generally the pH is very critical, whether the material is determined in aqueous medium or by solvent extraction into an organic solvent. If possible, it is best to work over a pH region where the fluorescence is constant even at the sacrifice of some sensitivity. In the extraction of the 8-hydroxyquinolates of aluminum, gallium, and indium, it is better to add the 8-hydroxyquinoline in an acetic acid solution and then to make the pH adjustment and finally the extraction with chloroform than the alternative of adjusting the pH of the solution and then extracting with a chloroform solution of 8-hydroxyquinoline. In the latter case, insoluble hydroxides of the three elements named will be formed and will reduce the pH range over which a quantitative extraction can be made.

(*c*) *Effect of Interferences.* Foreign cations and often anions constitute serious interferences in most fluorometric methods. They may diminish the fluorescence by absorbing the ultraviolet light (chromate ion is an example), by absorbing the emitted light (any colored substance), or by quenching the fluorescence. Occasionally, a foreign substance will fluoresce and lead to high results for a determination.

Quenching is the commonest and most serious source of error encountered. For example, a common method of determining traces of uranium is by measurement of the fluorescence of a uranium fluoride complex in a solidified fusion melt. When a 2.5% KF–97.5% $NaKCO_3$ flux was used, only aluminum of 29 common cations tested did not show appreciable quenching of the fluorescence. The amount of quenching is determined by the concentration of the foreign ion or ions present and can be experimentally determined by a "spiking" or "addition" method. The basis of this method is that any added uranium will be quenched in the same proportion as the uranium present in the original sample. An initial reading is made on a fused disk, then a known amount of uranium is added, and a second fusion and reading is made. Unless the difference between the first and second reading is equivalent to the amount of uranium added, quenching has occurred, and the original amount of uranium must be calculated from the quenching factor found. The same technique can be applied to a study of quenching in solution.† If quenching does occur, the best procedure is to remove the interfering elements by a suitable chemical separation. An alternate method is to employ a dilution technique by taking a small aliquot of sample and working at the lower limit of the calibration curve. Application of the dilution method is limited to samples in which the quenchers are present in ratios less than 1000 of quencher to 1 of the fluorescent material and then only to methods that give extreme sensitivity.

(d) *Stability of Solutions.* It is often found that the fluorescence diminishes as the solution is irradiated with ultraviolet light. This is a more important source of error in fluorimetry than in colorimetry because the radiant energy of the quanta emitted by the ultraviolet source is greater. In such cases, measurement must be made very rapidly or a series of successive readings must be taken and extrapolated to zero time. Occasionally the solution does not reach its full intensity of fluorescence for a considerable time after the reagents have been added. This is true for the Pontachrome-Blue Black R method for aluminum.[3] In such cases it is best to make the measurement in the center of a time interval in which the fluorescence is at a constant value.

(e) *Other Variables.* Usually the fluorescence increases as the temperature decreases, but for the sake of convenience most measurements are made at room temperature.

The order of adding reagents may also have a profound effect, as illustrated in the discussion on pH, and should be carefully considered in establishing a new fluorimetric method.

The standards employed for the initial setting required by most fluorimeters are worthy of mention. Quinine sulfate in 1 N sulfuric acid is very satisfactory in our opinion. The solution is stable in visible light for months, but does slowly decompose with prolonged exposure to ultraviolet light. For this reason, it is preferable to use a fresh standard with each new set of measurements. Fluorescent glass standards (uranium glass), sodium fluorescein, or a standard concentration of the material being determined are also employed as standards for setting the fluorimeter.

7.5 Applications. The main applications of fluorimetric analysis are in the inorganic, organic, and biological fields.

Two of the most important reagents in inorganic analysis are morin

† For a discussion of quenching in solution, see E. J. Bowen, *Analyst*, 72, 377 (1947).
[3] A. Weissler and C. E. White, *Ind. Eng. Chem., Anal. Ed.*, 18, 530 (1946).

and 8-hydroxyquinoline (oxine, 8-quinolinol). Morin may be used for beryllium,[4] aluminum, gallium, and zinc or for citrate, fluoride, oxalate, phosphate, tartrate and vanadate ions.[5] 8-Hydroxyquinoline yields a fluorescence in chloroform solution with aluminum,[6] gallium,[7] indium in an aqueous suspension with zinc [8] and in alcoholic solution with lithium.[9]

Other inorganic fluorimetric applications of considerable importance are the fluoride flux method for uranium [10] already discussed and the fluorescence of a complex of zirconium with flavonol in 0.2 N sulfuric acid solution,[11] as well as the analysis of gems and minerals.[12]

The organic and biological applications are difficult to classify inasmuch as they deal with such a variety of compounds. The determination of many vitamins, such as thiamine [13] (B_1) and riboflavin (B_2), of the alkaloids, and of the drugs, such as aureomycin,[14] are only a few of the examples that can be cited.

The excellent review articles [15] of C. E. White will give the reader a better idea of the increasing growth and importance of fluorimetric methods of analysis.

Bibliography

Books

H. C. Dake and J. De Ment, *Ultra-violet Light and Its Applications,* Chemical Publishing Co., Brooklyn (1942).
P. Pringsheim, *Fluorescence and Phosphorescence,* Interscience, New York (1949).
Cornell Symposium, *Preparation and Characteristics of Solid Luminescent Materials,* John Wiley, New York (1948).
J. A. Radley and J. Grant, *Fluorescence Analysis in Ultra-violet Light,* 3rd ed., Chapman & Hall, London (1948).

[4] E. B. Sandell, *Anal. Chim. Acta, 3,* 89 (1949).

[5] E. Bishop, *ibid., 4,* 6 (1950).

[6] L. G. Bassett, J. H. Harley, and S. E. Wiberley, *J. Chem. Education, 28,* 466 (1951).

[7] E. B. Sandell, *Anal. Chem., 19,* 63 (1947).

[8] L. L. Merritt, Jr., *Ind. Eng. Chem., Anal. Ed., 16,* 758 (1944).

[9] C. E. White, M. H. Fletcher, and J. Parks, *Anal. Chem., 23,* 478 (1951).

[10] C. J. Rodden, *ibid., 21,* 333 (1949).

[11] W. C. Alford, L. Shapiro, and C. E. White, *ibid., 23,* 1149 (1951).

[12] J. De Ment, *Handbook of Fluorescence, Gems and Minerals,* Mineralogist Publishing Co., Portland, Oreg. (1949).

[13] R. Patrick and J. F. H. Wright, *Analyst, 74,* 303 (1949).

[14] J. Levine, E. A. Garlock, and H. Fishback, *J. Am. Pharm. Assoc., 38,* 473 (1949).

[15] C. E. White, *Anal. Chem., 21,* 104 (1949); *22,* 69 (1950); *24,* 85 (1952).

CHAPTER 8

Apparatus for Emission Spectroscopy

Emission spectroscopy has become a very powerful tool for routine industrial analysis, particularly in the fields of metals and alloys. The instrumentation for quantitative emission spectroscopy is more complex and expensive than that for absorption measurements. Qualitative work may be done with simpler equipment, the major item being the spectrograph itself. This chapter will deal with the various components used for spectrographic analysis, and later chapters will deal with qualitative and quantitative methods.

Emission spectra are recorded in terms of wavelength, the Angstrom unit (A) which is equal to 10^{-8} cm. Tables may report wavelengths to six or seven significant figures, and the red line of cadmium, the international standard of wavelength, is known to eight significant figures (6438.4696 A). However, the wavelength (5460.7532 A) of green radiation from radioactive Hg^{198}, produced by transmutation of gold, is a new and finer ultimate standard since spectroscopic light sources containing this isotope of mercury emit spectral lines of greater sharpness than any found in nature.[1] Although this value has been checked in three independent laboratories[2] to ± 0.0001 A, in the usual analytical work an estimate of the first decimal place is sufficient.

8.1 Spectrographic analysis and equipment. In Chapter 2 it was shown that by measuring the frequency (or wavelength) of the quanta emitted by a substance a qualitative analysis may be obtained. Also, by measuring the relative number of quanta emitted at a particular frequency a quantitative analysis may be obtained. Emission spectrographic systems have been designed to fulfill the requirements for these measurements.

The major parts of the system for producing photographic spectra

---

[1] W. F. Meggers, *Sci. Monthly, 68,* 3 (1949).
[2] A. Perard and J. Terrien, *Compt. rend., 228,* 964 (1949).

may be listed as follows: (a) sample, (b) sample holder, (c) source of excitation, (d) illumination system, (e) spectrograph, (f) photographic processing equipment, (g) equipment for plate photometry. Though the above order is the logical, step-by-step sequence, the order of discussion has been selected to allow a clearer presentation of the process.

8.2   The spectrograph.   If two rods of an element are used as the electrodes for an electric arc, the spectrum of the hot vapor between the electrodes should be discontinuous, consisting of the characteristic discrete wavelengths of the electronic energy-level shifts in the element.   However, if the light from this source is dispersed by a prism or grating, an examination of the dispersed spectrum would show only broad bands of wavelengths.   The reason is that the source is a relatively large luminous area and its light cannot be brought to a sharp focus after dispersion.   A narrow vertical slit interposed between the arc and the grating or prism acts as a narrow source of all the wavelengths present.   This light may be dispersed and then focused on a screen or photographic plate, and the spectrum will appear as a series of lines.   Each line is an image of the slit and represents a wavelength present in the original source.

The parts of a spectrograph are the slit, the prism or grating, the optics for focusing the slit images, and the receptor for the dispersed images.   In this chapter we shall confine ourselves to the photographic emulsion as a receptor, reserving the discussion of other receptors until the chapter on quantitative analysis.

8.3   Spectrographic slits.   The width of the slit may vary considerably, a range of 10 to 200 microns covering most cases.   The edges forming the opening should be sharp to avoid reflections, and these sharp edges should be exactly parallel, or distorted lines will be produced.   The material for the jaws should be hard and resistant to corrosion.

The size of the slit opening regulates the amount of light admitted to the spectrograph, so that a wider slit will reduce the time necessary for a given source of light to produce a certain blackness of the plate image.   Increasing the slit width also produces wider lines on the plate, and may cause overlapping of nearby lines.   It is possible to calculate the optimum slit width, but the analytical spectrographer in practice would select the width that gives the shortest exposures without interference of neighboring lines.

Variation in slit width is obtained with a series of interchangeable fixed slits or with a slit with movable jaws.   The unilateral slit where one jaw is fixed and the other moves is open to the objection that the position of the center of the opening moves as the slit width changes. The bilateral slit where the two jaws move simultaneously is free from this objection but is more complex mechanically. Any movable slit should have a calibrated scale indicating the width, and must be checked periodically to insure that the calibration and parallelism of the jaws is remaining constant.

Fixed slits may be kept free of dust and dirt by a thin quartz cover plate cemented over the opening. Open slits of any type may be cleaned by wiping the edges with a sliver of soft wood moistened with alcohol.

8.4 Spectrographic prisms. The dispersion of light by a 60° prism is indicated in Fig. 8.1. The refractive index of the prism is

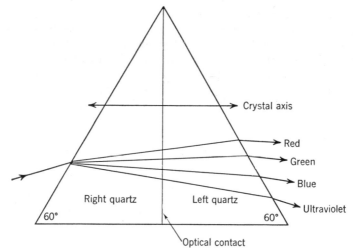

Fig. 8.1   60° Prism dispersion (Courtesy Bausch & Lomb Optical Company)

greater for shorter wavelengths; therefore the ultraviolet rays are deflected more than the visible light.

To obtain good definition of the spectral lines, the optical system shown in Fig. 8.2 is required. L_1, the collimator lens, is made so that its principal focus for light of the mean wavelength to be studied lies at the slit opening. Thus the rays striking the prism are parallel to the optical axis (dotted line). The diffracted rays leaving the prism must be focused on the plate P by L_2, the camera lens.

In the camera lens, as in the prism, the shorter wavelengths are refracted more strongly. The ultraviolet rays converge more, making the focal length of the lens shorter for them than for the visible. The spectrum is distributed in the plane P rather than in P' normal to the optic axis. The actual positions of focus may lie on a slight curve, in which case the plate may be bent in the holder, or, by lens correction, the focus may be made to lie on a plane.

Where the desired spectrum includes the ultraviolet region, quartz optics, transparent to below 2000 A, are necessary. Quartz exhibits double refraction, so that, if the prism is not cut so that the rays are transmitted parallel to the optic axis of the quartz, double images of the slit would be formed. The collimating lens produces the parallel rays and the prism is oriented to present its optic axis to the rays. Quartz also exhibits either right- or left-hand circular polarization which would also give double images. This may be corrected by using two 30° prisms, one of right-hand and one of left-hand quartz, placed back to back, as indicated in Fig. 8.1. This double or Cornu prism is used in most of the smaller-prism spectrographs.

For the complex spectra of the heavier elements, it is desirable to spread out the spectrum for examination. This increase in dispersion may be obtained by increasing the focal length and size of the spectrograph. However, two other factors must be considered, the resolving power and the speed. The resolving power, or the ability of the instrument to resolve two lines which are close together as being distinct entities, is a function of the size of the prism and the quality of the optics. Merely increasing the focal length of a spectrograph will not necessarily aid in distinguishing lines unless the resolving power is maintained. The two lines considered will be spread apart, but will also become more diffuse and thus seem to overlap as much as before.

The speed of a spectrograph, as of a camera, regulates the time necessary for a given intensity of light to produce a corresponding blackening on the plate. It may be expressed in terms of the aperture ratio, f/d, where f is the focal length and d is the diameter of the useful light path through the prism and lenses. A small aperture ratio means a high speed. Thus an increase in focal length will cut down on the speed of the spectrograph unless the diameter of the optics is also increased.

The arrangement shown in Fig. 8.2 becomes very cumbersome as the focal length of the spectrograph is increased. A more compact arrangement, the Littrow mounting, is shown in Fig. 8.3. A single 30° prism is aluminized on the back surface so that the light is reflected and traverses the prism twice. A single lens acts as both collimator and camera lens. The Littrow mounting is therefore more economical of quartz than an equivalent Cornu type.

The reflections produced at the front optical faces of the collimator and prism appear as stray light, called Littrow fog, which is revealed

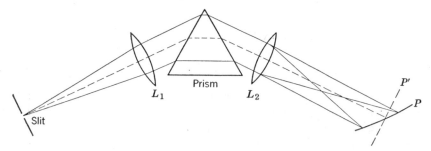

Fig. 8.2 Optical system of Cornu spectrograph or simple spectroscope

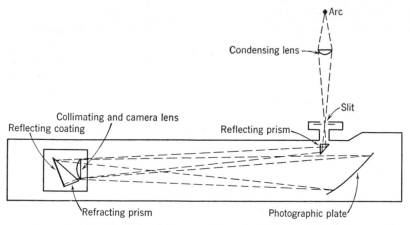

Fig. 8.3 Littrow mounting (Courtesy Bausch & Lomb Optical Company)

as an over-all darkening of the plate. This may be considerably reduced by masking out a portion of the collimator, or by tilting the collimator lens very slightly. The former method should be used only for qualitative work, as the line image produced is not uniform.

In Table 8.1, the characteristics of the typical sizes of quartz spectrographs are shown.

In choosing the size of the spectrograph, the desired dispersion is the chief factor. For materials such as ferrous alloys with complex spectra, a high dispersion is required. For simpler spectra, brass and

TABLE 8.1 *

Quartz Spectrographs

Size	Na$_D$ Line, Focal Length	Spectrum Length, 2000–8000 A
Small	20 cm	7.5 cm
Intermediate	38	14
Medium	60	22
Large (Littrow)	170	67

* From catalog data on Hilger instruments.

light alloys, the medium spectrograph may be more convenient. The normal photographic plate is 10 inches long, and so, although a single plate length will record the range 2000 to 8000 A on a medium instrument, a Littrow spectrograph requires three plate lengths. Rather than attempting to construct a long plate holder, the spectrograph is made adjustable so that different portions of the spectrum may be brought into focus on a single plate length.

To focus different portions of the spectrum it might be possible to move the plate along the focal plane or curve. The common procedure, however, is to rotate the prism until the desired range is on the plate. Owing to the change in focal length with wavelength, it is also necessary to move the prism and collimator along the optic axis. A final adjustment by rotating the plate in a vertical plane completes the focusing. The newer spectrographs have a mechanical system for maintaining the proper relationship among the three factors, a single control focusing the spectrograph for any desired wavelength range. Older instruments have calibrated manual controls for each function.

Prism spectrographs are stigmatic; a point-to-point correspondence exists between the slit and the line on the photographic plate. Any imperfection in the slit will be reproduced in the line. The advantage of the stigmatic feature is that one may adjust the height or position of the lines on the plate by diaphragming the slit or may reproduce nonuniform illumination of the slit when desired.

Glass optics transmit only in the visible region, but the index of refraction of glass is higher than that of quartz, so that the dispersion of a glass prism is greater. Some prism spectrographs are made with interchangeable glass and quartz optics to take advantage of the greater dispersion of glass in the visible range.

The dispersion of a spectrograph may be expressed as the number of millimeters on the plate covered by one angstrom, or the inverse ratio, angstroms per millimeter. A prism instrument does not show linear dispersion (Fig. 8.4), the dispersion becoming higher as the wavelength decreases.

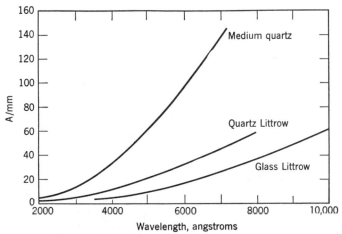

Fig. 8.4 Dispersion of prism spectrographs (Courtesy Bausch & Lomb Optical Company)

8.5 Spectrographic gratings. The function of a grating, like that of a prism, is to provide monochromatic light from light composed of all wavelengths. A diffraction grating consists of a number of equally spaced slits, which diffract the light by interference. Gratings are of two types: transmission gratings, in which the diffracted light passes through the slits, and reflection gratings in which the diffracted light is reflected back in the direction from which it entered. Since the light does not need to pass through a material whose transmittance depends upon the region of the spectrum involved, the reflection grating is superior to the transmission grating. In addition, the need for collimating and focusing lenses can be eliminated by employing a concave mirror as a reflecting surface and ruling the grating directly on this surface. Figure 8.5 shows the method of dispersion of light by a reflecting grating.

If i is the angle of incidence of monochromatic light of wavelength λ expressed in angstroms, and r is the angle of reflectance, the grating law is

$$n\lambda = d(\sin i \pm \sin r)$$

where $n = 1, 2, 3, \cdots$, i.e., the order of the spectra, and $d =$ the distance between the rulings or lines in angstroms.

The + sign applies when i and r are on the same side of the grating normal, and the − sign when they are on opposite sides.

As seen from this equation, light of submultiples of the primary wavelength (first order) may appear on the photographic plate. Thus, a first-order line at 8000 A may also represent a second-order line of 4000 A or a third-order line of 2000 A. Since the photographic emulsions usually have a short wavelength range in which they are sensitive, the higher orders do not interfere in ordinary work. By special ruling methods, approximately 80% of the light may be thrown into the desired order. The dispersion and resolving power are both raised in the higher orders, and for accurate wavelength measurements and similar work it is sometimes desirable to use the higher-order spectra. As the order increases, the intensity decreases so that the line intensity for third orders is just barely useful.

Modern diffraction gratings are ruled by cutting wedge-shaped grooves directly in special alloys such as speculum or in an aluminum coating on Pyrex glass, using a diamond point. In the case of the alloys, the ruled surface is coated with aluminum to prevent deterioration and to give more light in the ultra-violet region. Each ruling must be identical in depth and shape and must be straight and parallel to its neighbor. The spacing of the rulings must be identical as well, and so, when it is considered that gratings may have from 10,000 to over 100,000 rulings per inch and may

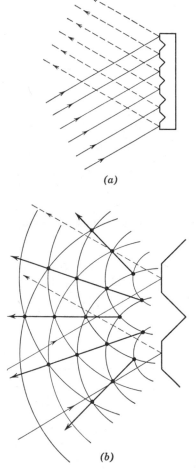

(a)

(b)

Fig. 8.5a Plane diffraction grating, showing incident and direct reflected beams.
Fig. 8.5b Grating diffraction. Heavy lines indicate diffracted beams for a single wavelength. This wavelength is equal to the radius difference of the circles showing the wave-front pattern.

have 6 inches or more ruled, the difficulties are seen to be enormous. Professor R. W. Wood of Johns Hopkins University has been a leading figure in the recent development of the grating, and it is only the painstaking efforts of many research workers that have furthered the art and lowered the cost of good gratings.

It is possible to make replicas of original gratings by casting a negative, and then a positive, with a suitable plastic. The replicas are aluminized and mounted on a rigid backing for use in spectrographs. Replica gratings are relatively inexpensive and good line quality can be obtained, but the poor replicas originally produced were the cause of some prejudice against such gratings.

In the ruling of gratings periodic errors of spacing cause the appearance of false lines known as "ghosts." Rowland ghosts consist usually of two or more pairs of equally intense lines symmetrically placed about every very intense line. Lyman ghosts are more difficult to identify since they are usually widely separated from their parent lines. Since they have the color of the parent line, they may be visually identified as lines of incorrect color for the spectral region under inspection. Ghost lines are becoming less of a problem to the spectrographer because they have been almost completely eliminated in modern gratings.

Spectrographs with these concave reflecting gratings may have the slit, grating, and plate combined in any one of several arrangements or mountings such as the Rowland, the Paschen-Runge, the Wadsworth, and the Eagle. These mountings will be shown in conjunction with the commercial instruments that employ them. However, the literature should be consulted for a detailed discussion of their operation.

The characteristics of grating spectrographs which interest the analyst are the same as for the prism types. By an increase in the focal length of the grating, a higher dispersion is attained, but this alone would not increase the resolving power. The theoretical resolving power is a function only of the total number of lines on the grating. Thus, for a given dispersion, the resolving power is increased by extending the width of the surface ruled. The dispersion also increases as the fineness of the ruling is increased. This method increases the resolving power also, provided the width of surface ruled is the same. As with prism instruments, an increase in dispersion by an increase in focal length cuts down the speed of the spectrograph. Higher speeds may be obtained with gratings having longer rulings, which give greater light-gathering power.

The dispersion of a grating spectrograph is essentially uniform and linear. This is useful in making analytical wavelength measurements, as simple interpolation or extrapolation from known lines may be used, once the dispersion has been determined.

With the exception of the Wadsworth mounting, the image produced by a concave grating is astigmatic; a point source produces a short line image. The effect of this is to average the light from the slit, so that the line on the plate is not an exact image of the slit. The averaging effect makes it less important to have the slit illuminated perfectly uniformly, but also makes it impossible to limit the height of the line by diaphragming the slit. However if the diaphragm is placed at the secondary focus of the grating [3,4] it will produce a stigmatic image.

8.6   Commercial spectrographs.   Prism spectrographs are made by several manufacturers, most of whom offer both the smaller Cornu instruments and the Littrow type. Grating spectrographs are available in several sizes and mountings. The selection of an instrument can best be made on the recommendations of experienced workers in the field.

Table 8.2 was prepared by J. R. Churchill [5] of the Aluminum Company of America. It is not all-inclusive, as it is restricted to the larger spectrographs and does not include every make now available.

The Bausch and Lomb large Littrow spectrograph (Fig. 8.6) covers the range of 2100 to 8000 A in 700 mm, requiring three exposures on 10-inch plates. The dispersion is about 2.5 A per mm at 2500 A and 10 A per mm at 4000 A. Interchangeable glass optics are provided which double the dispersion in the visible range. Ten focal positions are available, set with two controls.

The same company lists a medium quartz spectrograph, with Cornu prism, which covers the range of 2100 to 7000 A in 220 mm, requiring a single 10-inch plate. The dispersion is about 7.0 A per mm at 2500 A and 32.3 A per mm at 4000 A. A single-position fixed focus is used. The slit is bilateral and has a quartz cover plate.

The Gaertner large two-lens quartz spectrograph covers the range of 2000 to 8000 A with exposures on two 14-inch plates.[6] The dispersion is about 2.5 A per mm at 2500 A and 12 A per mm at 4000 A.

[3] N. H. Nachtreib, *Principles and Practice of Spectrochemical Analysis*, p. 62, McGraw-Hill, New York (1950).

[4] G. R. Harrison, R. C. Lord, and J. R. Loofbourow, *Practical Spectroscopy*, p. 338, Prentice-Hall, New York (1948).

[5] J. R. Churchill, *Ind. Eng. Chem., Anal. Ed., 16*, 653 (1944).

[6] S. Jacobsohn, *J. Optical Soc. Am., 32*, 164 (1942).

TABLE 8.2

Characteristics of Several Makes of Spectrographs

	ARL–Dietert	Baird (Large)	B. & L. (Littrow)	Gaertner (2 Lens)	Hilger (Littrow)	Jarrell-Ash (Grating)
Resolving power *	2	1	3	3	3	1
Dispersion *	3	1	2	2	2	1
Wavelength range (single spectrogram)	2	4	3	1	3	2
Scattered light	2	1	2	1	2	1
Resistance to vibration and shock	1	1	2	2	1	2
Auxiliary equipment available	1	2	3	3	2	2
Photographic speed	2	3	1	1	1	2
Slit	Adjustable	Fixed	Adjustable	Adjustable	Adjustable	
Wavelength setting	Semifixed	Continuously variable	Stepwise variable	Continuously variable	Continuously variable	Continuously variable

* Comparison limited to wavelengths most widely used in metallurgical analysis (2000–4000 A).

The numbers 1, 2, and 3 denote the rank of the various instruments when arranged in descending order with respect to the particular attribute or quality compared, based on the manufacturers' literature and the author's experience.

From J. R. Churchill, *Ind. Eng. Chem., Anal. Ed.*, **16**, 653 (1944). Reprinted by permission.

Interchangeable glass optics are available. The intermediate two-lens spectrograph covers the range of 2100 to 10,000 A on a single 14-inch plate. Although no dispersion curve was available to the author, the manufacturer states, "The dispersion . . . is 40 per cent greater than that of the usual medium-size quartz spectrograph."

The Hilger automatic large quartz spectrograph is a Littrow instrument and covers the range of 2000 to 8000 A in 670 mm, requiring three exposures on 10-inch plates. The dispersion is about the same as that of the Bausch and Lomb instrument.

Fig. 8.6   Bausch & Lomb large Littrow spectrograph (Courtesy Bausch & Lomb Optical Company)

Commercial grating spectrographs are available with a variety of mountings. The Rowland mounting (Fig. 8.7) should be mentioned first since it is of historical interest.[7] The three components, the slit, plate and the grating, lie on the radius of a common circle, the Rowland circle, which has a radius of curvature one-half that of the concave grating. The plate and grating are mounted at right angles to one another and must be mechanically moved to scan the spectrum. This disadvantage coupled with high astigmatism for incident angles greater than 40° has resulted in the development of other types.

The Paschen-Runge mounting (Fig. 8.8) is in the Applied Research Laboratories' 1½- and 2-meter grating spectrographs and in the Cenco grating spectrograph. Similar to the Rowland mounting, the

[7] H. A. Rowland, *Phil. Mag., 16*, 197 (1883).

slit, plate, and grating lie on the Rowland circle in fixed positions calculated to focus the desired region of the spectrum on the plate with minimum astigmatism. The ARL 1½-meter grating spectrograph has a first-order linear dispersion of 7 A per mm. The grating ruling is 24,000 lines per inch with 2 inches ruled, and has two fixed positions of 2150 to 4370 A and 4350 to 6570 A; these ranges cover-

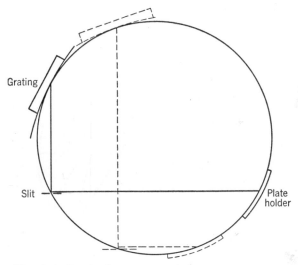

Fig. 8.7 Rowland mounting of the concave grating

The grating and plate holder are mounted on two rigid arms at right angles, with the slit at the intersection of the arms. The grating and plate holder may be rotated on the vertical axis to position them on the Rowland circle.

Two spectral positions are shown by the solid and the dotted lines, respectively.

ing a 32-cm length of 35-mm film. Separate optical benches and accessories are necessary for each range if rapid interchange is desired.

The ARL 2-meter grating spectrograph (Fig. 8.8) is available with two gratings, each having 2.5 inches ruled, one with 24,400 and the other with 36,600 lines per inch. The dispersions are 5.2 A per mm and 3.4 A per mm, respectively, in the first order. The spectrum range from 2100 to 9200 A is continuously covered by two cameras moving along an arc of the Rowland circle and encompassing 20 inches of 35-mm film. Either bilateral or fixed slits are available.

The Cenco 1-meter spectrograph has a first-order dispersion of 16

A per mm. A replica grating with 15,000 lines per inch is used. The spectrum range is continuously variable and covers 25 cm of strip film. The instrument is recommended by the makers for instructional use.

Bausch and Lomb manufactures a 1½-meter grating spectrograph in a modified Paschen-Runge mounting. A cylindrical lens inserted between the slit and the grating produces a stigmatic image. It is

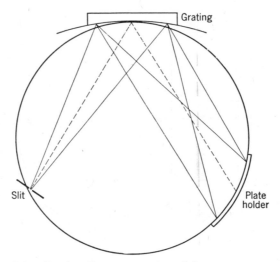

Fig. 8.8a   Paschen-Runge mounting of the concave grating

supplied with interchangeable fixed slits and a Hartmann diaphragm. The replica grating gives a dispersion of 15 A per mm in the first order. The range of 3700 to 7400 A is covered on 10 inches of 35-mm film. This instrument is of particular interest for academic work, as it is comparatively low in cost and offers the advantage of stigmatic operation.

The Eagle mounting (Fig. 8.9) has less astigmatism than the Rowland mounting and yields more intense higher-order spectra. To change the spectral region, it is necessary to rotate the plate holder, turn the grating, and change its distance from the plate. This mounting is in the Baird 3-meter grating spectrograph (Fig. 8.9) which has a first-order dispersion [8] of 5.6 A per mm. The three settings needed to adjust the spectrum range are set by three motor-

[8] W. S. Baird, A Practical Grating Spectrograph for Industrial Use, *Proc. 6th Summer Conference on Spectroscopy and Its Applications,* John Wiley, New York (1939).

driven controls at the front panel. The grating ruling has 15,000 lines per inch with 4 inches ruled. Ten-inch plates are required. A 2-meter instrument of the same design with proportional dispersion is available.

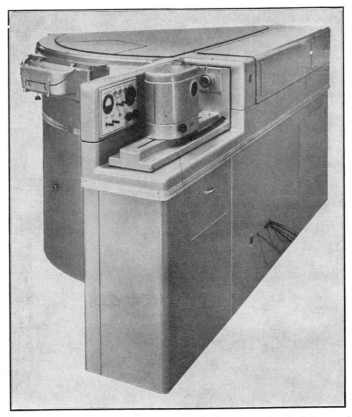

Fig. 8.8*b* ARL 2-meter grating spectrograph (Courtesy Applied Research Laboratories)

The three mountings, previously discussed, possess some degree of astigmatism. In the Wadsworth mounting (Fig. 8.10) the grating is illuminated by parallel light, which yields a stigmatic image. This mounting is available in the Jarrell-Ash 3.4-meter spectrograph [9] (Fig. 8.10). The light from the slit strikes a concave mirror which collimates the beam before it reaches the grating. The plate holder is mounted on the normal to the grating. To change the wavelength

[9] R. F. Jarrell, *J. Optical Soc. Am.*, 32, 666 (1942).

setting, the grating is rotated about a pivot directly under its face. As the grating is rotated, the plate holder must move in and out

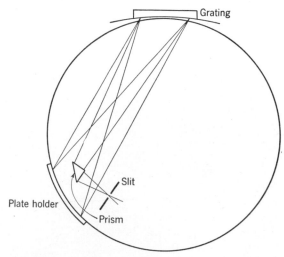

Fig. 8.9a   Eagle mounting of the concave grating

Fig. 8.9b   Baird 3-meter spectrograph (Courtesy Baird Associates, Inc.)

along the grating normal to maintain the focus. This spectrograph is supplied with a 6-inch-diameter, 15,000-line-per-inch grating. This gives a reciprocal linear dispersion of 5.0 A per mm in the first order,

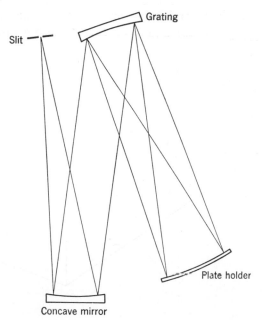

Fig. 8.10*a*   Wadsworth mounting of the concave grating

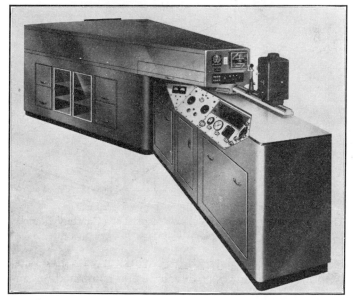

Fig. 8.10*b*   Jaco 3.4-meter spectrograph (Courtesy Jarrel-Ash Company)

2.4 A per mm in the second order, and 1.6 A per mm in the third order. Spectrographs of 2.5 and 5.5 meter are also available.

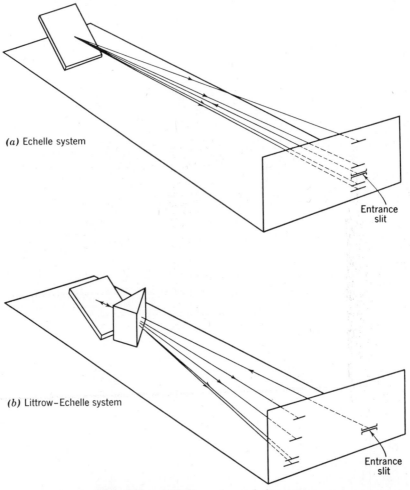

(a) Echelle system

Entrance
slit

(b) Littrow–Echelle system

Entrance
slit

Fig. 8.11a   Echelle system of dispersion
Fig. 8.11b   Combined prism and echelle dispersion (Courtesy Bausch & Lomb Optical Company)

Professor George R. Harrison,[10, 11] working with the Bausch and Lomb Optical Company has developed a combined prism-grating

[10] G. R. Harrison, *ibid.*, *39*, 522 (1949).

[11] G. R. Harrison and C. L. Bausch, London Conference on Optical Instruments, London (July 1950).

spectrograph that is a major contribution to spectrography. This instrument superimposes an echelle grating [10] dispersion on the normal prism dispersion, giving an increase in resolving power and dispersion of as much as 50 times that of the prism alone.

Figure 8.11 shows two diagrams which explain the operation of the combined system. The slit is horizontal, and with the prism alone the spectrum would consist of a series of overlapping horizontal

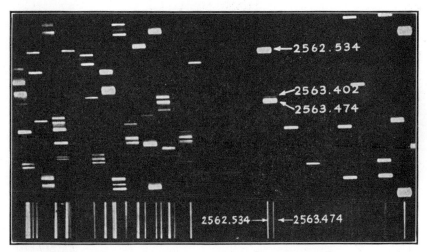

Fig. 8.12 Comparison of echellogram and prism spectrum of the 2500-A iron region (Courtesy Bausch & Lomb Optical Company)

lines at the level of the slit. With the echelle alone the spectrum would appear as a series of lines parallel to the slit with no horizontal displacement. The combination produces both horizontal and vertical dispersion, and the final spectrum is the echellogram. A typical echellogram is compared with the standard prism spectrum in Fig. 8.12.

The Littrow-Echelle system is available from Bausch and Lomb as a complete spectrograph or as an attachment for their Littrow spectrograph. The echelle has 200 grooves per inch, and the dispersion when combined with the prism is 0.39 A per mm at 2500 A and 0.57 A per mm at 4000 A. The increase in dispersion is even more marked at higher wavelengths.

Kirchgessner and Finkelstein [12] have described the application of echelle spectrographs to the quantitative analysis of boron in steel.

[12] W. G. Kirchgessner and N. A. Finkelstein, *Anal. Chem.*, 25, 1034 (1953).

8.7 Excitation sources. An excitation source is the system for supplying the excitation energy required to produce emission spectra. The exciting energy may be thermal or electric, there being no sharp dividing line between the two in practical equipment. It is evident from the equation $E = h\nu$ that relatively high energy is needed to produce the electronic spectra which appear in the visible and ultraviolet. Also, since we study the spectra of substances excited in the vapor state, we must consider the energy required for vaporization as well as for true excitation.

In Chapter 2 it was mentioned that, if we introduce the same average quantity of energy per atom into a given substance in a unit time, a probability function predicted that the same wavelengths would be produced and that their intensities would be the same. In the preceding paragraph we have added the restriction that the division of energy between vaporization and excitation be reproducible. And in a still more practical sense we also require that energy losses be reproducible. For qualitative analysis these requirements may be relaxed, but for quantitative analysis it is only by extreme control of the many factors involved that we can achieve the necessary goal, transfer of a reproducible quantity of energy per atom per unit time, and thus production of reproducible intensities for each wavelength.

The classical sources of energy are the flame, the d-c arc, the a-c arc and the spark.[13] In qualitative work we are chiefly interested in the sensitivity of a source; that is, its ability to produce spectral lines for traces of elements present in the sample. For quantitative analysis, the chief criterion is the reproducibility of the excitation, so that for a given sample repeated exposures record the same intensity for the various wavelengths produced. The sources mentioned will be examined with regard to sensitivity, reproducibility, and other considerations.

The excitation energy of a flame source is purely thermal. The thermal energy volatilizes the substance and also excites the vapors of the atoms or compounds introduced into the flame. The low temperatures involved as compared with other sources means that only the more volatile elements and compounds may be excited. The resulting spectra are simple and represent only electronic shifts in the neutral atoms.

[13] R. A. Sawyer and H. B. Vincent, Characteristics of Spectroscopic Light Sources, *Proc. 6th Summer Conference on Spectroscopy and Its Applications,* John Wiley, New York (1939).

The sensitivity of the source for suitable substances is high, and the reproducibility is good when uniform amounts of the substance can be fed into the flame. Both the qualitative and quantitative applications are limited by the volatilities of the elements sought. For quantitative work the source is most practical for solutions, the sample being introduced into the flame as a fine mist by an atomizer system. The recently developed flame photometers are direct-reading instruments using a solution-in-flame technique (see Chapter 11).

The ordinary gas-air flame temperature seldom exceeds 1100° C. and only the alkali and alkaline-earth elements are excited. The

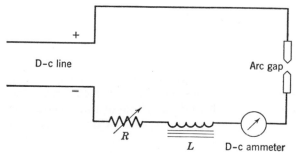

Fig. 8.13 D-c arc circuit

gas-oxygen, oxyacetylene, and oxyhydrogen flames give higher temperatures and increase the number of elements excited. For details on flame spectra, the monograph of Lundegardh listed in the bibliography is recommended.

The d-c arc circuit is shown in Fig. 8.13. A source of 110 to 220 volts direct current is connected in series with a variable ballast resistor, a large iron-core inductance, an ammeter, and the arc gap. When the current is turned on, the circuit is open at the gap, and current flow must be started by momentarily closing the gap or by short-circuiting the gap with an insulated carbon rod. The ballast resistor limits the current to the desired value, the resistance of the arc itself being very low. The inductance in the circuit acts to reduce surges and maintain a steady current.

The excitation is mostly thermal, the temperature in the arc stream ranging from 2000 to over 5000° C. The temperature varies with the current, the length of the gap, and the nature of the electrodes. The spectra produced are those of electron shifts in un-ionized atoms.

When the arc is struck, the electrodes heat up rapidly, and the electrode substance is volatilized into the arc stream. The process is essentially one of fractional distillation with the more volatile elements appearing first. The thermal energy of the arc is absorbed by the atoms and re-emitted as their arc spectra. The temperature in different portions of the stream varies, the cathode region being hottest, the anode region next, and the center of the gap being coolest. This *cathode-layer effect* [14] is utilized by illuminating the spectrograph with just the arc section around the cathode, the higher concentration of metallic ions and atoms in this region increasing the sensitivity of the excitation.

Arc lines are particularly prone to self-reversal which reduces the intensity of emission. *Self-reversal* is caused by the release of large amounts of atomic vapor which surrounds the arc gap. As this vapor is relatively cool, it absorbs its characteristic frequencies, reducing the intensity of these frequencies in the spectrum.

The d-c arc is simple and inexpensive, and its sensitivity is the highest of the classical methods. The reproducibility of the source is poor because of the instability of the current flow. The arc stream is not between the anode and the whole of the cathode, but is formed between the anode and a small spot on the cathode. This hot spot wanders from place to place on the cathode, causing a change in the electrode temperature, influencing volatilization, and, in the arc resistance, influencing the current, the arc temperature, and thus the excitation. For these reasons the d-c arc finds its main use in qualitative analysis.

The fractional-distillation effect may be minimized and the spectra of the less volatile elements produced by volatilizing a small portion of the material completely. A complete burn, as this process is described, is carried out by placing a small amount of the substance on an inert electrode, usually graphite, and continuing the excitation until the sample is completely gone.

The a-c arc circuit is shown in Fig. 8.14. The ordinary 110- or 220-volt, 60-cycle current is fed into the primary winding of a transformer. The secondary winding of this transformer is in series with the arc gap and a variable ballast resistor. The output of the transformer should be several hundred volts, the values 2200 or 4400 being popular because such transformers are stock items for power companies and are less expensive than custom-made units. The measurement of current in the circuit is usually made on the primary side of the transformer to avoid insulation difficulties.

[14] L. S. Strock, *Spectrum Analysis with the Carbon Arc Cathode Layer,* Adam Hilger, London (1936).

The discharge is self-starting, as the high voltage applied readily breaks down the gap. The excitation is both thermal and electric, and, though the body of the electrodes does not reach so high a temperature as the d-c arc, the atomic temperature in the vapor is higher. Although the spectra are predominantly those of neutral atoms, sufficient energy is involved so that ions and ionic spectra are formed.

As the current is alternating, there is no polarity effect, the arc striking alternately from each electrode on the half-cycle. The repeated striking and extinguishing of the arc minimizes any hot-

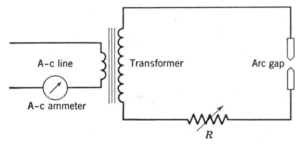

Fig. 8.14   A-c arc circuit

spot effect, such discharge being to a fresh spot on the electrodes, possibly the result of the formation of nonconducting oxides.

The a-c arc has a lower sensitivity and higher reproducibility than the d-c arc. It is more expensive and complex, but for quantitative analysis the advantage of the greater reproducibility renders these factors negligible. It ordinarily has no advantage over the d-c system for qualitative work and is seldom used for this purpose.

The basic circuit for spark excitation is shown in Fig. 8.15. A transformer is used to convert 110- or 220-volt, 60-cycle current to 10,000 to 100,000 volts. This high voltage is used to charge a condenser C, which then discharges across the electrode gap. By placing an inductance L in series with the gap, a high-frequency oscillating discharge is produced, whose frequency is determined by the LC product of the components. The gap discharge is a damped wave train (Fig. 8.15), with the majority of the power appearing in the first wave. The current flow in this wave may be several hundred amperes, but its duration may be less than a millionth of a second. Variable resistances may be added in the primary or secondary winding or both to increase the damping effect and to limit the current.

A spark discharge may also produce lines by excitation of the air molecules. This extraneous spectrum may be reduced by increasing the value of the inductance, with an accompanying decrease in the current flow. The current may be increased by increasing the size of the condenser or the voltage, both of which increase the stored power in the circuit.

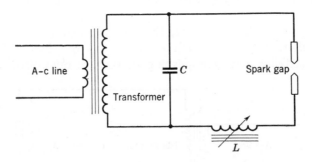

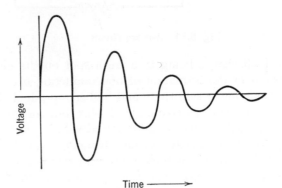

Fig. 8.15   Spark circuit and damped wave train

As with the a-c arc, the excitation is both electric and thermal; in comparison, the electrode temperature is still lower and the atomic temperature still higher (as high as 10,000° C). The spectra produced are largely ionic, the energy available being sufficient both to ionize the atoms and to excite the ions. Lines of neutral atoms may be considerably weaker than in an arc source, the energy absorption and emission appearing preferentially in the ionic spectra.

The spark discharge, like the a-c arc, does not show polarity and is formed and extinguished every half-cycle. One effect not present in the a-c arc is that the time at which the gap breakdown starts in relation to the voltage cycle of the 60-cycle high voltage is not uniform. Another is that the number of cycles in the damped wave train that occur before the discharge extinguishes may vary. These effects may be reduced by a rotary gap, driven by a synchronous motor (Feussner spark) to set the timing and duration of the discharge. Alternatively, a controlled jet of air may be directed on the electrode gap or preferably on an auxiliary series gap.[15] The spacing of the auxiliary gap regulates the voltage breakdown point, and the air jet blows out the damped wave train after a few cycles.

The spark source with a synchronous or air-jet gap is the most reproducible of the classical sources. Its sensitivity is low, as the most sensitive lines are usually neutral atom lines, which are not excited so much by a spark discharge as by the arc. It is the most expensive and complex circuit, but indispensable for quantitative analysis. The ARL spark-arc source unit features an 18,000-volt peak output spark, with variable inductance and capacitance and a rotating gap. The a-c arc section operates at 600 volts with a variable resistance for controlling the arc current.

Several attempts have been made to develop improved excitation units. The most notable of the commercial units is the Applied Research Laboratories Multisource.[16] A regulated direct voltage of about 1000 volts charges a variable high-capacity bank. The high power stored in this capacity bank is discharged by a rotary gap through variable resistance and inductance units in series with the electrode gap. In this way, the amount of energy in each discharge is made more reproducible than the conventional systems, and the wide variation possible in L, C, and R allows the formation of a variety of discharge types. Since the low voltage would not break down the electrode gap, a high-voltage–low-current source acts as an igniter in the system. The new model-4700 Multisource unit incorporates improvements in design based on the older models in industrial laboratories.

The dual source manufactured by the National Spectrographic Laboratories includes a 31,000-volt air-gap spark, an a-c arc with 2400 and 4800 volts available, and a rectifier unit for d-c arc excitation. The unit is mounted in a single cabinet with all controls and meters and the necessary valves and gages for the air gap.

At times it is desirable to start the excitation before starting the spectrographic exposure. This may be done with a shutter mecha-

[15] R. G. Fowler and R. A. Wolfe, *J. Optical Soc. Am.*, 35, 170 (1945).
[16] M. F. Hasler and H. W. Dietert, *ibid.*, 33, 218 (1943).

nism operated either manually or automatically. The pre-arc or pre-spark period has two possible advantages; to allow excitation equilibrium to be reached before exposing the plate, and to allow the removal of volatile elements before exposure when the desired elements are the least volatile.

Before a pre-arc or prespark time can be selected for either purpose, it is necessary to be sure that the lines to be measured are not affected, or that the effect is known and desirable. A good method for studying the intensity-time relationship is to move the plate vertically while the exposure is going on. A motor-driven mechanism is desirable, but some data may be obtained by moving the plate manually. The lines will vary in density along their length if a constant intensity-time relationship is not maintained.

8.8   Slit illumination. The slit appears to the spectrograph as the source of light, but the optical system between the actual source and the slit may change the effective illumination. To attain the maximum spectrographic speed the collimator lens or grating must be filled with light of maximum intensity and to obtain uniform lines on the plate the illumination must be equal at all points of the slit, particularly for stigmatic instruments.

The simplest method of illumination is to allow the light from the source to fall on the slit. Considering the arc or spark as a point source, the light travels outward in a spherical wave front. The illumination is proportional to the solid angle subtended on the source by the slit opening. When the source is considerably removed from the slit, and the incandescent electrodes are masked out, a point source is approximated, and the illumination along the slit is uniform. The subtended angle is small with a normal slit, and so the collimator is not filled with light, and the spectrographic utilization of the light is low. This may be improved by bringing the source closer to the slit, but the uniformity is impaired, and in any case the light utilization is still quite low.

The maximum utilization of light is obtained by focusing an image of the source on the slit with a short-focal-length lens. The source, lens, and slit may be close together to give a bright image. The uniformity of illumination is poor, as the light intensity varies within the source because of temperature gradients, and any wandering of the arc or spark will be reproduced at the slit. This method is most useful in qualitative work, and is required for the cathode-layer effect.

A method intermediate between the two mentioned is to place a long-focal-length lens as close to the slit as possible and focus an image of the source on the collimator or grating. This may be done by opening the slit and focusing an image of incandescent electrodes on a card or paper held close to the collimator or grating. In photographing a spectrum, the image of the electrodes must be masked out so that they do not contribute a continuous spectrum. The size and focal length of the lens must be selected to fill the grating or collimator with light. This method of illumination is excellent for quantitative analysis, as it furnishes a large amount of light without unduly sacrificing uniformity.

8.9   Spectrographic samples, electrodes, and holders.   Four general types of spectrographic samples are used: pins, flat surfaces, powders, and solutions, and several holders have been devised for handling these samples during excitation. Besides holding the samples, the holder should protect the operator from the ultraviolet radiation and from the high excitation voltages.

Pin electrodes, which may vary in diameter from small wires to ½-inch rods, can be held in clamps or clips using spring pressure to close on the sample. The clamps or clips must be isolated from each other and from any surrounding metal parts by insulation suitable for the excitation voltage. The leads from the excitation unit should fasten directly to the clamps. As pins may be excited with an arc or spark, it is desirable that the holder be suitably built and insulated for either source.

A suitable shield should protect the eyes of the operator from the ultraviolet light and make it impossible to come in contact with any electrically live parts. The shield should be hinged for easy access to the electrodes, and an interlock safety switch should be provided to automatically cut off the high voltage (a-c arc or spark) if the shield is opened. A unit fulfilling the requirements admirably has been designed by Scribner and Corliss [17] of the National Bureau of Standards. A simple fume-hood arrangement is desirable and can be constructed economically from a hand vacuum cleaner or a darkroom blower.

Commercial spectrographs are built with an optical bench to aid in the alignment of the electrode holder and other accessories with the optical path of the spectrograph. The construction of the bench differs from one manufacturer to another, so that accessories are not interchangeable without modification. However, each manufacturer puts out a reasonably complete line of accessories.

[17] B. F. Scribner and C. H. Corliss, *J. Research Natl. Bur. Standards, 30,* 41 (1943).

Useful refinements for a holder are provision for water-cooled clamps for high-current arc excitation, and a jig-loading system for speed and ease of electrode positioning. For jig loading a small auxiliary clamp holds the two electrodes with the proper gap spacing. The auxiliary clamp is built so that, when it is inserted into the main holder, the electrodes are transferred and automatically positioned.

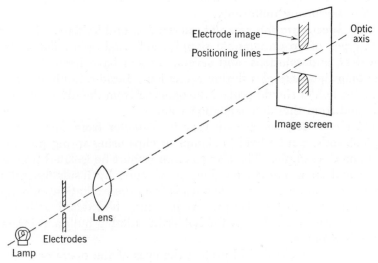

Fig. 8.16   Electrode positioning system

An arrangement for positioning the electrodes is shown in Fig. 8.16. A small incandescent lamp, which can be moved in and out of the light path, is combined with an auxiliary lens to throw an image of the electrodes on a screen behind the holder. After the proper position of the electrodes has been determined in relation to the spectrograph, the screen may be marked to show the required position of the image. This system is particularly necessary in d-c arc work, where the electrodes burn away during the exposure. The incandescent electrodes form an image on the screen, and the controls of the sample holder may be manipulated to maintain the image position during the exposure.

Samples from heats of metals or alloys are usually prepared by chill-casting pins or disks poured from a ladle sample from the furnace. The pins are ground to a conical point, and the disks are faced on a lathe or sanding drum to remove surface coatings before excitation. If the original melt is not available, pins or disks may be cut out and machined; a flat surface may be machined on an irregular object, or, if a flat surface is available, simple cleaning may be sufficient.

Flat-surface specimens act as one electrode with the other electrode (counterelectrode) usually being a pointed graphite rod.

Fig. 8.17   ARL Petrey stand (Courtesy Applied Research Laboratories)

Spark excitation is most common, and the sample may either rest on a flat plate with the graphite as the upper electrode or be supported on a Petrey stand (Fig. 8.17) above the graphite electrode.   The latter system has the advantage that only one side of the sample has to be flat, and so it is more adaptable for analyzing finished parts. The spark gap may be set with a lever spacing arm, as shown in the figure.   Petrey stands are automatically aligned horizontally by the optical bench, and, once the vertical adjustment is made, it need only be checked occasionally.

Powders or metallic samples in the form of drillings or turnings may be treated in several ways. For qualitative work, a small amount may be placed in a cupped graphite electrode and excited with the d-c arc, using a pointed graphite upper electrode. An alternative for quantitative analysis is to compress the particles into rods or small disks with a mold and hydraulic press. The rods may be excited with arc or spark, and the small disks may be sparked on a platform with a pointed graphite upper electrode.

Qualitative analysis on powdered samples is carried out with cupped graphite electrodes and the d-c arc. Low-volatility samples may be brought into the arc stream by mixing with a volatile carrier such as ammonium chloride. Nonconductors are more readily excited if they are mixed with graphite powder. For quantitative spark analysis, compressed pellets may be formed, and, if the sample will not cohere well, a weighed mixture with powdered graphite may be compressed to form the pellet. These pellets may be pin- or disk-shaped and may be excited like the metallic samples mentioned above.

Any sample that can be dissolved may be handled by a solution method, but it should be remembered that the concentration of the elements in the sample is lowered by the dilution. One device designed to handle solutions is the atomizer type which throws a fine mist into the spark gap between two auxiliary electrodes, into a flame, or into a mixing chamber in a burner for flame spectra. The atomizer should be easy to mount and easy to clean. A shield of some type is necessary to prevent corrosive spray from falling on other parts of the spectrograph equipment. Several other techniques have been developed. Graphite may be made very porous by heating at a high temperature, and these porous electrodes will absorb the solution to be analyzed.[18] The absorption is more rapid if alcohol is added to the solution. The prepared electrodes are suitable for any type of electric excitation. A more common method is to evaporate a small quantity of the solution in a shallow cupped graphite electrode. The electrode may be water-proofed by evaporating a drop of kerosene in the cup before adding the sample. These electrodes are most suitable for arc excitation.

Feldman,[19] at the Oak Ridge National Laboratory, introduced the porous-cup technique for handling solution samples. One-and-one-

[18] H. A. Sloviter and A. Sitkin, *J. Optical Soc. Am.*, *34*, 400 (1944).
[19] C. Feldman, *Anal. Chem.*, *21*, 1041 (1949).

half-inch lengths of graphite electrodes are hollowed out with a ⅛-inch drill so that the bottom thickness is about a millimeter. Approximately 0.25 ml of sample can be pipetted into the deep cup, which is made the upper electrode. This gives a continuously renewed thin film of solution when sparked with a graphite counter-electrode. The method is the most sensitive of the solution techniques for the less volatile elements and is recommended for aqueous and organic solutions.

To aid in sampling nonhomogeneous materials, a large portion may be dissolved and then evaporated to dryness. The salts or the oxides obtained upon subsequent ignition may be ground in a mortar and a small portion taken for analysis by one of the powder methods. An alternative procedure is to fuse the original material with a suitable flux and to crush and grind the fusion mixture to obtain a powder. Either of these methods should be checked for possible losses of the desired elements.

The graphite electrodes for sample cups and the pointed counter-electrodes are preferably of "spectroscopically pure" quality. The increased cost over standard grades is justified by their relative freedom from impurities and their uniformity. They are available from suppliers as prepared by the National Carbon Company or the Dow Chemical Company. The ¼-inch-diameter electrode is most common, but other sizes are available, and United Carbon Company supplies preformed shapes of purified graphite.

Graphite may be shaped readily, and many shapes of cups have been recommended for various purposes. The simple drilled cup may be formed with an easily made tool held in a chuck on a small motor. To prepare the tool, one end of a ¾-inch steel rod about 2 inches long is drilled so that the graphite rod fits easily. The other end is drilled out to accommodate a drill for the internal cup diameter desired, and the drill is held in place with a setscrew. A slot in the side to hold a thin steel blade for shaping the top of the cup may be added. A few right-angled holes to allow the graphite dust to escape are also advisable. Complete apparatus of this type is available commercially. More complex shapes may be turned on a lathe.

Graphite rods may be pointed easily in a pencil sharpener (reserved for this purpose). A more uniform pointed electrode for qualitative work may be prepared with a cutter of the type mentioned for making cups. The knife blade may be shaped to form a smooth point with a hemispherical end of the desired diameter. The blade design must give a cutting and not a burnishing action, for experience has shown that polished tips give less uniform results than the cut tips which retain the porosity of the original electrode.

8.10 Photographic processing equipment. After exposure in the spectrograph, the plate must be processed to produce the image. The ordinary steps of development, fixing, washing, and drying are followed, but certain differences from pictorial technique exist. For routine work the processing must be rapid, even at the expense of permanency of the plate, and in quantitative analysis uniformity of development is of utmost importance.

The Eastman spectrum analysis no.-1 emulsion was developed for the range (2400 to 3400 A) needed for routine spectrographic analysis. The uniformity, speed of processing, and contrast of the emulsion are excellent, the chief disadvantage being a rather wide variation in wavelength response. The emulsion is available on plates and on 35-mm film.*

When alkali metals are of interest, a plate responding to higher wavelengths is necessary. Ordinary panchromatic-process plates are quite satisfactory, and special emulsions are available. These plates in contrast to spectrum analysis no.-1 plates, must be processed in total darkness. A large number of other different emulsion types are available with varying wavelength response, sensitivity, and contrast. Figure 8.18 summarizes the spectroscopic plates available from Eastman Kodak Company.

The development process has as great an effect on the contrast of the image as the emulsion characteristic and the developer characteristic. As the developing time is increased, the contrast increases rapidly, then tends to level out. By setting the developing time in this plateau section, slight errors in timing are minimized. The effect of temperature within reasonable limits is a direct increase of contrast with increasing temperature; then a softening of the emulsion begins. The contrast varies with the type of developer and its concentration, and these variables should be controlled to obtain a satisfactory compromise between speed and uniformity.

Many of these factors are not critical for qualitative plates, but in quantitative analysis a close control over the developing factors is required. The goal is the production of plates where the contrast is identical, and the time, type, concentration, and temperature of the developing solution must be closely regulated.

---

* In the discussion of emulsion properties, the term plate should be understood to include both plates and film.

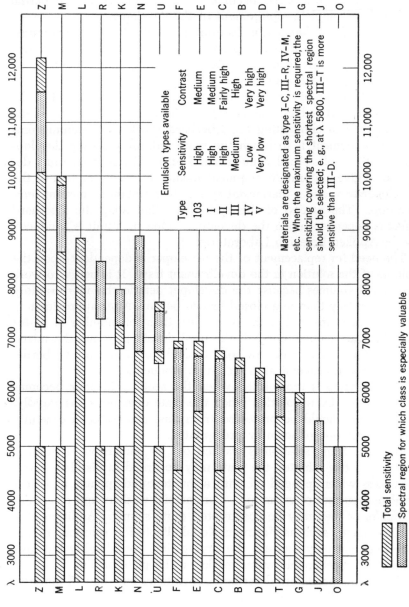

Fig. 8.18   Eastman Kodak plate chart (Courtesy Eastman Kodak Company)

The first few plates developed in a fresh solution sometimes are quite variable, and it has become common practice to use partial rather than complete replacement of the developer.

The end of development is fixed more exactly if the plate is immediately immersed in a shortstop bath of 5% acetic acid for a few seconds. The plate is then transferred to a fixing bath containing an emulsion hardener if necessary.

Local depletion of the developer causes a false development of the true image at its edges; this effect is known as the Eberhard effect. One method of eliminating the Eberhard effect and obtaining uniform development is to brush the plate uniformly during development with a soft, broad camel's-hair brush. Commercial units designed to give uniform development include a rocking motion of the developer tray, and a thermostat system to maintain a constant temperature. The success of this system in eliminating the Eberhard effect is dependent upon the developer. One such unit is produced by the Applied Research Laboratories.[20]

The need for replacement of the developer is dependent upon the volume of the solution in the development tray. It is better to work with small volumes because the developer deteriorates more rapidly in an open tray than in a closed brown bottle. After approximately 15 plates or at the end of the day if less than this number of plates have been developed, one-half the used developer should be mixed with an equal amount of new solution and stored in a brown bottle. This method is economical as well as reproducible.

The shortstop is replenished when the acetic acid odor becomes faint, and the fixing solution when the plate does not clear rapidly. All solutions should be protected from dust and watched carefully for the formation of scum or precipitates.

After the fixing solution is washed out by immersion in running water for a few minutes, the plate may be rinsed in distilled water, the excess water sponged off with a fine-textured sponge, and then dried in a current of warm air. Commercial washers and driers are available, or they may be constructed quite simply. Addition of a wetting agent, such as Eastman Kodak Photo-Flo solution, to the final wash not only shortens the drying time considerably but also eliminates objectionable water marks on the plate or film.

Though the procedure described above takes less than 15 minutes, even more rapid processing may be used. A comparison of the normal and rapid systems is given below:

[20] J. Schuch, *J. Optical Soc. Am.*, 32, 116 (1942).

	Normal	Rapid
Developer	D-19	D-19 (double strength)
Time	3 min	1 min
Shortstop	5% acetic acid	None
Time	5 sec	..
Fix	Eastman X ray	Eastman X ray
Time	3 min	To clear (about 20–30 sec)
Wash	5 min	Rinse in water
Dry	2 min	Use wet

The rapid system does not furnish a permanent record, as the plate becomes cloudy in a few hours.

8.11   The microphotometer.   The microphotometer or densitometer is used to measure the blackening of the photographic emulsion.[21]   The blackening may be related to the emitted intensity and thus to the concentration of an element.   The measurements are made in terms of the galvanometer or recorder pen deflection, with the clear emulsion usually rated as 100 and complete opacity rated as 0.

In the attempt to obtain more exposures on a plate, routine laboratories diaphragm the slit or plate to produce short line images.   This reduces the area available for measurement and makes the adjustment of the photometer system more critical.   To measure the blackening accurately, a large number of silver grains in the developed emulsion must be averaged by the photometer.   With fine-grained emulsions and operating with as wide a line as possible, the reduction in length is made possible.

The essential parts of a photoelectric microphotometer include a source of light (tungsten lamp), a slit to select the desired portion of the emulsion, a holder for the plate, a photocell or phototube, and a circuit and scale for reading the photocurrent.   Other features include a magnifying or projection system for viewing a reasonable portion of the spectrum, a wavelength scale for locating the lines, and a means of moving the plate horizontally (scanning) across the slit field to obtain the scale reading, and vertically (racking) to move from one spectrum to another.   In all instruments available commercially, the maximum excursion of the galvanometer or pen is read as the line is scanned.

The above paragraph describes a minimum microphotometer; the ease and comfort of operation should be considered when purchas-

[21] W. C. Pierce and N. H. Nachtrieb, *Ind. Eng. Chem., Anal. Ed.*, *13*, 774 (1941).

ing. For students and other inexperienced operators, the controls should be simple and convenient, and provision made for alignment of the plate with marked comparison spectrum. In all cases the instrument should be capable of being operated from a comfortably seated position without strain.

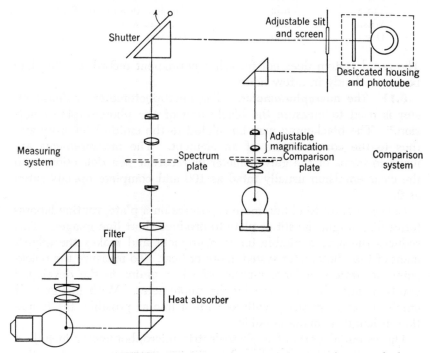

Fig. 8.19   Schematic diagram of optical system of the Bausch & Lomb densitometer (Courtesy Bausch & Lomb Optical Company)

A diagram of the Bausch and Lomb densitometer [22] is shown in Fig. 8.19 as a typical example. This instrument projects an enlarged image of a small portion of the spectrum onto a screen at eye level. The slit at the center of the screen passes the light transmitted by the spectral line to the phototube. An amplifier and microammeter give a direct reading on a 0–100 scale. Motor-driven and manual scanning are provided, and a comparison spectrum may be projected onto the screen for location of spectral lines.

Table 8.3, listing the characteristics of three makes of microphotometers, is reproduced from an article [5] by J. R. Churchill of the

[22] W. G. Kirchgessner, *Rev. Sci. Instruments*, 22, 289 (1951).

TABLE 8.3

Characteristics of Three Makes of Microphotometers

	Leeds & Northrup	University of Michigan	ARL–Dietert
Stability	1	2	3
Legibility of scale	1	1	1
Densitometered area	3	1	2
Field of view	3	2	1
Linearity	2	2	1
Provision of wavelength scale	No	No	Yes
Provision for reference spectrogram	No	Yes	Yes
Scanning	Synchronous motor	Manual	Synchronous motor
Racking	Rack and pinion	Manual	Rack and pinion
Plate or film holder	Plate	Plate	Plate and film
Position of film or plate	Vertical	Horizontal	Horizontal
Necessity for optical alignment	Each plate	Occasional	Occasional
Amplifier	Yes	No	Yes

Numbers 1, 2, and 3 denote rank of instruments when arranged in descending order with respect to the particular attribute or quality compared, based on manufacturers' literature and the author's experience.

From J. R. Churchill, *Ind. Eng. Chem., Anal. Ed., 16,* 653 (1944). Reprinted by permission.

Aluminum Company of America. The terms that are not self-explanatory may be defined as follows:

1. *Stability:* The ability of an instrument to maintain the 0 and 100 settings without frequent checking and correction. Instability is usually caused by light-source fluctuations and amplifier fluctuations.

2. *Linearity:* A linear relation between the transmitted intensity and the deflection is highly desirable. Nonlinearity may result from poor amplifier or galvanometer characteristics.

The Leeds and Northrup recording microphotometer, based on the design of Knorr and Albers,[23] has been described in the literature by Mackler.[24] The optical alignment is achieved by focusing an image of the lamp filament on the emulsion, and focusing this coupled system in turn on the slit. The measuring system includes a phototube, amplifier, and Micromax recorder. The initial adjustments of the electric system are complex but require only occasional correction. The chart record is convenient for wavelength measurement, as the scanning and chart drives are operated synchronously, allowing wavelength measurements to be made on the magnified scale of the chart record.

The University of Michigan microphotometer of Vincent and

[23] H. V. Knorr and V. M. Albers, *ibid.,* 8, 183 (1937).

[24] R. C. Mackler, A New Recording Microphotometer, *Proc. 7th Summer Conference on Spectroscopy and Its Applications,* John Wiley, New York (1940).

Sawyer [25] is now produced commercially by the Leeds and Northrup Company. The optical system is similar to the recording instrument, but the measuring system consists of a photocell and projection galvanometer. This instrument is probably the most rapid in operation and is widely used in routine laboratories.

The ARL comparator–densitometer (Fig. 8.20) has been described by Dietert and Schuch. [26] The slit is mounted in a retractible shoe which rides on the emulsion. The measuring circuit comprises a phototube, amplifier, and projection microammeter. The deflection scale and portions of the plate and a comparison spectrum are projected into a vertical translucent screen at eye level. This arrangement is convenient for qualitative work where comparisons of sample and standard spectra are to be made.

The Baird densitometer has been described by Baird. [27] The instrument in current production has been modified, chiefly in the electric circuits. A light beam is interrupted at a rate of 150 cps and split into two components, 180° out of phase. One beam passes through the plate and is reduced in intensity by the spectral line; the other is reduced by a circular step diaphragm and variable aperture until its intensity is equal to the measuring beam. The image density is then read off on the scales of the step diaphragm and variable aperture. The measuring circuit includes a multiplier phototube, illuminated alternately by the two beams, an a-c amplifier, and an electron-ray ("Magic-Eye") tube used as a null indicator. Racking and scanning adjustments are manual, and a viewing screen shows a magnified image of a small section of the plate, including the line being scanned.

The Jaco Projection Comparator microphotometer is produced by the Jarrell-Ash Company. A comparatively wide slit is illuminated by the lamp and a condenser lens, and this field is focused on the emulsion. A 10 x 20-mm portion of the emulsion is then projected onto the viewing screen and photocell slit at a ten times magnification. The photocell slit is a bilateral adjustable unit with provision for scanning line lengths of 0.1 to 3.5 mm. A photocell and projection galvanometer comprise the measuring circuit. The plate carrier handles two 10-inch plates end to end and is equipped for manual or motor-driven scanning. Provision is made for simultaneous pro-

[25] H. B. Vincent and R. A. Sawyer, *J. Optical Soc. Am.*, *31*, 639 (1941).

[26] H. W. Dietert and J. Schuch, *ibid.*, *31*, 54 (1941).

[27] W. S. Baird, *ibid.*, *31*, 179 (1941).

jection of an equivalent portion of a comparison plate for line identification.

The Gaertner spectrogram microdensitometer is the only visual

Fig. 8.20 ARL Comparator–Densitometer (Courtesy Applied Research Laboratories)

instrument offered at this time. The principle of operation is the comparison of the spectral line image with a linear neutral absorbing wedge. The optical system brings the spectrum image and the wedge image onto the eyepiece for matching, and readings are made on a millimeter scale. The instrument is recommended by the makers particularly when readings on a small number of lines are required.

Bibliography

Books

W. R. Brode, *Chemical Spectroscopy,* 2nd ed., John Wiley, New York (1943).
T. R. P. Gibb, Jr., *Optical Methods of Chemical Analysis,* McGraw-Hill, New York (1942).
H. G. Lundegardh, *Die Quantitative Spektralanalyse der Elemente,* I (1929), II (1934), Gustav Fischer, Jena.
R. A. Sawyer, *Experimental Spectroscopy,* Prentice-Hall, New York (1946).
F. Twyman, *Spectrochemical Analysis of Metals and Alloys,* Adam Hilger, London (1944).
Proc. 5th, 6th, and 7th Summer Conferences on Spectroscopy and Its Applications, John Wiley, New York (1938, 1939, 1940).

Articles

C. L. Guettel, Emission Spectrographic Equipment Used in Quantitative Analysis, *Ind. Eng. Chem., Anal. Ed., 16,* 670–75 (1944).
R. A. Sawyer and H. B. Vincent, Specifications and Testing of Spectrochemical Apparatus, *J. Optical Soc. Am., 31,* 47–53 (1943).
W. F. Meggers and B. F. Scribner, Index to the Literature on Spectrochemical Analysis 1920–1939, Am. Soc. Testing Materials, Philadelphia (1941).
B. F. Scribner and W. F. Meggers, Index to the Literature on Spectrochemical Analysis, Part II, 1940–1946, Am. Soc. Testing Materials, Philadelphia (1947).
B. F. Scribner and W. F. Meggers, Index to the Literature on Spectrochemical Analysis, Part III, in preparation.

CHAPTER 9

Qualitative Emission Spectroscopy

The elements that may be readily detected with the spectrograph include the metals and metalloids (such as P, B, As). By more complex techniques, it is possible to detect the presence of any element in a sample, as the spectra of all the elements may be excited by suitable means.

In the chapter on spectral theory, it was stated that the quanta emitted by an element when excited are characteristic of the elements. The magnitudes of these quanta are measurable in terms of wavelength or frequency. Thus, to perform a qualitative analysis, it is necessary to excite the sample, record the wavelengths produced, and identify the elements by reference to wavelength tables or charts. The intensity factor (number of quanta) at each frequency is not important, provided that it is sufficient to produce an image on the photographic plate.

The amount of an element that is detectable varies with its concentration, its relative volatility, the energy of excitation, and the function that describes the probability of the particular quanta which make up its spectrum being produced. For the common elements Table 9.1 shows the sensitivity with arc excitation.

9.1 Samples and excitation. In a qualitative analysis, it is desirable to have a high sensitivity, so that the presence of trace elements may be shown. For the metals and metalloids commonly analyzed for, the d-c arc shows the highest sensitivity. This source is increasingly important for the most difficultly excitable elements and nonvolatile and refractory compounds, as a complete burn of the sample may be obtained. It should be pointed out that any attempt to reduce excitation so that only major elements will appear in the spectrum may result in the nondetection of relatively high concentrations of elements which are difficult to excite.

The most common system of qualitative spectral analysis is to arc

TABLE 9.1

Arc Sensitivities of 50 Elements in the Range 2288 to 6717 A

0.1–1% Detectable
As, Cs, K, Cb, P, Rb, Ta, W
0.01–0.1% Detectable
B, Bi, Cd, La, Sb,
Si, Tl, Y, Zn, Zr
0.001–0.01% Detectable
Al, Au, Ba, Be, Ca, Fe, Ga, Ge, Hg,
Ir, Mn, Mo, Pb, Sc, Sn, Sr, Ti, V
0.0001–0.001% Detectable
Ag, Co, Cr, Cu, In, Li, Mg.
Na, Ni, Os, Pd, Pt, Rh, Ru

This table was reproduced from *Sensitive Arc Lines of 50 Elements* by J. W. Ryde and H. G. Jenkins, published by Johnson, Mathey and Company, by arrangement with the Jarrell-Ash Company.

the sample in a graphite cup, using a pointed graphite counterelectrode. Almost any sample may be reduced to a suitable size by grinding, milling, drilling, or any of the methods described in the preceding chapter. At times metallic pins are used, or flat samples may be treated with the spark on a Petrey stand.

The graphite electrode arc in air gives a cyanogen band spectrum in the near ultraviolet which may mask some of the interesting lines. This may be reduced by operating the arc in a stream of one of the inert gases, or by using metallic supporting electrodes. As the metals either burn away too rapidly, producing masking spectra themselves, or are difficult to obtain pure at low cost, graphite electrodes are used and the cyanogen spectrum is accepted as a necessary evil.

The exposure conditions for a particular type of sample must be determined by experiment. In all cases, a complete burn is desirable, to insure excitation of low-volatility elements. A sample of a few milligrams is sufficient, and, if the burn should give too dark an image, the exposure may be reduced by a variable angle sector. This consists of two disks with their opposite 90° segments cut out. The disks are rotated between the source and slit, and, by varying the relative angle of the opening, a variation of the exposure is possible from zero to 50%.

Nonconducting samples may be more easily excited by being mixed with an equal volume of graphite powder, and these, as well as all refractory materials, are often treated with a carrier to bring them into the arc stream. This carrier, usually a very volatile salt such as ammonium chloride, propels the entire sample smoothly up into the arc gap.

9.2   Methods of qualitative analysis.   While the entire pattern of lines produced by an element gives a positive identification, the location and measurement of all the lines for a particular element is extremely tedious, as the more complex elements may have several thousand lines in the range of 2000 to 10,000 A.   It has become customary to accept the identification of three lines of an element as positive proof of its presence,* and adherence to this practice will give excellent results.

De Gramont [1] and others made studies of the lines of the elements that persisted as the concentration of the element was decreased. These lines are spoken of as the persistent lines or raies ultimes (R.U.).   The identification of these lines will allow detection of elements present in low concentration, and all qualitative methods make use of the persistent lines.   (Tables of these lines may be found in chemical handbooks, references in the bibliography and in Appendix B.)

The identification of spectral lines may be done by comparison with known spectra or by the direct measurement of wavelength. These methods will be discussed in more detail in the following sections.

9.3   Wavelength measurement.   This process is the most tedious, but is the basic method upon which all others are based.   The measurements may be made directly on the plate, using a measuring microscope (Fig. 9.1) or on the trace produced by a recording densitometer.

In either case it is necessary to determine the dispersion or reciprocal dispersion of the plate or trace.   This may be done by measuring the separation of two lines of known wavelength and dividing the angstrom unit difference by the distance.   This value is valid for the complete range of a grating instrument, but for prism instruments it is only valid for interpolation between two lines that are separated in wavelength by only a few angstroms.   For interpolation between points spaced more widely, the Hartmann formula for nonuniform dispersion may be used.

---

* Absolute identification of a single line is positive proof, but the accuracy of wavelength measurement in the analytical laboratory (about 0.1 A) is not sufficient.   Three lines reduce the probability of mistaken identification.

[1] A. De Gramont, *Compt. rend., 171,* 1106 (1920).

Fig. 9.1   Measuring microscope (Courtesy Jarrel-Ash Company)

The dispersion of a prism instrument may be expressed approximately as

$$\lambda = \lambda_0 + c/(n - n_0)$$

where λ is the wavelength measured, n is the refractive index at λ, and λ_0, c, and n_0 are constants.

If we assume that the linear separation of two lines is proportional to the refractive indexes at the particular wavelengths, n may be replaced by d, the measured distance on the plate from some arbitrary line. The algebraic constants of the equation

$$\lambda = \lambda_0 + c/(d - d_0)$$

may be reduced to numerical constants by substituting values of λ and d for three known lines and solving the three simultaneous equations. The wavelengths of unknown lines may then be calculated.

To obtain reasonable accuracy, the three lines chosen should lie close together, and near the unknown line. Preferably the unknown should lie within the range of the three known lines.

The location of lines for the original measurements may be accomplished, using any readily recognizable groups of lines, but the most common comparison spectrum is that of iron. If iron is not present in the original sample in reasonable amounts, an iron spectrum should be run next to that of the sample. This is desirable in any event for easier reading. From the published charts (see bibliography) it should be possible to pick out characteristic groups of lines. If the manufacturer states the wavelength range covered for certain settings of the instrument, this will aid in finding the proper range for comparison. The identification of several iron lines will give an irregularly spaced wavelength scale for use in the measurements to follow.

For the prism instruments it is often helpful to prepare a prism calibration curve similar to those used in the infrared region. This curve is a plot of relative position (as measured on the scale of a traveling microscope) versus wavelength in angstroms. This curve can be prepared by means of the Hartmann dispersion formula, or by comparing the spectra of a mercury arc, a copper spark, and an iron spark with photographs with the wavelengths indicated. It is wise to start with the simple spectrum of mercury rather than the complex spectrum of iron (Fig. 9.2) in such a calibration.

Whether grating or prism instruments are used, it is desirable to interpolate as much as possible rather than to extrapolate, and, the shorter the interval between the known lines, the greater will be the accuracy of interpolation.

Once the wavelength scale has been established, there are two possible procedures. The first is to identify each line of the sample spectrum and assign it to the proper element. This method is extremely long, and it is difficult to assign every line accurately. The second method is to search specifically for the persistent lines of each element that may possibly be present. This method is much shorter, and, once three lines have been assigned to an element, no further search need be made for that element.

The problem of interference by other elements must be considered. The limitations of the spectrograph and the distance measurement cause an uncertainty in the measured wavelength. This uncertainty should be evaluated roughly in terms of angstrom units, and the inter-

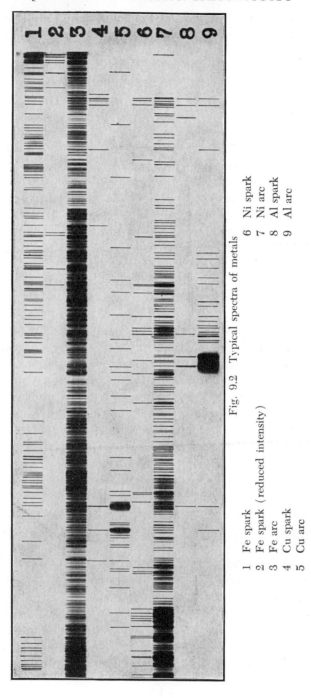

Fig. 9.2   Typical spectra of metals

1   Fe spark   6   Ni spark
2   Fe spark (reduced intensity)   7   Ni arc
3   Fe arc   8   Al spark
4   Cu spark   9   Al arc
5   Cu arc

ferences which appear in the range of the measured wavelength plus and minus the uncertainty noted. The decision concerning the presence or absence of a particular element can then be made on the basis of the over-all results. For example, if two or even three lines which may be due to zinc appear, and each of the lines may possibly be due to another element shown to be definitely present, other zinc lines must be checked to assure its presence or absence.

Either method of qualitative analysis by wavelength measurement is time-consuming, but the fundamental nature of the process makes it desirable that considerable practice in the techniques be obtained.

9.4 Standard-plate method. If a considerable number of qualitative analyses are to be run, it is desirable to build up a library of standard plates for comparison purposes. These may best be prepared by running arc spectra of pure elements or oxides at several concentrations, such as the pure element and 10, 1, and 0.1% dilutions made up with spectrographically pure graphite as a base. The spectra should be well separated on the plate, and each one should have a contiguous iron spectrum to allow registering of the standard and sample plates.

In the analysis, the sample and a contiguous iron spectrum are run on the plate and the elements picked out by comparison with the standard plates, first registering the two iron spectra. The lower concentrations are useful for picking out the persistent lines, whereas the higher concentrations show possible interferences with other elements.

It is not sound practice to estimate concentrations from the standard plates if the standard and sample matrixes are quite different. If an estimate is desirable, the beginner should run standard samples of composition similar to the unknown until he has gained sufficient experience to omit the standards.

The standard-plate method is suitable for routine analysis, particularly as an experienced operator recognizes many characteristic groups of lines without reference to any standards. It is less time-consuming than measuring each sample plate run, and, if the persistent lines and a few iron lines are marked on each standard plate, any necessary wavelength measurements can be made very rapidly.

9.5 The R.U. powder method. A prepared material is available that allows the spectrographer to show the persistent lines of 50 elements in one exposure. This material is known as R.U. powder and consists of a base mixture of calcium oxide, magnesium oxide, and zinc oxide, to which 47 other elements have been added in such amounts that only a few of the persistent lines appear for each element in the spectrum of the powder. The preparation was first made by J. W. Ryde and H. C. Jenkins of the research laboratories of the General Electric Company, Wembley, England, and is marketed in the United States through the Jarrell-Ash Company, Boston, Mass. Enlarged positive photographic prints of the arc spectra of iron, the oxide base material, and the R.U. powder are also available for identification work. This series of charts covers the range from 6717 A to 2288 A, and the R.U. and principal iron lines are marked on the prints. A table of the lines is given in Appendix B, and a portion of one of the charts is shown in Fig. 9.3.

For analysis with the powder, it is necessary to prepare a master plate of the R.U. powder arc spectrum, preferably with a contiguous iron spectrum. The master plate may be marked in ink on the emulsion side with the element symbols of the persistent lines in the R.U. spectrum and the wavelengths of a number of the lines in the iron spectrum marked by reference to the photographic enlargement mentioned above. After marking, the emulsion side of the master plate should be covered with a clear glass and the two plates bound together with cellulose tape or lantern-slide binding tape. This will protect the master plate from dirt and scratches.

A qualitative analysis is run by producing contiguous arc spectra of the R.U. powder, the sample, and the pure base element of the sample or a reference iron spectrum. The plate is processed, and the R.U. spectra of the master and sample plates are registered. The lines present in both the R.U. and sample spectra are noted, and the elements tabulated with the number of lines appearing. As in the preceding methods, three lines which are free from interference are considered positive proof of the presence of the element. The spectrum of the base element of the sample may be included to show interferences from this element, but the purity of the material must be high enough so that lines due to other elements do not appear.

The R.U. powder method is the simplest for nonroutine qualitative analysis for the 50 elements present in the powder. If an experienced operator is available, the standard plates or R.U. plates are not always necessary, but for casual qualitative analysis such aids allow a relatively inexperienced man to obtain accurate results.

The proof of the presence or absence of a single element is the easiest analysis to make. Although any of the methods described are satisfactory, it is frequently desirable to run a spectrum of the ele-

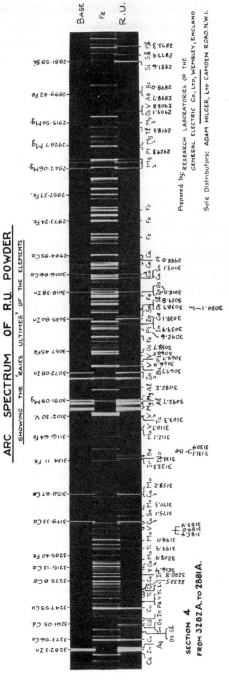

Fig. 9.3 R. U. spectrum chart (Courtesy Jarrel-Ash Company)

ment, suitably diluted with graphite powder, along with the sample and the iron or R.U. powder spectrum.

9.6   Operational notes.   The inclusion of blanks to compensate for impurities in the electrodes and the pickup of impurities during any preceding chemical treatment is very desirable.   The major electrode impurities may usually be removed by arcing the empty graphite cup for about 30 seconds, cooling, and then filling with the sample and arcing for the actual exposure.

Any system for producing contiguous comparison spectra must allow placing each exposure directly above the other, without any horizontal shifting of the spectra.   Stigmatic spectrographs use the Hartmann diaphragm, a steel slide which fits into grooves on the face of the slit.   When the slide is moved horizontally, any one of several apertures allows the light from the source to strike the desired section of the slit.

With astigmatic spectrographs, contiguous spectra are usually produced by plate racking (vertical motion to expose fresh sections of the plate), and slight horizontal shifts frequently occur.   It is worth while to make a mask with a narrow slot the length of the plate, and an attachment to move the mask vertically to expose contiguous sections of the plate without opening the spectrograph.   This eliminates any uncertainty in matching lines in successive spectra.

The various standard samples distributed by the National Bureau of Standards are frequently useful in qualitative work for producing comparison spectra.   As the complete analysis is available for most of these standards, they also are of value in estimating sensitivities under the particular conditions used.

For comparison of spectra, or for making master plates, a ground-glass screen with illumination behind the glass is an aid in reducing eye fatigue.   These are available from several manufacturers of spectrographic equipment, or may be made in the laboratory.

A more elaborate device is the Bausch and Lomb spectrum comparator.   An enlarged image of a section of the spectrum plate is projected onto a horizontal white screen at the base of the unit. Comparison spectra of iron and a wavelength scale are available for plates taken on the Bausch and Lomb Littrow spectrograph.

Bibliography

Articles

W. C. Pierce, O. R. Torres, and W. W. Marshall, Identification of Lines in Qualitative Spectrographic Analysis, *Ind. Eng. Chem., Anal. Ed., 11*, 191–93 (1939).
G. W. Standen, Qualitative Spectrographic Analysis, *Ind. Eng. Chem., Anal. Ed., 16*, 675–80 (1944).

Tables

W. R. Brode, *Chemical Spectroscopy*, 2nd. ed., John Wiley, New York (1943).
A. Gatterer and J. Junkes, *Atlas der Restlinien*, Specola Vaticana, Città del Vaticano (1937–49).
G. R. Harrison, *M.I.T. Wavelength Tables with Intensities in Arc, Spark, or Discharge Tube*, John Wiley, New York (1939).
G. R. Harrison, Compilations of Spectroscopic Data, *J. Applied Phys., 10*, 760–67 (1939).
H. Kayser and R. Ritschl, *Tabelle der Hauptlinien der Linien-spektren aller Elemente nach Wellenlange geordnet*, Julius Springer, Berlin (1939).
Tables of wavelengths also appear in the various chemistry handbooks.

Charts of Spectra

W. R. Brode, *Chemical Spectroscopy*, 2nd ed., John Wiley, New York (1943). (Spectrum of iron with positions of principal lines of other elements)
J. M. Eder and E. Valenta, *Atlas Typischer Spektren*, A. Holder, Wien (1928).
A. Hilger, *Spectrograms of Copper, Iron and R.U. Powder*, Adam Hilger, London.

CHAPTER 10

Quantitative Spectrographic Analysis

Quantitative spectrographic analysis is the most important tool of the metal industries for routine control. The methods require rigorous standardization and complex apparatus and are most useful where large numbers of similar samples are to be analyzed. These procedures are not feasible in the small laboratory, but simpler, less exact methods may often be applied to nonroutine estimation of small concentrations.

The intensity of emission for a single wavelength of the spectrum of an element is partly a function of the exciting energy and the concentration of the element in the matrix. The process of measuring the intensity introduces many more variables, so that the relationship becomes quite complex, and it is necessary to include the effects of the complete spectrographic system to evaluate the results of an analysis.

We have discussed the apparatus required to record emission spectra on a photographic plate, and this equipment must now be considered in relationship to quantitative analysis.

10.1 The photographic process. Photographic emulsions have been used for many years in photometric work to record the intensity of light. They possess the distinct advantage of allowing the measurement of low intensities by an increase in the time of exposure.

A photographic emulsion consists of a suspension of a silver halide such as silver bromide in gelatin. Upon exposure to radiation to which the emulsion is sensitive, a latent image is produced in the emulsion. Development of the emulsion causes the grains of silver bromide, in which the latent image exists, to be reduced to elemental silver. After development, the remaining silver bromide is removed in the "fixing" process by a solution of "hypo" consisting mainly of sodium thiosulfate.

According to the reciprocity law of Bunsen and Roscoe, the black-

174

ening of an emulsion is dependent solely upon the total energy striking the emulsion where the total energy is a product of the intensity
and the time.   For most emulsions, particularly with very short or
very long exposures with strong or weak light, the interchangeability
of time and intensity does not apply.   For example, this means that
a 100-second exposure at one unit of intensity does not yield the
same blackening as 100 units of intensity for 1 second.   Such a con-
tradiction is often referred to as failure of the reciprocity law.

For an approximation, the reciprocity law, combined with the
relationship between plate density and exposure, relates the density
or blackening of the image, the intensity, and the exposure time for
cases where the product of the intensity and time is a constant.

$$d = k \log I \cdot t$$

where d = the density (blackening) of the image, k = a constant,
I = the intensity, t = the time.

Though this approximation holds only over a rather limited range
for most emulsions, it demonstrates the principle involved.   We need
to determine intensity values for spectral lines, but we measure
density.

Since there is no exact mathematical equation relating image
density and the intensity of light producing the image, it is necessary to express this relationship graphically, and even then the intensities obtained from the graph are relative rather than absolute values.

The emulsion calibration curve, relating density and intensity is
frequently spoken of as the H and D curve, after Hurter and Driffield
who first prepared this curve for photographic work.   A typical curve
is shown in Fig. 10.1, the salient features of which are described
below.

It is noted that a certain threshold intensity is necessary before an
image is produced.   The density then increases to a maximum and
decreases again with overexposure.   The linear portion of the curve
is the most useful and is used to characterize the developed emulsion.   The slope ($\tan \theta$) of this portion is spoken of as the gamma,
or contrast, and the intercept on the horizontal axis as the inertia.
(Emulsions are classed as fast or slow by their relative inertia and
as high or low contrast by their linear slope.)

Several precautions are necessary in preparing an emulsion calibration curve.   The gamma is a function of the emulsion itself, its
age and condition, the development, and the wavelength of the light
producing the image (see Fig. 10.2).   These factors must be reason-

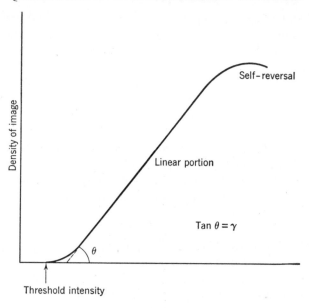

Fig. 10.1   Typical H and D curve

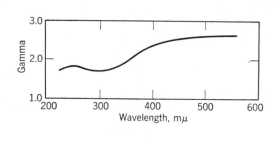

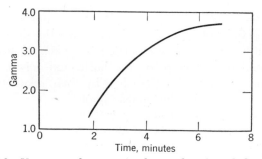

Fig. 10.2   Variation of gamma with wavelength and development

ably constant to reproduce a certain gamma. The gamma or contrast of an emulsion ranges from 0.6 to 7, being approximately 1 for emulsions of moderate contrast, the most common type for emission spectroscopy.

10.2 The analytical process. The two most variable operations in analytical spectrography are the excitation of the emission spectra and the recording of the number of quanta produced at each wavelength of the spectrum. We have seen that the excitation source energy must be divided between heating the sample, volatilization, ionization, and the actual excitation of the atoms or ions in the vapor state. If the fraction of the source energy devoted to excitation can be reproduced, the wavelengths and intensities of the spectral lines should be reproduced. The concentration of the element sought will control the intensity of its particular spectral lines, because the number of quanta produced at each of its wavelengths is a direct function of the number of atoms available.

The recording of the number of quanta or the intensity at any wavelength with a photographic emulsion has been shown to require a calibration of the emulsion. This is needed to translate the degree of blackening (density) measured into an intensity value for the radiant energy which produces the blackening.

It is very difficult to produce radiant energy intensities of known absolute intensity. Therefore, analytical spectrography has developed largely on the basis of using relative intensities as the function which is related to concentration.

The emulsion calibration curves obtained in practice are based on measurement of the density produced by several exposures of known intensity ratio. The relative intensity values are plotted against the corresponding densities to give the calibration curve. The methods vary in the means of producing the known intensity ratios, but the principle involved is the same in all cases.

10.3 Plate calibration methods. We shall now consider in more detail five methods of obtaining an emulsion calibration (H and D) curve.

(*a*) If the distance from the source to the spectrograph is varied and the light is allowed to fall directly on the slit, the intensity of illumination varies inversely as the square of the distance. This method is simple and direct but requires a lot of manipulation. Also the excitation and exposure time must be exactly the same for each distance.

(*b*) The intensity may be reduced in known ratios by the use of wire screens, optical wedges, and the like, if calibrations are available for these parts.

(*c*) A similar and more common method is to use a rotating step sector (Fig. 10.3) in front of the slit. This sector is cut to expose various portions of the slit in ratios of 1, 2, 4, 8, 16 and 32. If the spectrograph is stigmatic, the image will appear as in the figure, and the measurements of the densities in each step will give a calibration curve from a single exposure. This method is not applicable to astigmatic grating spectrographs unless the step sector can be placed at the secondary focus of the grating.

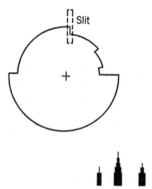

Fig. 10.3   Step sector and lines

(*d*) The Diecke method [1] is based on the principle that certain spectrographic lines (homologous lines) maintain a constant intensity ratio when slight changes in conditions of excitation and exposure occur. These homologous lines may therefore be used as standards once their relative intensity has been measured by some other method. A weakness of the system is that it is very difficult to find enough lines of the proper intensities which are truly homologous, as at least 10 or 12 points are desirable for plotting a calibration curve. The original article lists suitable lines in the iron spectrum.

(*e*) The "two-line" method developed at the Research Laboratories of the Aluminum Company of America [2] has many advantages and will be treated more fully here. It depends on the use of a single pair of homologous iron lines. Several exposures are taken on a plate, the optics of the system being varied to produce a range of densities. The relative values of these exposures need not be known, and practical methods are to decrease the grating aperture or to use a rotating sector with a variable angular aperture. The excitation or exposure time may not be the variable, although their reproducibility is not highly critical.

The image densities of the two homologous lines, Fe_1 and Fe_2, in each spectrum are caused by two intensities I_1 and I_2, which maintain a fixed ratio for all the spectra on the plate.

[1] G. H. Diecke and H. M. Crosswhite, *J. Optical Soc. Am.*, 33, 425 (1943).
[2] J. R. Churchill, *Ind. Eng. Chem., Anal. Ed.*, 16, 653 (1944).

$$I_1/I_2 = r$$

This gives us only a single ratio, whereas for plotting a complete calibration curve we need several interrelated ratios, one for each relative intensity.   To obtain the series of ratios required for the calibration curve, we first plot a preliminary curve of the deflection *
of Fe_2 against Fe_1, each point being the result of a separate spectrum. This curve gives us the equivalent of an infinite number of points, each one representing the galvanometer deflections caused by two intensities of fixed ratio.

On this preliminary curve (Fig. 10.4), we select a value of Fe_2

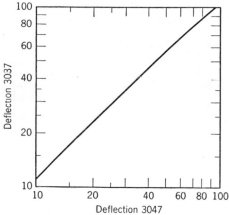

Fig. 10.4   Preliminary curve for plate calibration by the two-line method

with a deflection greater than any expected in our analysis, and from the curve we obtain the corresponding value of Fe_1.   Using this latter number † as a new Fe_2 value, we find the corresponding value for Fe_1 and repeat this procedure until we reach a deflection less than any expected in our analysis.

The procedure described gives us a series of deflection values, $D_0, D_1, D_2, \cdots, D_n$, each of which was produced by a corresponding intensity, $I_0, I_1, I_2, \cdots, I_n$.   Since

$$I_1/I_0 = I_2/I_1 = \cdots = I_n/I_{n-1} = r$$

* The quantity measured by most commercial densitometers is a galvanometer or recorder deflection and is based on the scale of 100 for a clear portion of the emulsion and 0 for complete opacity.

† Note that this allows cancellation of this number as shown in the equations which follow.

it is also true that

$$\frac{I_2}{I_0} = \frac{I_2}{I_1} \times \frac{I_1}{I_0} = r^2$$

or

$$I_n/I_0 = r^n$$

therefore

$$I_n = I_0 \cdot r^n$$

While we cannot evaluate I_n or I_0, it is apparent that, since I_0 is an arbitrary constant, r^n is a relative intensity. A logarithmic plot of D_n against r^n will give us an emulsion calibration curve in terms of

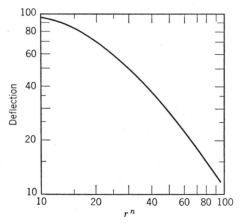

Fig. 10.5   Emulsion calibration curve

relative intensity (Fig. 10.5). The article cited recommends the following pairs of iron lines:

Pair		r
3047.6/3037.4	=	1.26
2966.9/3037.4	=	1.56
2755.7/2739.6	=	1.23

Any pair from the lines given by Diecke may be selected or any homologous pair in the spectrum of a suitable element. Section 10.5 gives an actual example of calibration curve preparation.

10.4   The internal standard method of analysis. The most universal photographic method of analysis is the method of homologous

pairs with an internal standard. A line of the element being determined (analysis line) and one of an element present or added in
fixed concentration (standard line) which are homologous are selected. The intensity ratio of the analysis and standard lines is the
operating function for determining the concentration of the unknown
element.

It is necessary to run a series of standards which approximate the
general composition and structure of the samples to be analyzed to
determine the concentration-intensity ratio function. Too much emphasis cannot be placed on the above restriction on the standards and
samples, as more faulty analyses may be traced to this point than
to any other part of the procedure.

The relationship between concentration and intensity is of the
form

$$\log c = A \log It + B$$

where B is a constant specific for the line and A is a constant that
is the same for the pair of homologous lines. For two elements in the
same sample and same exposure,

$$\log (c_1/c_2) = A \log (I_1/I_2) + B_1 - B_2$$

Then, since c_2 (the concentration of the internal standard) is constant, the equation will be of the form

$$\log c_1 = A \log (I_1/I_2) + B'$$

The straight line obtained from plot of $\log I_1/I_2$ against $\log c_1$ is
the concentration calibration curve (analytical curve). The useful-
ness of this curve over a period of time depends on the completely
homologous nature of the lines and the constancy maintained by
B_1, B_2, and c_2 which are included in B'.

This method of analysis allows a simplification of the two-line
method of emulsion calibration described in the preceding section.
It is apparent that the deflection of the analysis and standard line,
D_a and D_s, would yield relative intensities r^a and r^s. Their log ratio
would be

$$\frac{a \log r}{s \log r} = \frac{a}{s} \log r$$

If the value of r were not known exactly, it would be possible to
select any reasonable constant, and the only effect would be to

expand or contract the abscissa scale of the emulsion calibration and analytical curves without changing the results of the analysis.

To facilitate the computations involved, special calculating boards have been devised. These combine the functions of plotting scales for the emulsion calibration curve, and slide rule for determining intensity ratios directly. Still greater speed may be obtained by having concentration scales mounted on the intensity ratio scale of the calculating board.

The internal standard method with homologous pairs is the most accurate of the photographic methods. A relative accuracy of ± 5–10% is about average for analysis by this method. However, as the range of completely homologous behavior of two lines is limited, it is necessary to maintain the conditions of excitation, exposure time, development, and other variables as constant as possible.

10.5 Curve construction. The following description of the preparation of a calibration curve by the two-line method may aid in clarifying the method. A series of 15 exposures was made, sparking a steel plate on a Petrey stand with a graphite counterelectrode. The illumination was varied from exposure to exposure by means of a variable angle sector, and the deflection values for the 3037 and 3047 iron lines in each spectrum were read on the densitometer. The scale was read only to 0.5, and the following values were obtained:

Spectrum	D-3037	D-3047
1	11.0	10.5
2	13.5	12.5
3	15.0	14.0
4	20.0	18.0
5	22.0	19.5
6	27.0	24.0
7	33.5	30.0
8	39.0	35.0
9	47.5	43.5
10	55.0	50.0
11	75.0	70.5
12	85.5	83.0
13	88.0	85.0
14	92.0	90.0
15	95.5	95.0

These values were plotted on logarithmic paper (Fig. 10.4) giving the preliminary curve. With the value 95.5 on the vertical axis selected arbitrarily as being greater than any expected in the analyses, the corresponding point on the horizontal axis was found to be 95.0. For 95.0 on the vertical axis, 94.0 was found on the horizontal axis. Repeating this process gave the series

n	D	n	D	n	D
1	95.5	11	64.5	21	24.1
2	95.0	12	58.5	22	21.3
3	94.0	13	53.0	23	19.3
4	92.0	14	48.0	24	18.0
5	90.0	15	43.5	25	16.5
6	87.0	16	39.5	26	15.0
7	84.0	17	36.0	27	13.6
8	80.0	18	32.5	28	12.3
9	75.0	19	29.5	29	11.2
10	70.0	20	26.3		

These 29 values were plotted to prepare the calibration curve (Fig. 10.5). For demonstration purposes, log D was plotted against log a^n, the value of a being arbitrarily selected to fill the single-cycle logarithmic paper.

It is simpler to use semilog paper and plot log D against equally spaced linear distances selected to fill the paper, and this system is carried out in the laboratory. Both the preliminary and calibration curves are plotted on large (24 x 28-inch) plain paper with a calculating board. The logarithmic vertical scale runs from 2 to 100, while the horizontal scale is graduated the same way with an added 0–40 linear scale. In some cases the calibration curve is run down to a deflection of 5, which gives approximately 40 points for the full extent of the scale.

10.6 Comparison methods. If the excitation and exposure are maintained reasonably constant for a series of spectra of standards and samples exposed on one plate, it is possible to estimate the concentration of one or more elements in the samples by direct visual comparison with the standards. Measurement with a densitometer is a worthless refinement unless the complete procedure described in the preceding section is carried out.

The excitation and exposure variables affect the results considerably, so that a relative error of 20% is not uncommon. For determining elements present in amounts less than 0.01%, this relative accuracy is sufficient and in some cases may be good enough for estimating even larger amounts.

Comparison with permanent standards run on separate plates introduces the development and other emulsion variables into the system, and, if the emulsion batch is changed, new standards are necessary. Since the time and labor involved in the exposure of standards on each plate is relatively slight, separate standard plates are not recommended.

One of the earliest methods of quantitative analysis was based on the disappearance of certain lines in the spectrum of any element as its concentration is reduced. By the selection of the proper series of lines, it is possible to bracket a sample within the limits desired by noting which lines appear in the spectrum. The excitation, exposure, and photographic variables must be held constant to obtain reproducible results. As in the preceding method, the quantitative results are poor, but it is useful for estimating the order of magnitude of a constituent.

10.7   The log-sector method. The log sector shown in Fig. 10.6 may be used with a stigmatic spectrograph. If this sector is rotated between the source and the slit, the illumination varies logarithmically along the length of the slit, producing the line shapes shown. At some point along the line image, the illumination will be below the threshold intensity, and the line will fade out. Thus the length of the line image is a measure of the source intensity at that wavelength.

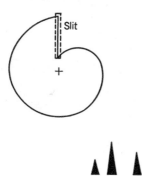

Fig. 10.6 Log sector and lines

Special micrometer magnifiers have been developed which allow the accurate measurement of line length. The emulsion calibration and analytical curves are prepared as in Section 10.5, the line-length values being used instead of the logarithms of the deflections. This allows the analyst to dispense with the microphotometer.

The log-sector method is only convenient with stigmatic spectrographs, so that, with the increasing popularity of astigmatic grating instruments, the method is becoming obsolete. The chief drawback is the requirement that the illumination striking the sector along the slit length must be reproducibly uniform. This requirement is extremely difficult to attain in practice. In measuring the line lengths it is difficult to determine exactly where the line ends, and the personal error involved in this visual measurement often exceeds 10%.

Two other effects may cause difficulties. The first is the intermittency effect; that is, a series of short exposures do not necessarily produce the same image density as a single long exposure of the same total time. A great deal of experimental work and theorizing on this subject have led to the conclusion that, if the number of interruptions are of the order of a few hundred per exposure, the densities are reproducible. A second effect, occurring with a-c sources, is caused by synchronization of the sector rotations and the flashes of light from the source. It may be seen that, if the individual flashes are not equally distributed around the sector, as it rotates, erratic exposures and densities will result.

10.8 Universal methods. All of the preceding methods require standards whose composition approximates that of the samples. While this is feasible for routine work, a laboratory with a large variety of samples to handle would need an equally large variety of standards. The development of a universal method for all types of substances would be very desirable, and several spectrographers [3, 4] have made valuable contributions.

One approach to a universal method is to dissolve the sample, add a known quantity of an element as an internal standard, and treat the solution by any of the available solution methods. A solution technique allows a simple preparation of synthetic standards, but has certain defects. Many elements, such as silicon and tungsten, are difficult to keep in solution. The sensitivity of solution methods is lower than that of other techniques. The possible effect of other elements on the spectrum of the desired one is not compensated for as well as with good individual standards. And the added internal standard must be rare enough so that it is not found in any of the samples and yet must have a simple spectrum with suitable standard lines.

To minimize the effect of different matrixes in a universal method, inert materials called buffers are added. By dilution, each sample is reduced to approximately the same matrix. The loss of sensitivity by dilution and the necessity of preparing a powdered sample limit the method.

Altogether, the problems involved in the development of a universal quantitative method are numerous and difficult. The solution of these problems, however, would lead to an increase in spectrographic analysis in nonroutine laboratories.

[3] J. van Calker, *Spectrochim. Acta, 2,* 333 (1944).
[4] G. Hansen, *ibid., 2,* 374 (1944).

10.9   Development of an analytical method. If a sufficient number of samples are to be analyzed, the time saved by setting up a spectrographic method may be considerable. This is particularly true if suitable standards are available.

The American Society for Testing Materials publishes a list of spectrographic standards [5] which are currently available. These have been prepared and analyzed by the National Bureau of Standards or large manufacturers. Almost all of the materials are metals and alloys, and so for other materials the analyst must prepare his own standards.

In the method of homologous pairs, the spectrographer will save much time and labor if the line pairs can be found in the literature. In such a case, he only needs to determine the excitation and exposure time necessary to produce the desired image blackenings for these lines. An extensive list of line pairs is to be found in the publication mentioned above.

It is possible to select homologous pairs on a theoretical basis, as such a pair must arise from similar electronic energy-level shifts. However, a second criterion for a usable pair is that they have an intensity ratio of unity for a concentration at about the middle of the desired concentration range. (The concentration for which unity ratio occurs is called the index value and is generally listed with published homologous pairs.) Thus the intensities of the two lines must be measured, although some indication is given by the relative intensity values shown in various wavelength tables (see bibliography). A purely empirical method is to select a large number of standard and analysis lines of suitable intensity and measure the intensity ratios of the various combinations while varying the excitation and exposure time. The closest approach to a homologous pair is the combination that gives the least variation in ratio.

The optimum excitation, prespark, and exposure must be experimentally developed, and, as they are mutually dependent, some compromises are necessary. A fruitful approach is to study the constancy of the homologous pairs in a single sample for each of the available excitation conditions with arbitrary prespark and exposure times. Several plates should be run, with duplicate or triplicate exposures of each condition on each plate.

After selection of the preliminary optimum excitation, a series of timed exposures of a continuous sparking period should be made, each

[5] W. R. Brode, and B. F. Scribner, Report on Standard Samples for Spectrographic Analysis, Am. Soc. Testing Materials, Philadelphia (1944).

one covering 10 seconds for example. A study of the ratios will indicate if the ratios are constant, if there is a plateau effect, or if they change constantly. The prespark time can then be selected and the exposure time determined for proper plate blackening. With this preliminary information, the process can be repeated to find the optimum conditions. Where several elements are to be determined, the compromises involved are considerable.

When the homologous pairs and the standard conditions of excitation and exposure have been selected, a series of standards is run to prepare the analytical curves for the desired elements. The samples may then be run with occasional checks of standards to be sure that the analytical curves remain valid. These checks may be run less often if experience indicates that they are unnecessary, but many routine laboratories run one standard on each plate to maintain rigid control.

Whenever a new emulsion batch is started, the emulsion calibration curve must be redetermined, and at this time it is preferable also to run a new analytical curve. The purchase of plates in large enough quantity to last 2 to 3 months reduces the labor involved, but, as the gamma of an emulsion changes slowly on aging, it is not advisable to purchase in larger lots.

It has been found that analytical curves tend to drift from time to time; that is, they move up or down slightly while remaining parallel to the original curve. The exact cause of this drift is not definitely known, but it can be corrected for by the standard checks discussed above.

When shifting from standard chemical analyses to spectrographic methods in routine laboratories, chemical checks may be run on a certain fraction of the samples. As time goes on, this fraction may be reduced. The chemical analyses allow the spectrographer to evaluate the accuracy of the spectrographic analysis, provided the precision and accuracy of the chemical method and the precision of the spectrographic method are known.

It should be pointed out that the amount of material consumed in a spark discharge is of the order of a few milligrams at most. The analysis depends on the composition of this minute sample, so that technique of sampling must be carefully considered and duplicate samples run if the results are to be of value.

The maintenance of routine spectrographic analysis at high accuracy is made easier by massive rigid construction of the component units. Rugged electrical components with high safety factors in the source, with a stable voltage supply, will greatly increase reproducibility. The spectrograph should be operated in an air-conditioned room at constant temperature and humidity. Variable humidity causes fluctuations in excitation and to some extent in emulsion characteristics.

10.10   Direct-reading instruments. So many of the faults of spectrographic analysis have been traced to the photographic plate that considerable research has been done in developing new receptors for emission spectroscopy. The energy of a single line is so low that it is extremely difficult to measure. However, the development of the photomultiplier tube ‡ has made possible the construction of direct-reading instruments.

With the photomultiplier tube each original electron is multiplied many times to give an appreciable current in the external circuit. The effect of a time integral of intensity is produced by using the current in the external circuit to charge a condenser. This builds up the voltage across the condenser according to the formula

$$V = I \cdot t / C$$

where I is the current, t the time, and C the capacity of the condenser. Thus the voltage measured across the condenser after a given time interval is proportional to the current, and thus to the intensity of the light.

In commercial instruments, such as the Applied Research Laboratories Quantometer [6] or the Baird Associates direct-reading spectrometer,[7] the exposure is continued until the voltage produced by the standard line reaches a given value.[6] The voltages produced by the analysis lines may then be considered directly as intensity ratios. By suitable amplification and recording devices, the excitation is shut off automatically when the standard voltage reaches the desired value, and the analytical line voltages operate dials reading directly in percentage of constituent. The high cost of this equipment is easily justified in routine laboratories, as an analysis for several elements may be made in a few seconds after the sample is placed in the electrode holder.

A direct-reading instrument is subject to the nonphotographic errors of the spectroscopic process plus the errors in its own record-

‡ See Section 6.2(e).

[6] M. F. Hasler and H. W. Dietert, J. Optical Soc. Am., 34, 751 (1944).

[7] J. L. Saunderson, V. J. Caldecourt, and E. W. Peterson, ibid., 35, 681 (1945).

ing system, but the relative accuracy attained is higher than by photographic methods, approaching 1% in some cases. It is definitely justified only for highly routine work and at the present time cannot replace the photographic method completely.

Bibliography

K. Henney and B. Dudley, *Handbook of Photography*, McGraw-Hill, New York (1939).

C. E. K. Mees, *The Theory of the Photographic Process*, Macmillan, New York (1942).

Eastman Kodak Co., Photographic Plates for Scientific Use, Rochester, N. Y. (1949).

Eastman Kodak Co., Kodak Materials for Spectrum Analysis, Rochester, N. Y. (1950).

CHAPTER 11

Flame Photometry

The quantitative separation and determination of the alkali and alkaline-earth elements by wet-chemical methods has always been a difficult analytical problem. Emission spectroscopy is an obvious instrumental approach to the determination of these elements. However, since the emission spectra of these elements contain few lines and can be readily excited by a suitable flame, a complex, high-dispersion spectrograph is not required. Flame photometers, which are in essence a highly simplified form of a direct-reading spectrograph, have been developed to satisfy the need for simple, inexpensive equipment.

The principle of operation of a flame photometer is based upon the quantitative measurement of the characteristic light emitted when a solution of the element being determined is atomized as a mist into a gas flame. If the flow of solution and the flame temperature are maintained constant, the emission intensity of the spectral lines will also be constant. By controlling the flame temperature, the number of elements excited may be regulated. For example, the standard gas-air flame will excite only the alkalies and alkaline earths, while the oxyhydrogen flame will excite over 40 elements.

Figure 11.1 shows the characteristic flame spectra [1] produced in an illuminating gas flame by the alkali and alkaline-earth elements, and Table 11.1 lists the flame spectra and the minimum quantity determinable of 24 elements. Not all the usable lines have been tabulated in Table 11.1, but only the strongest line, or, in those cases where the intensities are relatively close, the two strongest lines. The minimum amount detectable is the least concentration at which the element can be detected easily by comparison against a suitable blank. In general, it represents the least concentration required to give a

[1] R. B. Barnes, D. Richardson, J. W. Berry, and R. L. Hood, *Ind. Eng. Chem., Anal. Ed., 17,* 605 (1945).

reading of 0.5% of full scale on the meter of the instrument. The intensity values are only approximate and are given in units obtained by dividing into 100 the detection sensitivity in parts per million (ppm) for that particular wavelength.

Any of the characteristic radiations listed in Table 11.1, when isolated by a suitable monochromator or filters and allowed to strike a photocell or phototube with the proper spectral response, will yield an electric impulse which is proportional to the concentration of the

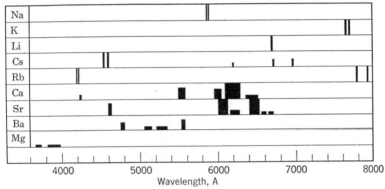

Fig. 11.1   Characteristic flame spectra produced in an illuminating gas flame
(Courtesy *Analytical Chemistry*)

element present in the flame. This relationship between light intensity and concentration requires constant burning conditions in the flame and a constant rate of atomization.

11.1   Development of flame photometers.   One of the earliest flame photometers was described by Schuhknecht.[2] This instrument consisted of a Lundegardh [3] acetylene flame source, placed before a box containing suitable filters for isolating the red wavelengths of potassium, and a phototube as a receptor. Two commercial German instruments based on this design have been described by Schmitt and Breitweiser.[4]

In 1945 a flame photometer designed in the United States was described in an article by Barnes et al.[1] This instrument was developed for the rapid quantitative determination of the alkali metals

[2] W. Schuhknecht, *Angew. Chem.*, **50**, 299 (1937).

[3] H. Lundegardh, *Die Quantitative Spektralanalyse der Elemente*, Part I (1929), Part II (1934), Gustav Fischer, Jena.

[4] L. Schmitt and W. Breitweiser, *Bodenkunde u. Pflanzenernähr.*, **9–10**, 750 (1938).

TABLE 11.1

Flame Spectra of Elements *

Element	Minimum Detected ppm	Wavelength, mμ	Intensity
Barium	1	745 †	100
		830 †	50
Boron	5	548 †	20
		521 †	15
Cadmium	500	326.1	0.2
Calcium	0.3	624 †	300
		554 †	200
Cesium	0.1	852.1	1,000
Chromium	3	359.3	30
		645 †	30
Cobalt	5	350.2	20
		352.7	20
Copper	1	324.8	100
		327.4	90
Gallium	1	417.2	100
Gold	50	267.6	2
Indium	1	451.1	100
Iron	10	373.6	10
Lead	300	405.8	0.3
Lithium	0.05	670.8	2,000
Magnesium	10	285.2	10
		370.8	10
Manganese	1	403.4	100
		561 †	70
Mercury	50	253.6	2
Nickel	3	352.4	30
Palladium	50	340.5	2
		363.5	2
Potassium	0.05	766.5 ⎫ 769.9 ⎭	2,000
Rubidium	0.1	780.0	1,000
Ruthenium	30	372.7	3
		378.6	3
Silver	2	338.3	50
Sodium	0.01	589.0 ⎫ 589.6 ⎭	10,000

Also determinable are the rare earths, selenium and tin.

* P. T. Gilbert, Jr., R. C. Hawes, and A. O. Beckman, *Anal. Chem.*, *22*, 772 (1950).

† An oxide band with its maximum value at this wavelength.

(primarily sodium and potassium) and also proved satisfactory for the analysis of calcium. Both Meker-type Fisher burners and Fisher blast lamps were used to excite the flame spectra while a barrier-layer photocell was the receptor. Although an average accuracy of 3% of the total element present in the sample in a single determination was attained with this instrument, it was noted [5] that the presence of acids or salts reduced the apparent sodium content and yielded serious errors. For example, the presence of 1% sulfuric acid in a solution containing 100 ppm of sodium reduced the light emitted by the flame by 15%. An obvious solution to this problem is to prepare standard solutions with the same amount of the interfering acid or salt in proportions similar to the unknowns to be analyzed. This method yields correct results but is not completely satisfactory because it involves laborious compounding of standard solutions for each type of unknown to be analyzed. For those truly unknown solutions with a varying composition, the analyst is at a loss as to how to prepare suitable standards. Subsequent investigators [6,7] using a commercial version of the initial instrument described by Barnes et al.[1] confirmed these results.

For this reason an improved version of this instrument was developed.[5] This instrument was built with a dual optical system so as to utilize the conventional internal standard principle of emission spectroscopy. In this method light-intensity ratios are measured rather than absolute light intensities, and the errors, introduced by the presence of foreign acids and salts, by organic compounds and viscosity effects, and by gas- and air-pressure fluctuations, are considerably reduced. Figure 11.2 shows a comparison of these errors for the internal standard method and for the absolute method, where direct-intensity measurements are made.

The choice of a suitable element as an internal standard was naturally limited to those elements excited by a flame. Lithium was finally chosen as the internal standard because the need for the determination of this element is much less than for such elements as sodium and potassium; it emits only a single intense line at 6708 A, which is about equidistant in the spectrum between the lines of sodium and potassium, and finally it is well within the wavelength sensitivity of the photodetecting devices available. The only fault

[5] J. W. Berry, D. G. Chappell, and R. B. Barnes, *Ind. Eng. Chem., Anal. Ed.,* 18, 19 (1946).

[6] P. M. Hald, *J. Biol. Chem.,* 167, 499 (1947).

[7] T. D. Parks, H. O. Johnson, and L. Lykken, *Anal. Chem.,* 20, 822 (1948).

with lithium as an internal standard is that lithium is not too uncommon an element, and the existence of any appreciable quantities

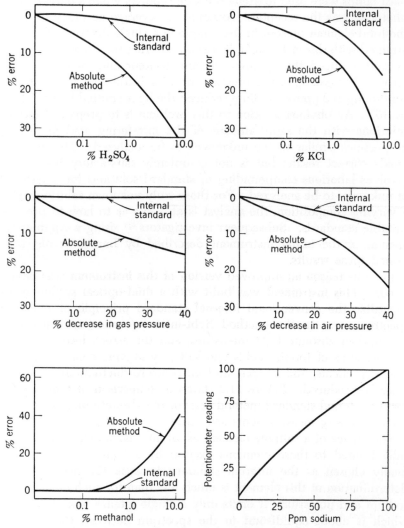

Fig. 11.2 Effect of various factors on the error of flame photometry and a
typical calibration curve (Courtesy *Analytical Chemistry*)

of lithium in an unknown sample would decrease the intensity ratio
and lead to low results for the element being determined.

11.2 Commercial flame photometers. Table 11.2 contains a
brief summary of the commercial flame photometers available. All

TABLE 11.2

Comparison of Flame Photometers *

Model	Monochromator	Measuring Circuit	Fuel	Elements Determinable
Barclay	Glass filters	Photocells and galvanometer	Propane	Na, K
Baird	Multilayer filters	Photocells and galvanometer	Propane or illuminating gas	Na, K, Ca, Li
Fox	Glass filters	Photocells and galvanometer	Propane or illuminating gas	Na, K
Beckman	Glass or quartz prism	Phototube and amplifier	Natural, illuminating gas, or hydrogen	Minimum 30 elements, maximum not determined
Perkin-Elmer 52A	Glass prisms	Phototubes and amplifier	Propane or acetylene	Na, K, Li, Ba, Ca, Sr, Mg, Mn, Cr

* Other flame photometers of interest have been described by Bowman and Berliner,[8] Weichselbaum and Varney,[9] and Leyton.[10]

of these flame photometers need a compressed air supply for most efficient operation of the atomizer and, with the exception of the Beckman, are designed with a split or dual light path so that an internal standard can be used. However, by first measuring the intensity of the lithium line and then that of the element to be determined, intensity ratios can also be obtained on the Beckman flame photometer.

The Barclay flame photometer has a dual optical path. A different feature of this instrument is that hypodermic needles furnish the fine spray in the atomizer. A simple d-c circuit with the two photocells and galvanometer as a null indicator serves to measure the intensity of the light emitted.

The Baird flame photometer has been described in detail by J. U. White.[11] This instrument is unique in its employment of multilayer interference filters, which are an improved type of filter having a band width of less than 8 mμ, peak transmission over 70%, and transmission of unwanted wavelengths less than 0.03%.

The Fox flame photometer [12] is unusual in that the atomizer sprays into the periphery of a centifugal separator chamber adapted from a design of Bartholomew.[13] This chamber collects and condenses large

[8] R. L. Bowman and R. W. Berliner, *Federation Proc.*, 8, 14 (1949).

[9] T. E. Weichselbaum and P. L. Varney, *Proc. Soc. Exptl. Biol. Med.*, 71, 570 (1949).

[10] L. Leyton, *Analyst*, 76, 723 (1951).

[11] J. U. White, *Anal. Chem.*, 24, 394 (1952).

[12] C. L. Fox, Jr., *ibid.*, 23, 137 (1951).

[13] W. H. Bartholomew, *ibid.*, 21, 527 (1949).

liquid droplets, passing only very minute droplets, which result in a fine aerosol.

The Beckman flame photometer [14] is available as an attachment for either the model-DU or the model-B spectrophotometers and uses

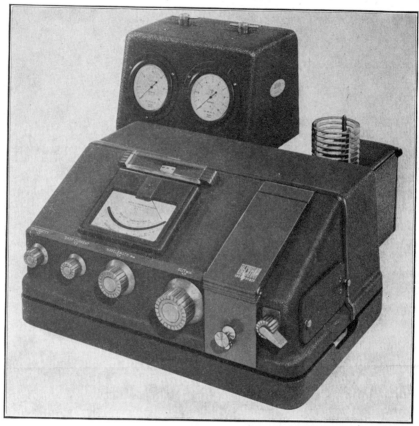

Fig. 11.3 Beckman model-B spectrophotometer with flame attachment (Courtesy Beckman Instrument Company)

their monochromator systems (see Fig. 11.3). The high resolution of these monochromators allows high-temperature excitation of less volatile elements, and a large number of elements can be determined (see Table 11.1). For example, a recent paper [15] describes the de-

[14] P. T. Gilbert, Jr., R. C. Hawes, and A. O. Beckman, *ibid.*, 22, 772 (1950).
[15] P. T. Gilbert, Jr., *ibid.*, 23, 1053 (1951).

termination of lead in gasoline with this photometer.   In order to modify the model-DU spectrophotometer, the only adjustment needed is to install a 10,000-megohm phototube resistor to increase the sensitivity fivefold.   The burner source will operate with the following flames when oxygen is used for atomizing: artificial gas with a little air, natural gas with very little additional oxygen, air–acetylene, and hydrogen alone.   The atomizer burner is smaller and simpler than the initial design.[15]   It incorporates a straight, large-diameter, noble-metal atomizer tube discharging directly into the flame.   The instrument may be standardized with either internal or external standards.

The Perkin-Elmer model 52A shown in Fig. 11.4 has a conventional-type Meker burner for compressed air–propane mixtures which may be modified by the addition of a Venturi tube for compressed air–acetylene mixtures.   The light emitted by the burner is chopped at the rate of 17 to 18.5 cps by a magnetically driven reed, permitting a-c amplification of the photocurrent.   After passing through a double-prism monochromator, the light is split into two beams.   One beam is focused for the lithium line at 6708 A on a fixed slit and falls on a phototube whose spectral response covers the lithium line.   The other beam passes through a slit which can be adjusted by means of the large dial shown on the panel of the instrument.   This selects the wavelength for the particular element to be determined.   Depending on the slit adjustment, the light falls on one of two phototubes whose spectral response is sensitive to the wavelength of the emitted line of the element being determined.   The outputs of the reference phototube for lithium and the phototube for the element being determined are connected to two potentiometer-type attenuators; their outputs in turn, after one stage of amplification, are connected in opposition, so that either may be read directly when the other is set to the end of its range, or the two may be balanced against each other with the output meter acting as a null indicator.   In this way, absolute measurements can be made for all of the alkali and alkaline-earth elements, and internal standard measurements for all of these elements except lithium.

11.3   Instrument reproducibility, calibration, and sample handling.   Some of the important factors that govern the reproducibility of a given instrument are the atomizer, the air and gas supply, and the stability of either the electronic-amplifier circuit or the photocell circuit.

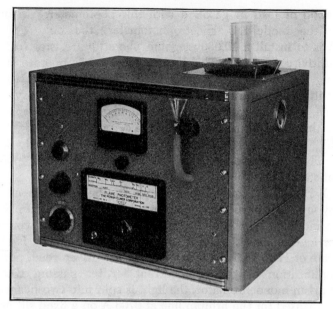

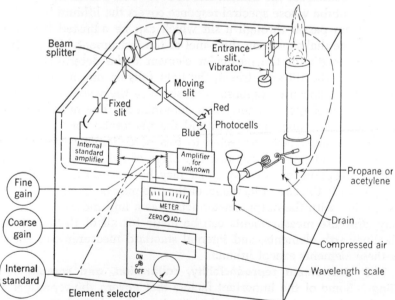

Fig. 11.4   Perkin-Elmer model-52A flame photometer (Courtesy Perkin-Elmer Corporation)

The atomizer construction is critical since it has been found that atomizers of apparently identical construction require separate calibration. Large errors can result if the atomizer is not kept extremely clean. The presence of very small amounts of dirt or dust will often clog an atomizer so slightly that it is difficult to see that the atomizer is not behaving properly. Usually this will yield low results for the element being determined, particularly with the absolute method of measurement. Improper drainage of the atomizer will also cause trouble. It is generally a good idea to clean the atomizer with distilled water and alcohol after each series of determinations, followed by periodic cleanings with appropriate mineral acids or organic solvents, depending on the material that is being analyzed.

If the air supply is not clean, it should be filtered to prevent dust particles from clogging the atomizer or from producing luminous flame spots which will lead to erratic results. Diaphragm-type pressure regulators do not usually give so steady a flow of gas as is required and should be followed by needle valves for added manual control.

Errors in the analysis can also result from lack of uniformity or stability of the electronic-amplifier tubes. These errors can be minimized by selecting by trial and error tubes that yield the most reproducible results in a given instrument. Line-voltage fluctuations, if serious, can be stabilized somewhat by constant-voltage transformers.

Surface-tension effects influence the rate of atomization and the sensitivity and can be minimized by measuring with dilute test solutions or with alcohol as a solvent for organic and biological samples. In the analysis of such samples as food products and plant material, it is necessary to eliminate the organic material by ashing before analysis. In certain cases such as dried plant material, a simple extraction with hot water will remove the potassium quantitatively.

For very accurate analyses standards should be prepared from spectroscopically pure materials. If the internal standard method is not used, the standards should be carefully compounded to the composition of the unknowns. Usually four standard solutions are adequate for the preparation of a calibration curve (see Fig. 11.2). In the case of sodium and potassium, accurate standard solutions can be prepared by weighing a known amount of a suitable salt and diluting it in a volumetric flask to a known volume. The more dilute solutions should be prepared by taking a suitable aliquot (50 ml or more) and again diluting to a known volume. If deliquescent salts such as lithium chloride or nitrate must be weighed, they can be dried by storing over phosphorus pentoxide in vacuo for several days, and then weighed rapidly when preparing the standard solutions. It is better, however, to standardize such solutions gravimetrically.

11.4 Applications. Although most of the applications of flame photometry deal with sodium and potassium analysis, the determination of calcium and the other alkaline earths is increasing in importance.[16] As an indication of the type of analyses being performed, Table 11.3 contains a list of some recent contributions to the field.

TABLE 11.3

Typical Applications of Flame Photometry *

Material Analyzed	Elements	Reference
Lubricating oils	K, Li, Ba, Ca	A. L. Conrad and W. C. Johnson, *Anal. Chem.*, *22*, 1530 (1950)
Portland cement	Na, K	W. R. Eubank and R. H. Bogue, *J. Research Natl. Bur. Standards*, *43*, 173 (1949)
Plasma, urine, and tissues	Na, K	C. L. Fox Jr., *Anal. Chem.*, *23*, 137 (1951)
Lithium metal	Na, K	W. R. Inman, R. A. Rogers, and J. A. Fournier, *ibid.*, 482 (1951)
Milk	Na, K, Ca	R. J. Keirs and S. J. Speck, *J. Dairy Sci.*, *33*, 413 (1950)
Minerals	Na, K, Ca	S. B. Knight, W. C. Mathis, and J. R. Graham, *Anal. Chem.*, *23*, 1704 (1951)
Magnesite and brucite ores	Ca	R. E. Mosher, E. J. Bird, and A. J. Boyle, *ibid.*, *22*, 715 (1950)
Water	Na, K, Ca	P. W. West, P. Folse and D. Montgomery, *ibid.*, 667 (1950)

* See ASTM Symposium on Flame Photometry, *Anal. Chem.*, *23*, 1053 (1951).

[16] An excellent bibliography on flame photometry is available from Patwin Instruments, 41 Brown St., Waterbury, Conn.

CHAPTER 12

Colorimetric pH Measurement

The spectroscopic methods previously discussed are based upon the absorption or emission of radiant energy by elements, ions, or molecules in the gaseous, liquid, or solid state. In contrast, electrometric methods are based on the changes in the electrochemical properties (electrode potential, resistance) of a solution caused by changes in the concentration of ions or molecules in aqueous or nonaqueous media. The ions or molecules may produce an electromotive force if combined in a simple cell, or may transmit a measurable current if acted upon by an impressed emf with suitable electrodes.

It may seem odd to the reader that the colorimetric measurement of pH is included in the section on electrometric methods. This has been done because the principles of equilibrium, mass action, dissociation, and hydrolysis are as intimately connected with colorimetric pH measurement as they are with electrometric pH measurement. Although the spectrophotometer and filter photometer are occasionally involved in the colorimetric measurement of pH and in studies of the behavior of indicators, the usual colorimetric measurement of pH is made with simpler visual instruments.

The measurement of pH as an analysis in itself and as an adjunct to other analytical methods is one of the most important determinations made in the laboratory. The necessity of close pH control of many industrial and analytical processes makes it the most common analytical measurement.

The pH notation as a means of expressing hydrogen-ion concentration was suggested by Sorenson.[1]

$$pH = -\log (H^+), \quad \text{or} \quad (H^+) = 10^{-pH}$$

This is a convenient definition to remember for converting from pH to hydrogen ion concentration. Thus, for a solution of pH 8.2,

[1] S. P. L. Sorenson, *Biochem. Z.*, *21*, 131 (1909).

$(H^+) = 10^{-8.2} = 10^{+0.8} \times 10^{-9.0}$ (antilog $0.8 = 6.3$) and $(H^+) = 6.3 \times 10^{-9}$.

A more exact relationship would be that based on the activity of the hydrogen ion rather than its stoichiometric concentration. If we employ stoichiometric concentrations in dealing with such properties as conductivity or freezing-point lowering for electrolytes in *dilute* solution, we obtain good agreement with the experimentally determined values. However, as the solutions of the electrolytes are made more concentrated, the experimentally determined values are less than those calculated. This phenomenon can be explained by assuming that electrolytes are 100% ionized only in infinitely dilute solutions and are less ionized in more concentrated solutions. A more satisfactory explanation assumes that the electrolytes are 100% ionized in both concentrated and dilute solutions, but that, because of attractive forces between positive and negative ions, the effective concentration, or *activity* of the ions, is decreased in the concentrated solutions. Therefore, activities rather than stoichiometric (molar) concentrations yield more accurate results in calculations. This is equally true in mass-action equilibria which will be discussed in the following section. The activity a of an ion or molecule is equal to the product of its molar concentration c and its activity coefficient f

$$a = fc$$

Some typical activity coefficients are shown in Table 12.1

TABLE 12.1

Activity Coefficients (f) at $25°$ C

	0.01 M	0.05 M	0.10 M	1.0 M	2.0 M	3.0 M
HCl	0.92	0.86	0.80	0.81	1.01	1.32
KOH	0.92	0.84	0.80	0.76	0.89	1.08
NaCl	0.92	0.84	0.78	0.66	0.67	0.71

In general, activity coefficients vary inversely with the temperature and decrease with increasing concentration. Exceptions may be noted; in 3.0 M HCl, the activity coefficient is greater than 1. This may be caused by a change in the hydration of ions with increasing concentration. The activity coefficients also depend upon the total ion concentration of the solution, but have the same numerical value for solutions with the same *ionic strength*. This term was first introduced by Lewis and Randall and is a measure of the electric field present in solution. The ionic strength is defined as one half of the sum obtained by multiplying the molar concentration of each ion by the square of its electric charge. Thus, a solution 0.01 M in HCl and 0.02 M in $BaCl_2$ has the following ionic strength:

$$H^+: \quad 0.01 \times 1 \quad = 0.01$$
$$Ba^{++}: \quad 0.02 \times 2^2 = 0.08$$
$$Cl^-: \quad 0.05 \times 1 \quad = 0.05$$
$$\overline{}$$
$$0.14 \times \tfrac{1}{2} = 0.07$$

If we base our pH calculations on the activity of the hydrogen ion, we have

$$p a H = - \log a_{H^+}$$

The analytical chemist, however, either measures pH against standards with known activities or is interested only in the effect of various materials on the relative pH of a solution. In either case, activities are not necessary for calculations, and we shall confine ourselves to stoichiometric concentrations. Since the effective concentration or activity changes with the total ion concentration of a solution, however, we must realize that our calculations are only approximations.

12.1 Equilibrium and mass action. The calculations involved in pH determination are based on the law of mass action. In any equilibrium where $A + B \rightleftarrows C + D$, the product of the molar concentrations of the reaction products, C and D, divided by the molar concentrations of the reactants, A and B, is a constant K,

$$\frac{(C)(D)}{(A)(B)} = K$$

The equilibrium "constant," K varies with the ionic strength, and with the temperature T according to the equation

$$\frac{d \ln K}{dT} = \frac{\Delta H}{RT^2}$$

where ΔH is the heat of reaction.

When the reaction involves more than one atom or molecule of a particular kind, such as

$$2NH_3 \rightleftarrows N_2 + 3H_2$$

our mass action expression becomes

$$\frac{(N_2)(H_2)(H_2)(H_2)}{(NH_3)(NH_3)} = K \quad \text{or} \quad \frac{(N_2)(H_2)^3}{(NH_3)^2} = K$$

Many reactions of interest to the analytical chemist are ionic, and the ion concentrations may be treated the same as molecular concentrations, for example,

$$H_2O \rightleftarrows H^+ + OH^-, \qquad \frac{(H^+)(OH^-)}{(H_2O)} = K$$

12.2   Dissociation and the strength of acids and bases.   Any acid in solution dissociates at least partially into its ions.   For a monobasic acid,

$$HA \rightleftarrows H^+ + A^-, \qquad \frac{(H^+)(A^-)}{(HA)} = Ka$$

The value of the dissociation constant Ka indicates the strength of the acid, being extremely large for strong acids and nearly zero for weak acids.

If the fraction of the acid dissociating is represented by α, and the original concentration by c,

$$(H^+) = (A^-) = \alpha c, \qquad (HA) = (1 - \alpha)c$$

The mass-action expression becomes

$$\alpha^2 c/(1 - \alpha) = Ka$$

This quadratic equation may be solved for α if Ka is known.   If the acid is weak, $1 - \alpha$ is approximately 1, and

$$\alpha^2 c = Ka, \qquad (H^+)^2 = Kac, \qquad (H^+) = \sqrt{Kac}$$

The quantity α is called the *degree of dissociation* and is sometimes a more convenient expression for the strength of an acid than the dissociation constant.

The dissociation of bases may be given similar treatment, in which case we obtain the concentration of hydroxyl ions.   The OH-ion concentration may be readily converted to hydrogen-ion concentration because of the relationship

$$H_2O \rightleftarrows H^+ + OH^-, \qquad \frac{(H^+)(OH^-)}{(H_2O)} = K$$

Since the degree of dissociation of water is small, the quantity (H_2O) remains essentially constant in aqueous solution, and

$$(\mathrm{H}^+)(\mathrm{OH}^-) = K(\mathrm{H_2O}) = Kw$$

Kw, the ion product constant for water is approximately 1×10^{-14} at 25° C, and, knowing either (H^+) or (OH^-), we can readily calculate the other. Also, $pH + pOH = 14$, and, knowing either pH or pOH, we can obtain the other by subtraction. Similar to the pH terminology, the terms pW and pA or pB are often employed where $pW = \log\ 1/Kw = -\log\ Kw$, $pA = \log\ 1/Ka = -\log\ Ka$ and $pB = \log\ 1/Kb = -\log\ Kb$. The dissociation constants Ka and Kb of several acids and bases are given in Appendix G.

It is apparent that molar solutions of all monobasic acids have the same stoichiometric concentration, and yet, if their degree of dissociation values differ, the hydrogen-ion concentrations will differ. This instantaneous hydrogen-ion concentration must be measured under equilibrium conditions, not by titration, and the measurement must not disturb the equilibrium.

For example, in a 0.01 M solution of a strong, 100% ionized acid such as hydrochloric, the hydrogen-ion concentration is equal to 1×10^{-2} (pH 2.0). But in acetic acid, $Ka = 1.75 \times 10^{-5}$, a 0.01 M acetic acid solution is only 4.2% ionized, and the hydrogen-ion concentration equals 4.2×10^{-4} (pH 3.4). Thus, for equal molar concentrations, the pH of the solution of a strong acid is not the same as the pH of the solution of a weak acid. In a titration with a base such as sodium hydroxide, however, equal volumes of the two 0.01 M acids would require the same amount of sodium hydroxide. A titration then disturbs the equilibrium of a weak acid or base and releases "reserve" acidity as the titration proceeds. The completed titration then yields a measure of "total" acidity. In contrast, the determination of pH is a measurement of the "momentary" acidity which exists in the solution.

A polybasic acid such as $\mathrm{H_2S}$ may be considered as dissociating in stages; for example,

$$\mathrm{H_2S} \rightleftarrows \mathrm{H}^+ + \mathrm{HS}^-$$

$$\mathrm{HS}^- \rightleftarrows \mathrm{H}^+ + \mathrm{S}^=$$

$$\frac{(\mathrm{H}^+)(\mathrm{HS}^-)}{(\mathrm{H_2S})} = K_1 \qquad (K_1 = 9.1 \times 10^{-8})$$

$$\frac{(\mathrm{H}^+)(\mathrm{S}^=)}{(\mathrm{HS}^-)} = K_2 \qquad (K_2 = 1.2 \times 10^{-15})$$

These expressions may be combined to give

$$H_2S \rightleftarrows 2H^+ + S^=, \qquad \frac{(H^+)^2(S^=)}{(H_2S)} = K_1K_2 = K$$

The separate dissociation constants for many polybasic acids and polyacid bases have been measured and are available for calculations. Since the first dissociation is usually considerably greater than subsequent ones, an approximate calculation for (H^+) is possible by considering only the first dissociation. With this approximation, the treatment follows that of the simple acids.

12.3   Hydrolysis of salts.   If we titrate a solution of a strong base such as sodium hydroxide with a strong acid such as hydrochloric acid and measure the pH at frequent intervals, the plot of the data will appear as shown in Fig. 12.1.

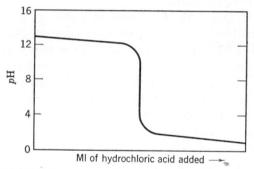

Fig. 12.1   Titration curve of a strong base with a strong acid

Such a plot of pH versus milliliters of reagent added is called a *titration curve*.   At the equivalence point of the titration, i.e., the point at which equivalent quantities of the acid and base have reacted, the pH is 7 and the solution is neutral, having an excess of neither H^+ nor OH^- ions.   The sodium chloride which is formed as a result of this titration is a strong electrolyte and may be considered to be completely dissociated in solution.

On the other hand, in salts of weak acids or bases, a combination with water or hydrolysis may occur.   These salts can be formed by the reaction of a strong base with a weak acid, a weak base with a strong acid, or a weak base with a weak acid, and for the purpose of discussion we shall consider them in this order.

(*a*) *Strong-Base–Weak-Acid Salt.*   If we titrate 25 ml of a 0.1 N solution of a strong base such as sodium hydroxide with a 0.1 N

solution of a weak acid such as acetic acid and measure the pH at frequent intervals, a plot of the data will appear as shown in Fig. 12.2. It can be seen from Fig. 12.2 that at the equivalence point of this

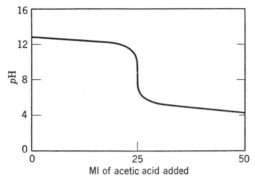

Fig. 12.2   Titration curve of a strong base with a weak acid

titration the pH will be approximately 8.7 and the solution is basic. We can explain why the solution is basic if we consider that the acetate ion hydrolyzes as follows:

$$Ac^- + H_2O \rightleftarrows HAc + OH^-$$

and K, the equilibrium constant for this hydrolysis equals

$$\frac{(HAc)(OH^-)}{(Ac^-)(H_2O)} = K$$

or, since (H_2O) is constant,

$$\frac{(HAc)(OH^-)}{(Ac^-)} = K_h$$

where K_h is called the hydrolysis constant.   In order to express this equation in terms of available constants, we find that

$$K_h = \frac{(HAc)(OH^-)}{(Ac^-)} = \frac{(H^+)(OH^-)}{\underset{(HAc)}{(H^+)(Ac^-)}} = \frac{Kw}{Ka}$$

thus the hydrolysis constant may be readily calculated from the ion-product constant of water and the ionization constant of the acid.

In order to calculate the pH at the equivalent point in this titration, we may neglect the slight (OH^-) contribution from the water, and, since, from the original hydrolysis equilibrium, $(OH^-) = (HAc)$,

$$\frac{(OH)^2}{(Ac^-)} = \frac{Kw}{Ka}, \qquad (OH^-) = \sqrt{\frac{Kw}{Ka}(Ac^-)}$$

and since $(H^+) = \dfrac{Kw}{(OH^-)}, \qquad (H^+) = \dfrac{Kw}{\sqrt{(Kw/Ka)(Ac^-)}}$

Since hydrolysis is slight, the (Ac^-) may be considered equal to the concentration c of the salt formed at the equivalence point, and

$$(H^+) = \frac{Kw}{\sqrt{(Kw/Ka)(c)}}$$

or $\quad p$H $= -(\log Kw - \tfrac{1}{2}\log Kw + \tfrac{1}{2}\log Ka - \tfrac{1}{2}\log c)$

$\quad\quad p$H $= -\tfrac{1}{2}\log Kw - \tfrac{1}{2}\log Ka + \tfrac{1}{2}\log c$

$\quad\quad p$H $= \tfrac{1}{2}p$W $+ \tfrac{1}{2}p$A $+ \tfrac{1}{2}\log c$

In the example considered, pW $= 14$, $Ka = 1.86 \times 10^{-5}$, pA $= 4.73$, $c = 5 \times 10^{-2}$, and pH $= 7 + 2.37 - 0.65 = 8.72$.

(b) *Weak-Base–Strong-Acid Salt.* If we titrate 25 ml of a 0.1 N solution of a weak base such as ammonium hydroxide with a 0.1 N solution of a strong acid such as hydrochloric acid, the titration curve obtained will be as shown in Fig. 12.3. At the equivalence point of

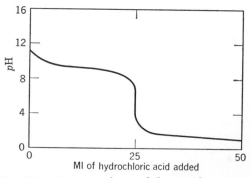

Fig. 12.3   Titration of a weak base with a strong acid

this titration the measured pH will be approximately 5.3 and the solution is acid. Again, we can explain the pH of the solution at the equivalent point if we consider that the ammonium ion hydrolyzes as follows:

$$\mathrm{NH_4^+ + H_2O \rightarrow NH_4OH + H^+}$$

and, by a treatment similar to that used for the strong-base–weak-acid salt, we obtain

$$(\mathrm{H^+}) = \sqrt{(K_w/K_b)(c)}$$

or

$$p\mathrm{H} = -(\tfrac{1}{2}\log K_w - \tfrac{1}{2}\log K_b + \tfrac{1}{2}\log c)$$

$$p\mathrm{H} = -\tfrac{1}{2}\log K_w + \tfrac{1}{2}\log K_b - \tfrac{1}{2}\log c$$

$$p\mathrm{H} = \tfrac{1}{2}p\mathrm{W} - \tfrac{1}{2}p\mathrm{B} - \tfrac{1}{2}\log c$$

and in the example considered

$$p\mathrm{H} = 7.00 - 2.38 + 0.65, \qquad p\mathrm{H} = 5.27$$

(c) *Weak-Base–Weak-Acid Salt.* The titration of 25 ml of a 0.1 N solution of a weak base such as ammonium hydroxide with a 0.1 N solution of a weak acid such as acetic acid gives a titration curve as shown in Fig. 12.4. At the equivalence point of this titration the

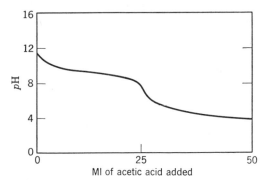

Fig. 12.4 Titration curve of a weak base with a weak acid

pH will be approximately 7.0. However, it can be seen from this curve that there is no sharp inflection at the equivalence point. Such titrations are of little analytical value, as it is difficult to detect the equivalence point of the reaction.

The formula for calculating the *p*H value at the equivalence point is also derived on the basis that the salt formed hydrolyzes. In ammonium acetate both cation and anion undergo hydrolysis, and

$$\mathrm{Ac^- + H_2O \rightarrow HAc + OH^-}, \qquad \mathrm{NH_4^+ + H_2O \rightarrow NH_4OH + H^+}$$

and

$$\frac{K_w}{K_a} = \frac{(\mathrm{HAc})(\mathrm{OH^-})}{(\mathrm{Ac^-})} \qquad (1)$$

$$\frac{Kw}{Kb} = \frac{(NH_4OH)(H^+)}{(NH_4^+)} \tag{2}$$

In this case (NH_4OH) does not equal (H^+), since the (H^+) ions react with (Ac^-) to form HAc. However, since the solution is neutral, (H^+) and (OH^-) are very small and the amounts of (HAc) and (NH_4OH) can be considered to be equal. Since the NH_4Ac formed is a strong electrolyte, $(NH_4^+) = (Ac^-) = c$.

By multiplication of equations 1 and 2,

$$\frac{(NH_4OH)(HAc)}{(NH_4)(Ac^-)} = \frac{Kw}{KaKb} \quad \text{and} \quad \frac{(NH_4OH)(HAc)}{c^2} = \frac{Kw}{KaKb}$$

or $$(NH_4OH)^2/c^2 = (HAc)^2/c^2 = Kw/KaKb$$

but $$(HAc) = (H^+)c/Ka$$

and $$(H^+)^2/Ka^2 = Kw/KaKb, \qquad (H^+) = \sqrt{KwKa/Kb}$$

$$pH = -(\tfrac{1}{2}\log Kw + \tfrac{1}{2}\log Ka - \tfrac{1}{2}\log Kb)$$

$$pH = -\tfrac{1}{2}\log Kw - \tfrac{1}{2}\log Ka + \tfrac{1}{2}\log Kb$$

$$pH = \tfrac{1}{2}pW + \tfrac{1}{2}pA - \tfrac{1}{2}pB$$

and in the example considered

$$pH = 7.00 + 2.37 - 2.38 = 6.99$$

Hence, in the hydrolysis of the salt of a weak acid and a weak base the hydrogen-ion concentration is independent of the concentration of the salt.

The calculations described are useful in the selection of an indicator or other method for detecting the equivalence point in an acid-base titration. The approximations are justified, as the exact calculation of the equivalence point is not necessary. In all cases but the weak-acid–weak-base titration, the change of pH with volume of titrant added is great enough that the simplified calculation is sufficient.

12.4   Buffer solutions. In analytical procedures, it is frequently desirable to adjust the pH of a solution to a fixed value and to be able to maintain this pH despite small additions of acid or base. Solutions possessing these properties may be prepared by combining salts of weak acids or salts of weak bases with the corresponding free acid or base. Such solutions are called *buffer solutions.*

From the dissociation constant,

$$(H^+)(A^-)/(HA) = Ka$$

we can obtain

$$(H^+) = \frac{(HA)}{(A^-)} Ka$$

The corresponding dissociation,

$$HA \rightleftarrows H^+ + A^-$$

shows that, if we add an appreciable amount of the salt of the acid (with a strong base), the dissociation will be repressed by the salt and the hydrolysis, $A^- + H_2O \rightleftarrows HA + OH^-$, will be repressed by the acid. The quantities (HA) and (A^-) then approach the stoichiometric values for the acid and salt added to the solution.

If a small amount of base is added to the solution, some of the hydrogen ion will be used, but the dissociation will then proceed to replace it. If a small amount of acid is added, the equilibrium will cause it to be used in the formation of more weak acid. As long as the amounts of acid or base added are small compared with the concentrations of the weak acid and its salt, the pH change will be negligible. Therefore, by increasing the concentration of the buffer ingredients, an increased resistance to change (*buffer capacity*) is obtained.

The preceding paragraph relates to buffer capacity only. A buffer solution may be diluted without appreciable change * in pH, even though its buffer capacity is strongly reduced. Standard buffers where the concentrations are of the order of 0.1 M may be diluted twofold without change.

From the expression

$$(H^+) = \frac{(HA)}{(A^-)} Ka$$

we see that by varying the ratio of salt to acid we can obtain hydrogen-ion concentrations centered about the point, $(H^+) = Ka$. This equality exists when equimolar quantities, (A^-) and (HA), of the salt and acid are present. In a practical sense we are limited by our assumption of negligible hydrolysis and dissociation. If (HA) is too low, we must consider the acid formed by hydrolysis of the salts, and if (A^-) is too low, we must consider the dissociation of the

* A slight change occurs because the ionic strength is decreased.

acid. The usual limits of the ratio are considered to be 0.1 to 10, and the useful pH range of a buffer mixture is

$$pH = pKa \pm 1$$

For a weak base and its salt,

$$BOH \rightleftarrows B^+ + OH^-, \qquad \frac{(B^+)(OH^-)}{(BOH)} = Kb, \qquad (H^+) = \frac{(B^+)}{(BOH)} \frac{Kw}{Kb}$$

Similar considerations apply to this system, but we must include the effect of the Kw term which appears. In contrast to most Ka and Kb quantities, Kw has a high temperature coefficient. So, in the preparation of buffer solutions, weak base-salt combinations are avoided whenever possible.

Acid salts are useful buffer materials, since in solution, they behave approximately as equimolar mixtures of the acid and its salt.

12.5 Standard buffer solutions. Unless some special purpose is to be served, the preparation of buffer solutions based on the calculations described is a waste of time and effort. Specific directions for making up several series of standard buffers, ordinarily in steps of 0.2 pH units, have been published in the literature. These buffers are formulated according to the pH scale based on hydrogen-electrode measurements and are simple to prepare.

The first such series was described by Sorenson. His buffers for the range 7.5 to 10.0 were mixtures of borax (sodium tetraborate) with hydrochloric acid or sodium hydroxide, and the pH values were given for 18° C, a room temperature evidently more common in Europe than in the United States. The most common series are those of Clark and Lubs, Kolthoff and Vleeschouwer, and McIlvaine. The instructions for preparation of the Clark and Lubs buffers are given in Appendix C.

For measurement of pH to ± 0.1 unit, the reagent-grade chemicals available commercially are suitable for direct buffer preparation. For more exact work, the salts must be purified by recrystallization. Such purified salts are available from the National Bureau of Standards.

Buffers may be prepared rapidly with several acid salts by dissolving a weighed quantity of the salt in water. Some of these salts are listed in Table 12.2, with the pH obtained at 25° C.

12.6 Acid-base indicators. Many organic substances when dissolved show a color change as the pH of the medium is changed. These have been utilized to indicate the pH of solutions or the end-

TABLE 12.2

Acid Salts for Buffer Mixtures

Concentration and Type of Salt	pH
Saturated potassium acid tartrate *	3.57 ± 0.02
0.05 M potassium acid phthalate †	4.004
0.05 M sodium tetraborate	9.180

* J. J. Lingane, *Anal. Chem.*, *19*, 810 (1947).

† pH values from M. Dole, *The Glass Electrode*, John Wiley, New York (1941).

point of acid-base titrations. Some indicators show different colors in acid and in basic solution (methyl orange) while others are colorless in one and colored in the other (phenolphthalein). Since all of the useful indicators are weak acids or weak bases, it is considered that the action of an indicator acid might be explained as follows:

$$\text{H}In \rightleftarrows \text{H}^+ + In^-$$

$$\frac{(\text{H}^+)(In^-)}{(\text{H}In)} = K_{In}$$

where K_{In} is called the indicator constant

$$(\text{H}^+) = \frac{(\text{H}In)}{In^-} K_{In}$$

If the ionized (In^-) and un-ionized ($\text{H}In$) forms of the indicator have different colors, the color shown in solution will depend on the ratio of the two forms present, and thus on the hydrogen-ion concentration. This simplified explanation is not strictly valid, as it may be necessary for one or both forms of the indicator to undergo a tautomeric change for the production of the color. However, since the ionization process appears to be the limiting reaction in all cases, we can consider only the simplified form in our discussion.

A single indicator is useful over a limited pH range. If the color of the solution were measured spectrophotometrically, it might be possible, for example, to detect one part of the acid form in the presence of one hundred parts of the ion form, or vice versa. This would mean that our concentration ratio would vary from 0.01 to 100, and our useful pH range would be

$$p\text{H} = pK_{In} \pm 2$$

However, indicators were originally developed for visual comparison, and the published ranges are given a maximum ratio of ten to one. Since the average eye is unable to distinguish changes outside of these limits, the useful pH range is given as

$$pH = pK_{In} \pm 1$$

Several hundred indicators have been described in the literature, but the best ones for pH work are the sulfonphthalein group. The sulfonic acid group of these indicators must be neutralized when preparing their solutions. This is done by making a paste of the indicator with a measured quantity of standard 0.01 M NaOH and diluting with water to the desired concentration. The properties of these and a few other common indicators are given in Table 12.3.

TABLE 12.3

Properties of Some Common Indicators *

Name	pH Range	Color Change, Acid to Alkaline	Absorption Maximum, $m\mu$		pK
			Acid	Alkaline	
Thymol blue	1.2–2.8	Red to yellow	545	435	1.5
Methyl orange	3.0–4.5	Red to yellow	510	460	. . .
Bromcresol green	3.8–5.4	Yellow to blue	440	615	4.7
Methyl red	4.2–6.3	Red to yellow	517	430	. . .
Bromthymol blue	6.0–7.6	Yellow to blue	434	617	7.0
Cresol red	7.2–8.8	Yellow to red	518	572	8.3
Thymol blue	8.0–9.6	Yellow to blue	435	595	8.9
Phenolphthalein	8.5–10.0	Colorless to red	. . .	553	. . .

* For more complete data on indicators, see W. M. Clark, *The Determination of Hydrogen Ions*, 3rd ed., Williams and Wilkins, Baltimore (1928).

The choice of a proper indicator depends upon the general type of acid-base reaction. In the titration of a strong acid with a strong base, the change in pH as the equivalent point is passed, is very broad (see Fig. 12.1), and almost any common indicator is satisfactory; for example, methyl orange (pH range 3.0 to 4.5), methyl red (pH range 4.2 to 6.3), bromthymol blue (pH range 6.0 to 7.6), cresol red (pH range 7.2 to 8.8) or phenolphthalein (pH range 8.5 to 10.0) could be selected.

For a strong-base–weak-acid titration (see Fig. 12.2) only cresol red would be suitable from the group of indicators just discussed.

For a weak-base–strong-acid titration (see Fig. 12.3) methyl red would be chosen, whereas for a weak-base–weak-acid titration bromthymol blue would be chosen (see Fig. 12.4).

12.7 The colorimetric measurement of pH. The pH of a simple, colorless, dilute, buffered solution may be measured by comparison with series of standards with an indicator having a suitable range. The proper indicator may be chosen with the aid of test papers. The common practice is to prepare a series of Pyrex tubes containing 10 ml of the standards made at intervals of 0.2 pH, and a tube with 10 ml of the sample. A carefully measured amount (0.2 to 0.5 ml of a 0.2% solution) of the indicator is added to each tube. The pH of the sample may be estimated to 0.1 pH unit by visual comparison. For best results, the pH of the solution should lie near the center of the indicator's pH range where the color change is most marked.

Of course it would be possible to set up a photoelectric colorimeter and measure the color more accurately, but it is seldom that the conditions of the analysis or the required accuracy would warrant such a procedure. Such difficulties as the variation of indicators from lot to lot, and the accuracy required for the standard buffers used to calibrate the instrument would be serious, but the many errors inherent in colorimetric pH measurements would be even more important.

Interferences with the indicator method include: (1) High salt concentration (change in activities of hydrogen and indicator ions), (2) Colored or turbid samples (optical interference), (3) Unbuffered samples (change in pH on addition of indicator acid or base), (4) Oxidizing agents (destruction of indicator), (5) Colloidal materials (adsorption of indicator), (6) Nonaqueous samples (change in indicator constant).

Though the last three interferences cannot readily be avoided, it is possible to compensate for the first three. The effect of high salt concentration may be minimized by using buffers with approximately the same ionic strength as the sample. The effect of color or turbidity in the sample may be taken care of with a comparator block (Fig. 12.5). The holes 1, 2, and 3 are used for test tubes of the sample, only tube 2 having indicator added. Tube 5 contains distilled water, while tubes 4 and 6 contain standard buffer solutions with added indicator. When viewed horizontally, the three pairs of tubes present to the eye the same amount of glass, sample, indicator, and water, and any color difference must be caused by a difference in pH. The sample may be bracketed to the desired accuracy by two buffers with suitable pH values.

Unbuffered or very slightly buffered solutions may change in pH

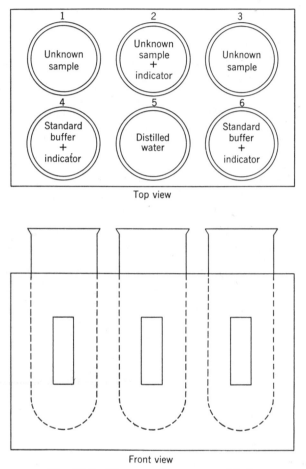

Fig. 12.5 Diagram of comparator block

upon addition of the indicator, because of its weakly acidic or basic character. This can be compensated for by an isohydric indicator solution. This is an indicator solution whose pH is the same as that of the sample, and therefore the apparent pH of the sample will not change as the amount of the indicator is varied. This can be tested by preparing dilute (0.01%) solutions of the indicator in the acid and basic forms. To a portion of the sample add 5 drops of each indicator, and to another portion add 10 drops of each. If the pH is less with the larger amount of indicator, the indicator mixture is too acid. Then try a third portion with 3 drops of the acid form and 7 drops of basic and a fourth portion with twice as much of each. In this way it should be possible to select the proper ratio of acid form to basic form for the particular sample. This procedure is tedious, and some experience is required to avoid confusing the change in depth of color for different indicator concentrations with a change in pH.

12.8   Instrumental aids for colorimetric pH determination. The preparation and maintenance of a series of buffer standards for a considerable pH range is a nuisance, and several systems of permanent standards have been devised. Liquid and glass standards are typified by the LaMotte Roulette comparator and the Hellige comparator (Fig. 3.10), respectively. Both instruments are available with standards covering the common indicators at 0.2 pH intervals, allowing estimation to 0.1 unit.

The Roulette comparator is a convenient form of the comparator block. A fixed holder has space for the three sample tubes, the indicator being added to the center tube. A manually rotated holder contains alternate tubes of standard buffers plus indicator and tubes of distilled water, allowing any two consecutive buffers to be brought into position. A light bulb at the center furnishes uniform illumination.

The Hellige comparator has space for two sample tubes, one with and one without indicator. The standards are small glass disks mounted on a wheel which can be rotated for comparing any standard with the sample. Each wheel covers one indicator, and they can be easily interchanged. Comparisons are made by holding the instrument up to a light source, a ground-glass diffusing screen on the back of the case helping to give uniform illumination. The pH corresponding to the standard in position appears at a small window.

These two instruments should be calibrated for the proper amount of each indicator required to match the depth of color of the standards. This may be done with a known buffer in each pH range. After the number of drops required for a match has been determined, the data should be recorded on the bottle of indicator solution, along with instructions for preparing the solution.

Measurements with a photoelectric colorimeter require that a calibration curve be set up for each indicator, using a filter whose maximum transmittance is at the wavelength of maximum absorbance for one form (acidic or basic) of the indicator. This eliminates the preparation of standards for each measurement, but the indicator concentration must be controlled very accurately. By measuring at two wavelengths the maximum absorbance for the two forms of the indicator, it is possible to obtain concentrations of both forms. From the relation

$$(H^+) = \frac{(HIn)}{(In^-)} K_{In}$$

it is apparent that the concentration ratio is a function of (H^+) which is independent of the total indicator concentration. This allows measurements to be made without the concentration of the indicator being reproduced exactly, but the process is lengthier than standardizing the indicator initially.

In spite of its limitations the colorimetric measurement of pH remains an important analytical technique in most academic and industrial laboratories because of the advantages it offers in simplicity and low cost relative to electrometric pH measurements. The same statement can be made concerning indicators in acid-base titrations. Although there is an increasing tendency to replace these conventional visual methods by more elaborate instrumental methods, their importance should not be minimized.

Bibliography

I. M. Kolthoff and H. A. Laitinen, *pH and Electro Titrations,* 2nd ed., John Wiley, New York (1941).

CHAPTER 13

Electrode Potential and
pH Measurements

In this chapter the elementary theory of electrode potentials for electrolytic solutions is presented. This potential is a function chiefly of the electrolyte, its activity, and the measuring electrodes. Because of the fundamental difference between activity and concentration, the electrode potential is not a direct absolute measure of concentration. The pH, or hydrogen-ion concentration, may be determined by comparison with standards and the change in ion concentration during the course of a titration may be followed. These are the major applications of electrode-potential measurement.

13.1 Electrode potential. An element in contact with water or other ionizing medium will tend to go into solution as the corresponding ion with the gain or loss of electrons. For a metal placed in water the reaction

$$M \rightleftarrows M^+ + e$$

will proceed until equilibrium is established, leaving the electrode negatively charged with respect to the solution. If the concentration of the metal ion is changed, a shift in the equilibrium and in the potential difference between the electrode and the solution occurs. Thus, if we can measure the potential difference between the electrode and the solution, we obtain a measure of the concentration * of the metal ion.

For the measurement of the potential difference, it is necessary to have a second electrode to make contact with the solution. This electrode should maintain a constant potential with respect to the solution, regardless of any change in the concentration of the specific ion and is called the *reference electrode*. The first electrode, whose

---

* The molar concentrations should be replaced by activities for precise calculations.

potential depends upon the concentration, is called the *indicator electrode.*

Since many elements react spontaneously with water, they may not be used as indicator electrodes for determining concentration of solutions of their ions. In a few of these cases, it is possible to measure indirectly, but suitable indicator electrodes are not available for many common elements. There is seldom any difficulty, however, in finding a reference electrode for ordinary analytical systems.

13.2   Electrolytic cells. The notation for an electrode-solution system may be shown in the example

$$M \mid M^+ (a = 1)$$

where the bar indicates the phase boundary between solid and liquid and the activity of the ion is given in parentheses. Such a system is described as a half-cell or a couple. When two half-cells are connected, the resulting electrolytic cell may be written

$$A \mid A^+ (a = 0.5) \mid B^+ (a = 1) \mid B$$

the center bar indicating the junction of the two liquid phases. Since ions may move across this junction, a so-called liquid junction potential is set up because of the difference in mobilities of the cation and anion which exists for most electrolytes. The value of this potential may be calculated, or it may be minimized by a salt bridge. (A salt bridge is simply an electrolytic conductor connecting the two solutions. Saturated agar solutions of salts such as KCl or NH_4NO_3 which have equal anion-cation mobilities are recommended.) The above cell would then be written

$$A \mid A^+ (a = 0.5) \parallel B^+ (a = 1) \mid B$$

the double bar indicating that the liquid junction potential has been eliminated by a salt bridge.

13.3   Standard potentials and potential conventions. The experimental measurement of the absolute potential of a half-cell is very difficult. For this reason there are no tables available with the absolute potentials of the common half-cell reactions. Since we are concerned only with potential differences in ordinary chemical calculations involving cells, we do not need to know absolute potentials. We select, therefore, arbitrarily some half-cell as a standard and call the potential of this half-cell zero volts. The hydrogen-gas–hydrogen-ion half-cell reaction has been selected as such a standard,

$$\tfrac{1}{2}H_2 \text{ (1 atmosphere)} \rightleftarrows H^+ \text{ (unit activity)} + e$$

and is referred to as the *standard hydrogen electrode*. The standard potentials of other half-cells have been obtained by measuring the emf of a cell composed of the given half-cell (with the reactants and products at unit activity) and the standard hydrogen electrode as the other half-cell. These standard electrode potentials are called $E°$ values. Appendix D contains the $E°$ values for the more common half-cell reactions.

Having obtained these values, we are then faced with the problem of what sign we should ascribe to them. For example, if the reduced form of the substance is a better reducing agent than hydrogen, shall we give the emf value a positive or a negative sign? Again the choice is an arbitrary one. We must also choose between writing the half-cell reactions as reductions

$$Cu^{++} + 2e \rightleftarrows Cu$$

or as oxidations

$$Cu \rightleftarrows Cu^{++} + 2e$$

Since chemists have not agreed universally on the sign convention or on the choice of writing the half-cell reactions as reductions or oxidations, much confusion has resulted. We can only be thankful that at least there is universal agreement that the hydrogen electrode is the reference standard.

In this text we shall follow the notation of W. M. Latimer [1] and write all half-cell reactions as oxidations with the electrons on the right-hand side of the equation. A positive value for $E°$ will mean that the reduced form of the half-cell is a better reducing agent than hydrogen gas (H_2) while a negative value for $E°$ will mean that the oxidized form of the half-cell is a better oxidizing agent than hydrogen ion (H^+). Consequently, according to this convention a positive sign will result for the over-all potential of any complete reaction which goes spontaneously in the direction as written. In addition, the available free energy F will always be negative for spontaneous reactions,

$$\Delta F = -nFE$$

where ΔF is the free-energy change in joules, n is the number of electrons involved, F is the Faraday (96,484 absolute coulombs), E

[1] W. M. Latimer, *Oxidation Potentials*, 2nd ed., Prentice-Hall, New York (1952).

is the emf of the cell in volts. If E is positive for the cell, ΔF will be negative, and the reaction will proceed spontaneously as written.

When a complete cell is written as $A \mid A^+ \parallel B^+ \mid B$, the position indicates that the left-hand half-cell represents an oxidation

$$A \rightleftarrows A^+ + e$$

while the right-hand half-cell represents a reduction

$$B^+ + e \rightleftarrows B$$

The over-all reaction is the sum of the half-cell reactions,

$$A + B^+ \rightleftarrows A^+ + B$$

A corollary of this relationship is that, since the left-hand half-cell is an oxidation, the electrode will be negatively charged with respect to the other electrode, which would become positively charged because of the reduction reaction, $B^+ + e \rightarrow B$. According to the conventional nomenclature for electrodes in electric circuits, the electrode at which oxidation has taken place is the cathode. It may be noted, however, that in the inner or solution circuit the "current" may be considered to flow from the electrode where oxidation takes place through the salt bridge to the electrode where reduction takes place. In this sense, then, the electrode at which oxidation takes place becomes the *anode* and the electrode at which reduction takes place becomes the *cathode*. In this text we employ the latter convention which has been universally adopted by chemists who always speak of *anodic oxidation* and *cathodic reduction*.

It is helpful to illustrate the convention with several examples. Thus, if we consider the cell

$$Cu \mid Cu^{++} (a = 1) \parallel Ag^+ (a = 1) \mid Ag$$

we find in the table of standard oxidation potentials ($E°$ values) in Appendix D.

$$Cu \rightarrow Cu^{++} + 2e, \qquad E° = -0.337 \text{ volt} \qquad (1)$$

$$Ag \rightarrow Ag^+ + e, \qquad E° = -0.799 \text{ volt} \qquad (2)$$

and, to obtain the same number of electrons, we have

$$2Ag \rightarrow 2Ag^+ + 2e, \qquad E° = -0.799 \qquad (3)$$

(Note that the standard electrode potential for silver is not multiplied by 2.)

It should be noted that in the previous example we wrote one half-cell as an oxidation and the other as a reduction, and to obtain the over-all reaction we added the two half-cell reactions. In the convention that we have adopted all $E°$ values are given as *oxidation potentials*, and to obtain the over-all reaction we must subtract reaction 3 from 1 and likewise subtract the $E°$ values which yields

$$Cu - 2Ag \rightleftarrows Cu^{++} - 2Ag^+$$

and $E_{over-all} = -0.337 - (-0.799) = +0.462$ volt

Now, transposing, we have

$$Cu + 2Ag^+ \rightleftarrows Cu^{++} + 2Ag, \qquad E_{over-all} = +0.462 \text{ volt}$$

Since E for the over-all reaction is positive, ΔF is negative, and the reaction proceeds spontaneously as written. The student may ask how we know which reaction to write first if we have no previous information concerning how the reaction proceeds. With a little thought it should be realized that, if we always write the half-cell with the most positive $E°$ value first, upon subtraction, E for the over-all reaction will always be positive, and the reaction will proceed spontaneously as written.

13.4   The Nernst equation. The potential of the half-cell $M \mid M^{+n}$ for the half-cell reaction $M \rightleftarrows M^{+n} + ne$ may be written in the form of the Nernst equation,

$$E = E° - RT/nF \ln (M^{+n})$$

where $E°$ = standard electrode potential (unit activity), R = gas constant, 8.3144 joules per degree mole, n = number of electrons involved per atom, F = the Faraday, 96,484 coulombs, T = the absolute temperature. The ion concentration rather than the activity is shown because it is the quantity of analytical importance, and it is sufficiently accurate for our calculations.

In the general case,

$$E = E° - RT/nF \ln Q$$

where Q is the ratio obtained by dividing the product of the *prevailing* molar concentrations of the resulting substances by the product of the *prevailing* molar concentrations of the reacting substances, each molar concentration being raised to that power whose exponent is the coefficient of the substance in the chemical equation. Hence, Q has the same general form as an equilibrium constant but differs in that the concentrations involved are *not* those at equilibrium but the *prevailing* concentrations. Of course, at equilibrium Q equals K, the equilibrium constant. In expressing Q, in line with the convention we have adopted, we must write all reactions as oxidations.

At 25° C this equation simplifies to

$$E = E° - 0.0591/n \log Q$$

and in this form we can calculate the effect of concentration on electrode potential. For example, in the cell,

$$Pb \mid Pb^{++} (1\ M) \parallel H^+ (1\ M) \mid H_2, Pt$$

we can calculate the cell potential as in the preceding section.

$Pb \rightleftarrows Pb^{++} + 2e,$	$E° = 0.126$ volt
$H_2 \rightleftarrows 2H^+ + 2e,$	$E° = 0.000$ volt

$Pb - H_2 \rightleftarrows Pb^{++} - 2H^+,$	$E_{\text{over-all}} = +0.126$ volt
and $Pb + 2H^+ \rightleftarrows Pb^{++} + H_2,$	$E_{\text{over-all}} = +0.126$ volt

However, if the same constituents are at different concentrations,

$$Pb \mid Pb^{++} (2\ M) \parallel H^+ (0.00001\ M) \mid H_2, Pt$$

the potential of the lead electrode is

$$E = 0.126 - 0.0591/2 \log 2 = 0.117$$

and the potential of the hydrogen electrode is

$$E = 0.000 - 0.0591/2 \log (10^{-5}) = 0.148 \text{ volt}$$

and

$Pb \rightleftarrows Pb^{++} + 2e,$	$E = 0.117$ volt
$H_2 \rightleftarrows 2H^+ + 2e,$	$E = 0.148$ volt

$Pb - H_2 \rightleftarrows Pb^{++} - 2H^+,$	$E_{\text{over-all}} = -0.031$ volt
and $Pb + 2H^+ \rightleftarrows Pb^{++} + H_2,$	$E_{\text{over-all}} = -0.031$ volt

The reaction will not be spontaneous as written since the cell potential is negative. In such a cell then the lead electrode would be positive, whereas with molar solutions the lead electrode was shown to be negative.

13.5 Practical electrodes. The relationships discussed so far are based on thermodynamic principles, requiring that the measurements be made under equilibrium conditions on systems that are reversible. In adopting potential measurements for analysis, we find that it is possible to use nonreversible electrodes in some cases, but that it is still necessary to make measurements under equilibrium conditions. For practical purposes, therefore, it is necessary that our indicator electrodes come to equilibrium rapidly and that any practical electrode either have a long life or else be easily prepared.

Since the determination of concentration by direct potential measurement is applied mainly to pH work, this chapter will deal with pH electrodes. For indicator electrodes, the hydrogen, glass, and quinhydrone types are most common; the calomel electrode is almost exclusively the reference one.

(a) *The Hydrogen Electrode.* The hydrogen electrode is the primary standard of pH measurement, and it is discussed for this reason only, as very few analytical chemists use it in their work. The standard buffer solutions for calibration of pH meters and similar equipment are prepared with fundamental hydrogen-electrode measurements, and thus the analyses made by comparison with these buffers are based on secondary standards rather than the primary standard of pH. The reaction $\frac{1}{2}H_2 \rightarrow H^+$ $(a = 1) + e$ describes the standard hydrogen electrode, whose potential is arbitrarily assigned the value of zero volts. The general reaction

$$\tfrac{1}{2}H_2 \rightleftarrows H^+ + e$$

at 25° C has the potential

$$E = E° - 0.0591 \log a_{H^+}/(p_{H_2})^{1/2}$$

and since, by definition, $E°$ for the hydrogen electrode at unit activity of hydrogen ions and at 1 atmosphere pressure is zero volts,

$$E = -0.0591 \log a_{H^+}/(p_{H_2})^{1/2}$$

and, for 1 atmosphere pressure,

$$E = -0.0591 \log a_{H^+} \quad \text{and} \quad E = 0.0591 \ pH$$

Hence, at 1 atmosphere pressure the emf of the hydrogen electrode is only dependent upon the activity or for practical purposes the molar concentration of the hydrogen ions in solution.

Gaseous hydrogen, being a nonconductor, cannot act as the electrode, and so the electrode is formed by passing a stream of hydrogen gas over a platinum strip which makes contact with the solution. If the strip is coated with platinum black to increase the surface area, a small amount of hydrogen is adsorbed on the surface, and the electrode as a whole behaves as a hydrogen electrode. (Other gases such as oxygen may be handled similarly for the corresponding electrode.)

The hydrogen electrode has many disadvantages for analytical work. The hydrogen must be pure; particularly it must be free of oxygen. Many substances interfere with the action of the electrode; sulfides and compounds of arsenic poison the electrode, destroying its response to pH changes. Oxidizing agents act to produce their redox potential at the electrode while metals more noble than hydrogen are reduced and may deposit on the electrode. Colloidal materials are adsorbed on the platinum black, making the electrode slow in response, and the bubbling hydrogen may sweep out volatile materials such as carbon dioxide, changing the pH of the sample.

In general, it takes several minutes for the hydrogen electrode to reach equilibrium with the solution being measured and such slowness of response is an important drawback for titration methods. This fact plus the comparative complexity of the apparatus and the short life of the electrode under analytical conditions have led to the abandonment of the hydrogen electrode for routine work.

(*b*) *The Glass Electrode.* If a thin glass membrane separates two solutions, it is found [2] that a potential difference appears between the two solutions which is a function of the pH difference. The half-cell,

$$\text{Ag, AgCl} \mid \text{HCl (0.1 } M) \mid \text{glass} \mid$$

may be used to determine the pH of a solution by measuring its potential against a suitable reference electrode.

The glass electrodes available commercially consist of a thin-walled glass bulb sealed to a supporting tube. The inside of the bulb may be a quinhydrone electrode,

$$\text{Pt} \mid \text{HCl (0.1 } M) \text{ quinone·hydroquinone (sat)}$$

or a silver–silver chloride electrode,

$$\text{Ag, AgCl} \mid \text{HCl (0.1 } M)$$

Within the pH range of 0 to 10, the potential of the glass electrode follows that of the hydrogen electrode very exactly, indicating that the reaction involved is $\frac{1}{2}H_2 \rightleftarrows H^+ + e$.

[2] F. Haber and Z. Klemensiewicz, *Z. physik. Chem., 67,* 385 (1909).

Even with identical solutions in contact with the inside and out-side glass surfaces, each glass electrode has a small, residual emf across the glass membrane. This emf is known as the "asymmetry potential" of the glass.

The exact potential of the glass electrode will therefore vary from one electrode to another, the $E°_g$ term in the equation

$$E_g = E°_g - 0.0591 \; pH$$

varying with the individual electrode. The pH relationship is evaluated by standardizing the electrode with a standard buffer. Since the equation is linear and the slope is fixed, one known point determines the line.

The action of a glass electrode has been explained by Dole[3] on the basis of the curve showing the potential energy of a hydrogen ion in the glass-solution interface as a function of its distance from the glass surface (Fig. 13.1). It is seen that as the ion approaches

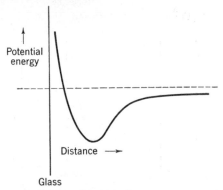

Fig. 13.1 Potential energy of hydrogen ion near glass surface

the glass surface there is an attraction and then a repulsion. (This general picture has been used in explaining a number of surface phenomena and should be applicable to this case.) Likewise, as the ion approaches a water molecule an attraction and then a repulsion results and a similar potential-energy–distance curve is obtained (Fig. 13.2). If we combine the two curves, there are three possibilities; the ion is attracted more strongly to the glass (Fig. 13.3a), to the solution (Fig. 13.3b), or equally to both (Fig. 13.3c).

[3] M. Dole, *The Glass Electrode,* John Wiley, New York (1941).

If hydrogen ions are attracted more strongly to the glass (lower-potential-energy valley near the glass surface), they will tend to make the transition to the glass, giving it a positive charge and leaving the solution negatively charged. Equilibrium will be established when the electric-potential difference set up just balances the difference in the potential-energy levels.

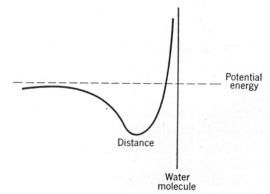

Fig. 13.2   Potential energy of hydrogen ion near water molecule

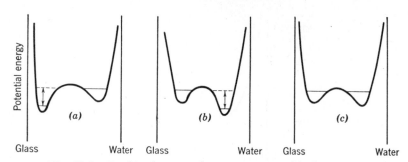

Fig. 13.3   Combined potential energy curves of hydrogen ion

Similar considerations apply to the reverse process. The tendency for the hydrogen ions to make the solution-glass transfer or vice versa will depend on the concentration of the hydrogen ions in solution, and the potential established at the electrode surface will be a function of the *p*H.

Thus the inner and outer glass surfaces may assume potentials dependent on the solution with which they are in contact. If a sealed electrode is used, in which the inner solution is at a constant concentration, the glass electrode potential varies only with the *p*H of the external solution.

Although the exact cause is somewhat doubtful, it is found that when the two surfaces are immersed in the same solution the electrode assumes a small potential. As previously mentioned, this asymmetry potential is of no great moment in practical work as it is compensated for when the glass electrode is standardized against a buffer.

In the presence of high concentrations of alkali salts, the glass electrode gives low values for solutions with a pH above about 9, the error being a function of the alkali ion and its concentration. Sodium shows the greatest error whereas the effect of ammonium ion is negligible. Dole explains this in terms of his electrode mechanism theory by stating that, in alkaline solution, the solution-glass transition for the hydrogen ion is less probable and that the alkali-metal ions make this transition instead. In this way the glass electrode acts as a mixed hydrogen–alkali electrode causing an error in pH measurements. The use of the Beckman type-E high-pH glass electrode reduces this error considerably. In highly acid ($pH < 0$) and nonaqueous solutions, the glass electrode gives erroneous results.

These disadvantages are notable, but the convenience and other advantages of the glass electrode far outweigh them. It is suited for colored or turbid solutions; it is not affected by oxidizing or reducing agents, and may measure the pH of solutions containing colloids, proteins, and moderate concentrations of salts without error. The glass electrode does not affect the solution being measured, which allows measurement of unbuffered solutions and solutions containing dissolved gases. The high electrical resistance of the glass membrane requires special apparatus for the measurement of its potential, but such apparatus is readily available.

Commercial electrodes will be shown in connection with the section on pH meters. The variety and dependability of these electrodes make it unnecessary for the analyst even to consider preparing his own for determining pH.

A comprehensive study of the pH response of glasses of more than 500 different compositions has been made by Perley.[4]

(c) *The Quinhydrone Electrode.* The quinhydrone electrode is based on the redox system

$$HO\!-\!\langle\ \rangle\!-\!OH \rightleftarrows O\!=\!\langle\ \rangle\!=\!O + 2H^+ + 2e$$

[4] G. A. Perley, *Anal. Chem.*, 21, 391 (1949).

The potential of the redox system may be followed with a bright (unplatinized) platinum electrode. Since the redox equilibrium is a function of pH, the potential will indicate the pH. The potential of the electrode at 25° C is given by

$$E = E° - \frac{0.0591}{2} \log \frac{(\text{quinone})(\text{H}^+)^2}{(\text{hydroquinone})}$$

In practice, a small amount of quinhydrone is added to the sample solution and a platinum wire is used for the electrode. Since quinhydrone is an equimolar mixture of hydroquinone and quinone, the above expression reduces to

$$E = E° - 0.0591 \log (\text{H}^+), \qquad E = E° + 0.0591 \, p\text{H}$$

The quinhydrone electrode is simple and easy to prepare, and it comes to equilibrium rapidly. Unlike the glass electrode, it requires no calibration. Its disadvantages are that oxidizing or reducing agents destroy the value of the equilibrium for hydrogen-ion measurement, and, at a pH of about 8 or above, hydroquinone ionizes sufficiently to affect the pH. In addition, oxygen reacts readily with hydroquinone, and the presence of large concentrations of electrolytes causes an appreciable salt error.

(d) *The Calomel Electrode.* The calomel electrode consists of a paste of mercury and calomel. Connection to the solution to be measured is accomplished with a solution of potassium chloride saturated with calomel; the electric connection is made by a platinum wire in contact with a layer of mercury underlying the paste. The half-cell reaction is

$$2\text{Hg} + 2\text{Cl}^- \rightleftarrows \text{Hg}_2\text{Cl}_2 + 2e$$

The potential for the half-cell at 25° C is

$$E = E° - \frac{0.0591}{2} \log \frac{1}{(\text{Cl}^-)^2}$$

as the activities of solid components are unity. By fixing the chloride concentration, the potential of the cell is fixed. In Table 13.1 are given the potentials of calomel electrodes as a function of chloride concentration and temperature.

Two forms of the calomel electrode are shown in Fig. 13.4. Both of these have a separate salt bridge for connection to the solution. If the chloride ion may affect the sample, a solution of KNO_3 or

TABLE 13.1

Calomel Electrode Potentials

Electrode	Emf at 25° C	Temperature Coefficient
0.1 N calomel	0.3338	$-7 \times 10^{-5}(t - 25)$
1.0 N calomel	0.2800	$-2.4 \times 10^{-4}(t - 25)$
Saturated calomel	0.2415	$-7.6 \times 10^{-4}(t - 25)$

NH_4NO_3 may be substituted in the salt bridge instead of potassium chloride.

The only noteworthy defect of the calomel electrode is its variation in potential with temperature, a defect common to all electrode systems. The 0.1 N calomel electrode has the smallest temperature variation while the saturated calomel electrode has the highest.

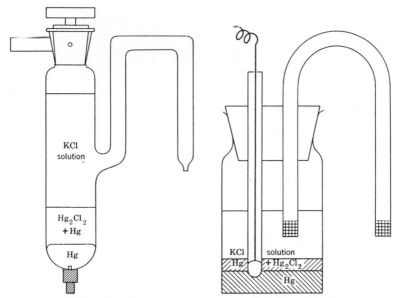

Fig. 13.4 Two types of calomel electrodes (I. M. Kolthoff and H. A. Laitinen, *pH and Electro Titrations*, John Wiley, New York, 1948)

13.6 The measurement of electrode potential. Electrode potential is an equilibrium phenomenon, and in its measurement we must not disturb the equilibrium, or the potential value obtained will be false. If our measuring device draws appreciable current from the cell, the equilibrium is shifted, so that the ordinary voltmeter is not applicable.   Two methods are available, a null-balance system using the potentiometer principle and the vacuum-tube voltmeter.

In the potentiometer, an equal and opposite voltage is applied to the electrolytic cell.   The balance point is detected by a galvanometer, and the cell potential measured as the potentiometer voltage required for balance.   The simple potentiometer and a practical instrument are shown schematically in Fig. 13.5.

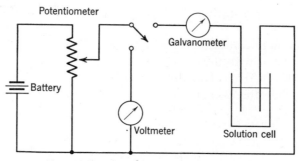

Fig. 13.5*a*   Simple potentiometer circuit

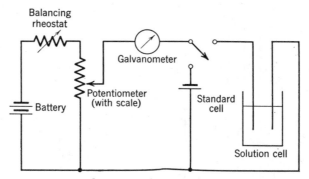

Fig. 13.5*b*   Practical potentiometer circuit

The former instrument has one or two dry cells as a source of balancing voltage, and the slide wire is adjusted to balance the galvanometer.   A switch then disconnects the electrolytic cell and connects a voltmeter to the balancing circuit, allowing the cell potential to be read directly.   This circuit is simple, but not highly accurate unless an expensive precision voltmeter is available.

In the practical instrument a uniform slide wire with an attached scale calibrated in volts is the potentiometer proper.   A switch substitutes a standard cell for the cell to be measured.   The slide-wire scale is set to the standard cell potential, and the voltage applied to the slide wire is varied by the rheostat until the galvanometer balances. The potentiometer then reads directly in potential. Instantaneous measurements are made by depressing a tap key to complete the circuit.

The potentiometer is simple and relatively trouble-free, requiring only that all electric contacts be firm and clean. The accuracy depends on the uniformity of the slide wire, the degree of scale subdivision, and the sensitivity of the galvanometer. If a sensitive galvanometer is used, a second tap key with a series resistor is desirable. This series resistor reduces the sensitivity of the galvanometer so that it will not be damaged by swinging off-scale if the system is far out of balance.

The chief disadvantage of the potentiometer is that it cannot measure the potential of a high-resistance system such as a cell using a glass electrode.

The commercially available instruments are usually of three grades: student models, portable models, and precision potentiometers. Other special instruments are available for particular purposes, but these three cover the analytical field.

13.7 The pH meter. The ordinary vacuum-tube voltmeter built for radio and electrical measurements is a versatile instrument, but its accuracy does not meet the requirements for analytical work. For this reason, a special type of vacuum-tube potentiometer has been developed. Since these meters were designed for pH determination with the glass electrode, they are called pH meters, but they are generally capable of measuring the potential of any electrode system.

In operation, the electrodes are connected across a high resistance at the input grid of a vacuum-tube amplifier. Because of the high resistance, only a small current, a fraction of a microampere, will flow. This current is not sufficient to affect the cell equilibrium, but after amplification it is sufficient to operate a galvanometer or sensitive microammeter.

The first instruments built were battery-operated in order to achieve high stability, and used the potentiometer principle to give a null balance on a galvanometer, the potentiometer scale being calibrated directly in pH units. The commercial instruments are typified by the Beckman model G (Fig. 13.6), the Leeds and Northrup, and the Coleman.

A later development was the replacement of the galvanometer with a microammeter scale to give direct pH readings, as in the battery-operated Beckman model M. More recently, several line-operated meters, using a voltage-regulated power supply for the tube voltages,

Fig. 13.6 Beckman model-G *p*H meter (Courtesy Beckman Instrument Company)

have been introduced. Line operation is considered to be a desirable feature, although the usual life of the batteries is of the order of six months.† The Leeds and Northrup model 7664 is a typical

---

† It is the opinion of the authors that the battery-operated type is the most versatile and satisfactory for general laboratory work.

example of the line-operated pH meter, although they are available from several manufacturers.

The manufacturers mentioned produce a complete line of electrodes, particularly glass, platinum, and calomel, for their own instruments (Fig. 13.7). These electrodes are not interchangeable between instruments of different manufacturers without modification.

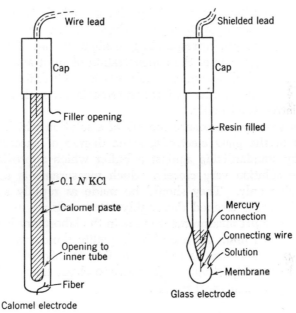

Fig. 13.7 Typical commercial electrodes

Ready-made electrodes are more convenient and reproducible than those made in the laboratory, and types for macro and micro quantities of solution are available at reasonable cost.

13.8 The measurement of pH. In the analytical laboratory, the pH meter with a glass-calomel electrode system is used almost exclusively for pH measurement. The convenience and direct-reading features of these instruments have led to an increase in the number of methods utilizing pH control. However, this convenience has led to many erroneous results because the limitations of the method are not realized.

While some of the errors inherent in the glass electrode have been discussed, it may be well to approach them from the viewpoint of measurement. Like any analytical instrument, the pH meter requires accurate adjustment and standardization.   For this reason, a selection of buffers of known pH should be available.   Certain of these are supplied by the instrument manufacturers or chemical supply houses.   The standards may be solutions or tablets, and the makers specify a tolerance of ± 0.01 pH, which is well within the limits of measurement.   Simple, less expensive standards are listed in Table 12.2.

The error resulting from activity change, which is caused by a change in ionic strength, is usually slight, as the standard buffers have an ionic strength corresponding to about 0.1 M.   0.1 M is also the order of magnitude of the concentration of most analytical solutions.   The effect of nonaqueous solvents is more difficult to assess, and it is wise to consider pH measurements on such solutions as having relative values only.

If it is necessary to measure the pH of a solution which is outside the range of the glass electrode, some degree of success may be attained by standardizing against a buffer which approximates the pH of the solution very closely.   Such measurements again have relative value only.   They should be made as rapidly as possible and the electrodes cleaned thoroughly afterwards.

The ordinary pH measurement made in the laboratory has an error of 0.05 to 0.1 pH unit.   By use of high-quality standards and careful operation the error may be reduced to 0.02 to 0.05 pH unit, but it is doubtful if the reporting of pH values to closer than 0.05 unit has any meaning for analytical results.

CHAPTER 14

Potentiometric Titrations

In the preceding chapter we considered electrode-potential measurements mainly for the determination of the hydrogen-ion concentration of a solution. Electrode-potential measurements are of equal importance for following the course of a titration and determining the equivalence point. Such methods are termed *potentiometric titrations*. Normally, any stoichiometric reaction may be made the basis of a titration if a suitable indicator is available for locating the equivalence point. Chemical indicators which give a color change are available for the majority of reactions, but there are some reactions where no chemical compound suitable for a visual indicator has been found. In such cases, potentiometric titrations have made volumetric analyses possible.

Potentiometric titrations are conveniently classified by three distinct types of reactions, acid-base, oxidation-reduction (redox), and precipitation and complex formation reactions. For acid-base and redox reactions, indicator electrodes are readily available, being the glass and bright platinum electrodes, respectively. For precipitation and complex formation we are limited to indicator electrodes involving silver, mercury, or the common halogen ions. Only the more noble metals may act as electrodes without affecting the equilibrium of the systems, and so many precipitation and complex-formation reactions cannot be followed because of the lack of an indicator electrode.

14.1 Acid-base titrations. The apparatus described for pH measurement may follow the course of an acid-base titration, the pH meter with a glass–calomel-electrode system being most convenient. Any acid-base titration may be made, provided the reaction is stoichiometric. Color or turbidity in the sample or the presence of oxidizing agents or other materials that would interfere with visual indicators do not cause difficulty. The method offers no advantage over visual titrations in many cases but is indispensable in others.

If increments of the titrating solution are added until the end point has definitely been passed, the pH values measured after each addition may be plotted against the volume added to give the familiar titration curves. The four examples of strong base–strong acid, strong base–weak acid, weak base–strong acid, and weak base–weak acid were shown in Figs. 12.1 to 12.4, inclusive.

In each instance it may be seen that the equivalence point is at an inflection point on the curve, where the slope is at a maximum. The equivalence point may be calculated by means of the equations derived in Chapter 12. Thus, the pH at the equivalence point for a strong-base–weak-acid titration is given by

$$pH = \tfrac{1}{2}pW + \tfrac{1}{2}pA + \tfrac{1}{2}\log c$$

and for a weak-base–strong-acid titration by

$$pH = \tfrac{1}{2}pW - \tfrac{1}{2}pB - \tfrac{1}{2}\log c$$

and for a weak-base–weak-acid titration by

$$pH = \tfrac{1}{2}pW + \tfrac{1}{2}pA - \tfrac{1}{2}pB$$

In general, it is necessary to check the pH value at the equivalence point experimentally, rather than by calculation. This requires determination of the complete titration curve.

The equivalence point may also be located by visual estimation or graphically. The first graphical method (Fig. 14.1) is to draw

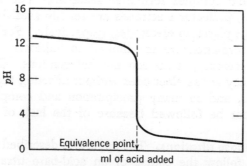

Fig. 14.1   Graphical method of determining equivalence point

a line, through the center of the inflection region, perpendicular to the abscissa, and take the equivalence point as the intersection of the perpendicular line and the abscissa. Or the nearly horizontal lines at the start and end of the titration may be extended and a parallel line drawn midway between, and the intersection of this line with the titration curve will be the endpoint.

The second graphical method is possible because the equivalence point lies at the maximum slope of the curve. The values of $\Delta pH/\Delta V$ are calculated for each increment and plotted against V, the volume added (Fig. 14.2).

The maximum of this curve is the equivalence point. Both graphical methods require small increments near the equivalence point to establish the exact shape and position of the curve. The second method is the most sensitive in this respect, and, unless a large number of readings are taken near the equivalence point, it is difficult to select the peak value. However, if the curve is assumed to be symmetrical, it is possible to select two points on opposite arms of the $\Delta pH/\Delta V$ curve having equal ordinates and take the midpoint of the corresponding volume values as the equivalence point.

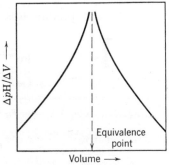

Fig. 14.2 Determination of equivalence point with differential plot

The process of taking this amount of data and plotting the results is tedious but is only necessary when studying a new system. Once the pH at the equivalence point has been established, it is only necessary to titrate to the proper pH and read the buret volume as in any standard titration. The titrant must be added slowly near the equivalence point, as the glass electrode takes a few seconds to reach equilibrium. By following the pH roughly and noting the increased rate of change as the endpoint is approached, the titration may be slowed down at the appropriate time.

The precision and accuracy of the potentiometric method equals that of a visual method, and it is applicable in more special cases, but it is also subject to error in some instances. Any chemical interference where the pH is affected, such as absorption of atmospheric carbon dioxide, will render the titration worthless. The inherent errors of the glass electrode do not all affect the titration, as we need only relative pH values. Thus the glass-electrode system has been used for titrations in nonaqueous solutions and concentrated salt solutions with considerable success.

The highly colored, concentrated solutions of plating baths can best be titrated with the glass electrode. Dye baths and bleaching solutions are other outstanding applications in which visual methods fail. One of the few failures of the glass-electrode system is in the titration of acid fluoride solutions, where the attack on the thin-glass membrane of the electrode is too severe.

14.2   Redox titrations.   If we consider a typical oxidation-reduction titration such as the titration of iron with ceric ammonium nitrate, we know from our laboratory experience that the reaction proceeds as follows:

$$Fe^{++} + Ce^{++++} \rightarrow Fe^{+++} + Ce^{+++}$$

We could also predict this reaction from an inspection of the $E°$ values, thus:

$$Fe^{++} \quad \rightarrow Fe^{+++} + e, \qquad\qquad E° = -0.771 \text{ volt}$$

$$Ce^{+++} \rightarrow Ce^{++++} + e, \qquad\qquad E° = -1.61 \quad \text{volt}$$

$$Fe^{++} - Ce^{+++} \rightarrow Fe^{+++} - Ce^{++++}, \quad E_{over-all} = +0.839 \text{ volt}$$

$$\text{or } Fe^{++} + Ce^{++++} \rightarrow Fe^{+++} + Ce^{+++}, \quad E_{over-all} = +0.839 \text{ volt}$$

Since $E_{over-all}$ is positive, ΔF is negative and the reaction proceeds spontaneously as written.

In the titration of ferrous iron with ceric ammonium nitrate the emf may be followed with a bright platinum strip or wire as an indicator electrode and a calomel cell as the reference electrode. If ferrous ions are present in a beaker and the ceric solution in the buret at the start of the titration, the potential of the platinum electrode will be dependent upon the ratio of the concentration of ferrous to ferric iron. The equilibrium

$$Fe^{++} \rightleftarrows Fe^{+++} + e$$

would be shown by the half-cell

$$Pt \mid Fe^{++}, Fe^{+++}$$

and the potential would be given by the Nernst equation as

$$E_1 = E°_1 - 0.0591 \log (Fe^{+++})/(Fe^{++})$$

As the ceric solution is added to the beaker, the ratio of the oxidized iron to the reduced iron changes, and consequently the emf indicated by the platinum electrode changes. For each tenfold change in the redox ratio, a potential change of 59 millivolts will be observed, until the equivalence point is reached. At this point the titration involves not only the ferrous–ferric-ion equilibrium but also the ceric–cerous-ion equilibrium. There are now two half-cells to deal with, and their potentials are given by

$$E_1 = E^{\circ}_1 - 0.0591 \log (Fe^{+++})/(Fe^{++})$$

and

$$E_2 = E^{\circ}_2 - 0.0591 \log (Ce^{++++})/(Ce^{+++})$$

Adding the two equations yields

$$E_1 + E_2 = E^{\circ}_1 + E^{\circ}_2 - 0.0591 \log \frac{(Fe^{+++})(Ce^{++++})}{(Fe^{++})(Ce^{+++})}$$

In the system at equilibrium $E_1 = E_2$, and at the equivalence point they equal the equivalence potential, E_{eq}.

$$2E_{eq} = E^{\circ}_1 + E^{\circ}_2 - 0.0591 \log \frac{(Fe^{+++})(Ce^{++++})}{(Fe^{++})(Ce^{+++})}$$

Also, at the equivalence point,

$$(Ce^{+++}) = (Fe^{+++}), \qquad (Ce^{++++}) = (Fe^{++})$$

and, therefore,

$$2E_{eq} = E^{\circ}_1 + E^{\circ}_2, \qquad E_{eq} = \frac{E^{\circ}_1 + E^{\circ}_2}{2}$$

and, in this particular example,

$$E_{eq} = \frac{-0.771 + (-1.61)}{2} = -1.19 \text{ volts}$$

This relationship shows that the equivalence potential is a function only of the E° values of the two half-cells involved.

After the equivalence point the redox ratio of the substance being added, namely the ceric solution, controls the potential, and the potential is given by

$$E = E^{\circ} - 0.0591 \log (Ce^{++++})/(Ce^{+++})$$

It is possible to plot the potential values of the platinum electrode during the course of a redox titration, just as we plotted pH during the course of a neutralization. Significant points are the equivalence potential and the potential when the redox ratios are one. In the first half of the titration, the ratio is one when the reaction is 50% complete, and the potential is the E° value for the substance titrated. After the equivalence point, the redox ratio for the titrant is one when twice the required amount has been added. At this point, the potential is the $E°$ value for the titrant.

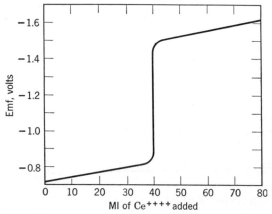

Fig. 14.3 Titration of ferrous sulfate with ceric ammonium nitrate

A theoretical redox-titration curve for the titration of 40 ml of 0.1 M ferrous sulfate with 0.1 M ceric ammonium nitrate is shown in Fig. 14.3, and a corresponding set of calculations for the titration is shown in Table 14.1.

TABLE 14.1

Emf Values for the Titration of 40 ml of 0.1 M Ferrous Sulfate with 0.1 M Ceric Ammonium Nitrate

Ml Ce^{++++} Added	$E° - 0.0591 \log \left[\dfrac{(\text{oxid})}{(\text{red})} \right]$	$E_{\text{over-all}}$	$\Delta E / \Delta \text{ml}$
10	$-0.771 + 0.0591 \log 3$ *	-0.743	. . . . . .
20	$-0.771 - 0.0591 \log 1$	-0.771	0.0028
30	$-0.771 - 0.0591 \log 3$	-0.799	0.0028
39.0	$-0.771 - 0.0591 \log 39$	-0.865	0.0073
39.9	$-0.771 - 0.0591 \log 399$	-0.925	0.0666
39.99	$-0.771 - 0.0591 \log 3999$	-0.984	0.6555
40.00	$\dfrac{-0.771 - 1.61}{2}$	-1.19	20.7
40.01	$-1.61 + 0.0591 \log 4000$	-1.40	20.6
40.10	$-1.61 + 0.0591 \log 400$	-1.46	0.656
50.00	$-1.61 + 0.0591 \log 4$	-1.52	0.0060
80.00	$-1.61 - 0.0591 \log 1$	-1.61	0.0032

* $- \log \frac{1}{3} = + \log 3$.

As the (Fe^{+++}) is zero at the start of the titration, the potential break with the first drop of titrant added would be infinite. In practical work, ferrous ions free from at least a trace of ferric ion do not exist, and the break is not very marked. However, in many titrations, a sharp change of potential upon addition of the first drop of titrant may be noted.

14.3 Redox reactions involving hydrogen ion. If one or both of the half-cell reactions involve hydrogen ion, the electrode potential becomes a function of pH. Thus, for the reaction

$$2Cr^{+++} + 7H_2O \rightleftarrows Cr_2O_7^= + 14H^+ + 6e$$

the electrode potential would be expressed

$$E = E^\circ - \frac{0.0591}{6} \log \frac{(Cr_2O_7^=)(H^+)^{14}}{(Cr^{+++})^2}$$

The potential at any point in the titration is dependent on the pH. It is possible to rewrite the previous equation as

$$E = E^\circ - \frac{0.0591}{6} \log \frac{(Cr_2O_7^=)}{(Cr^{+++})^2} - \frac{0.0591}{6} \log (H^+)^{14}$$

From this expression, it is apparent that, if the original (H^+) is large enough so that no appreciable change occurs during the reaction, the last term will be constant. The potential change will still be expressed by the redox ratio, but the absolute potential would vary if the initial pH is changed. A series of titration curves for differing initial pH values would merely be shifted vertically along the potential axis.

The practical significance of this shift is that it is not possible to titrate a redox system involving hydrogen ion to a definite potential value, as it is impossible to control the pH of the solution to the required precision. Another factor involved is that the common reagents such as potassium permanganate and potassium dichromate do not act as completely reversible half-cells. While the potential change during a titration is measurable, the absolute potentials involved may not be calculated.

14.4 Redox potentials and equilibrium constants. Equilibrium constants can be determined for redox reactions in the following manner. If we consider the reduction of ferric to ferrous iron by stannous chloride, the two half-cell reactions are

$$Sn^{++} \rightarrow Sn^{++++} + 2e \tag{1}$$

$$2Fe^{++} \rightarrow 2Fe^{+++} + 2e \tag{2}$$

and the over-all reaction is given by

$$Sn^{++} - 2Fe^{++} \rightarrow Sn^{++++} - 2Fe^{+++}$$

or $\qquad Sn^{++} + 2Fe^{+++} \rightarrow Sn^{++++} + 2Fe^{++}$

The equilibrium constant for this reaction is

$$K_{eq} = \frac{(Sn^{++++})(Fe^{++})^2}{(Sn^{++})(Fe^{+++})^2}$$

But the potentials for the half-cell reactions 1 and 2 are given by

$$E_{Sn} = E^\circ{}_{Sn} - \frac{0.0591}{2} \log \frac{(Sn^{++++})}{(Sn^{++})}$$

and $\qquad E_{Fe} = E^\circ{}_{Fe} - \dfrac{0.0591}{2} \log \dfrac{(Fe^{+++})^2}{(Fe^{++})^2}$

At equilibrium, these two potentials are equal,

$$E^\circ{}_{Sn} - \frac{0.0591}{2} \log \frac{(Sn^{++++})}{(Sn^{++})} = E^\circ{}_{Fe} - \frac{0.0591}{2} \log \frac{(Fe^{+++})^2}{(Fe^{++})^2}$$

and $\qquad E^\circ{}_{Sn} - E^\circ{}_{Fe} = + \dfrac{0.0591}{2} \log \dfrac{(Sn^{++++})(Fe^{++})^2}{(Sn^{++})(Fe^{+++})^2}$

or $\qquad E^\circ{}_{Sn} - E^\circ{}_{Fe} = + \dfrac{0.0591}{2} \log K_{eq}$

and, finally, $\qquad \log K_{eq} = \dfrac{E^\circ{}_{Sn} - E^\circ{}_{Fe}}{0.0591/2}$

It is possible, then, to calculate the equilibrium constant for a redox reaction and to estimate how complete the reaction should be, using only the tabulated E° values for redox half-cell reactions. In this example, $K_{eq} = 10^{21}$, indicating complete reduction of ferric iron by stannous tin.

If the hydrogen-ion concentration is involved, the calculation must include this factor. The relative oxidizing power of acid and alkaline permanganate solutions have been encountered in organic chemistry and are a familiar example of how it is possible to direct the course of redox reactions by adjustment of the acidity.

14.5 Other factors influencing redox potential. In our previous calculation involving the ions of tin and iron we considered only the ions engaged directly in the redox reaction. It must be stressed that ions in solution are seldom present as the simple ions but exist in the form of complexes. For example, solutions containing tin ordinarily contain hydrochloric acid, and in such solutions the tin does not exist merely as stannous (Sn^{++}) and stannic (Sn^{++++}) ions but may be in the form of complexes such as $SnCl_4^=$ and $SnCl_6^=$. In like manner, in hydrochloric acid solution, iron is often present as $FeCl_4^-$, $FeCl_2^+$ and $FeCl^{++}$. As a consequence, the numerical value of the electrode potential often only serves as a rough approximation of the true state of affairs. Exact calculations would require a knowledge of the activities of the simple and complex ions and of the $E°$ values for both. Such activity values are not always available, and, therefore, on a practical basis, solutions involving complex ions must be treated experimentally.

A practical example in which complexes alter redox potential is the permanganate titration of ferrous iron. The reduction to ferrous iron takes place in a chloride solution, and it is apparent from the $E°$ values involved that the permanganate would oxidize the chloride ion to chlorine as well as the ferrous iron to the ferric state. The permanganate reaction

$$Mn^{++} + 4H_2O \rightarrow MnO_4^- + 8H^+ + 5e$$

gives the potential

$$E = E° - \frac{0.591}{5} \log \frac{(MnO_4^-)(H^+)^8}{(Mn^{++})}$$

By adding a large excess of manganous ion to the solution, it is possible to reduce the permanganate potential so that the oxidation of chloride ion to chlorine no longer occurs. The increase in manganous-ion concentration, of course, also reduces the difference between the potential values for permanganate and iron, which makes the desired reaction less complete. If we consider the reaction,

$$Fe^{++} \rightleftarrows Fe^{+++} + e, \qquad E = E° - 0.0591 \log (Fe^{+++})/(Fe^{++})$$

we see that we cannot increase the potential difference by raising the (Fe^{++}) as that is our substance being titrated. Thus we must lower (Fe^{+++}), and this is done by adding an excess of phosphoric acid, forming a stable ferric complex $Fe(PO_4)_2^=$, and reducing the effective (Fe^{+++}).

In any redox titration, therefore, it is advantageous to consider the effect of the anions present on the potential change at the endpoint. Depending on the particular case it may be worth while to add complexing ions or to assure their absence.

14.6   Precipitation and complex formation.   Precipitation reactions are the third general type of reaction that can be followed by a potentiometric titration.   Potentiometric titrations may involve the precipitation of chloride or iodide ion with silver ion or the reverse process.   Metal ions such as silver which can form a stable soluble complex, i.e., $Ag(CN)_2^-$, can be titrated potentiometrically with the complex-forming compound.   In general, the lack of suitable indicator electrodes has limited the application of potentiometric methods in precipitation and complex-formation titrations.

A special case is the titration of zinc or other heavy metals with ferrocyanide.   Redox electrodes are used, and the first excess of titrant causes a large increase in the ferrocyanide–ferricyanide redox ratio and a corresponding potential break.   Sufficient ferricyanide is ordinarily present in the reagent to complete the cell.   Similar methods should be possible with iodide, chromate, or mercurous ions as precipitants.

As was true of acid-base and redox reactions we can calculate the emf at the equivalence point of a precipitation reaction.   According to the solubility-product principle, in a saturated solution of a slightly soluble electrolyte, the product K_{sp} of the total molar concentrations of the ions is a constant, provided each molar concentration is raised to that power whose exponent is the coefficient of the substance in the chemical equation.*

Thus, for the slightly soluble electrolyte A_mB_n,

$$A_mB_n \rightleftarrows mA^+ + nB^-$$

$$K_{sp} = (A^+)^m(B^-)^n$$

Like other equilibrium constants, the solubility-product constant K_{sp} for any given compound varies with the temperature.

If we consider a common example with which we are all familiar, the precipitation of chloride ion with silver ion,

$$K_{sp} = (Ag^+)(Cl^-)$$

At the equivalence point, for every silver ion present there will be one chloride ion, and

* The molar concentrations should be replaced by activities for precise calculations.

$$(Ag^+) = (Cl^-) = \sqrt{K_{sp}}$$

From the Nernst equation the emf will be given by

$$E = E° - 0.0591 \log (Ag^+)$$

or

$$E = E° - 0.0591 \log \sqrt{K_{sp}}$$

and

$$E = E° - 0.0591/2 \log K_{sp}$$

If we know the solubility or the solubility product of the substance being titrated, we can calculate the emf at the equivalence point. Conversely, by accurately measuring the emf at the equivalence point for a given substance, we can determine its solubility product. Hence, we should remember the importance of potentiometric titrations not only for their analytical value but also for their application in physical chemistry.

Potentiometric titrations have a special value in the analysis of mixtures. For example, as illustrated in Fig. 14.4 it is possible to

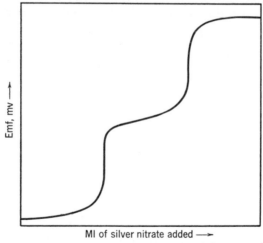

Emf, mv ⟶

Ml of silver nitrate added ⟶

Fig. 14.4   Titration of a mixture of chloride and iodide ion with silver nitrate

determine both the chloride and iodide content in a mixture of the two without resorting to an indirect method of analysis. From Fig. 14.4 it can be seen that there are two distinct breaks in the curve. The first break occurs with iodide ion which is the first to precipitate, being more insoluble than silver chloride. The second occurs as all the chloride ions are precipitated as silver chloride.

14.7 Electrode systems. For acid-base reactions, the most common electrode pair is the glass–calomel system. In addition to the glass electrode, the quinhydrone or hydrogen electrodes are occasionally used as indicator electrodes. In redox titrations the platinum–calomel system is most common, although there is some variation in the selection of a reference electrode in place of the calomel half-cell. The criterion for a reference electrode is that it must maintain a constant potential with respect to the solution during the course of the titration. If the pH remains constant during the titration, the glass electrode is not sensitive to redox conditions and may act as reference electrode in potentiometric titrations. As in pH work, a high input-resistance measuring system is needed. The glass electrode offers little advantage over the calomel electrode unless traces of chloride ion (from the calomel-electrode salt bridge) cause difficulty in the solution.

The bimetallic-electrode systems of Willard and Fenwick[1] and Van Name and Fenwick[2] depend on the metallic reference electrode taking a relatively long time to reach equilibrium. One common system is the platinum–tungsten pair, in which the tungsten lags behind the platinum in following the redox potential. If the titration is carried out rapidly, there will be a sharp break in potential at the equivalence point. The tungsten electrode tends to form an oxide film and become very insensitive. This coating may be removed by dipping the tungsten into molten sodium nitrite followed by rinsing in water.

Two pieces of platinum wire may act as an electrode system if a polarizing current of a few microamperes is allowed to flow during the titration. The difference in the rate of response of the two polarized electrodes is similar to that of the platinum–tungsten pair. The polarized platinum system is very convenient, and many commercial titrimeters include a polarizing circuit.

For precipitation reactions, the indicator electrode is usually the metal itself if it is more noble than hydrogen (i.e. has a negative $E°$ value) while a calomel or mercurous sulfate half-cell acts as the reference electrode.

Table 14.2 contains a brief list of electrode systems for various potentiometric titrations. This list is by no means complete but should serve as a general guide.

[1] H. H. Willard and F. Fenwick, *J. Am. Chem. Soc.*, **44**, 2504, 2516 (1922); **45**, 84, 623, 645, 715, 928, 933 (1923).

[2] R. G. Van Name and F. Fenwick, *ibid.*, **47**, 9, 19 (1925).

TABLE 14.2

Some Typical Electrode Systems

	Electrodes	
System	Indicator	Reference
Acid-Base Reactions		
Acid-base, all types	Glass	Calomel
Acid-base, limited	Quinhydrone	Calomel
Acid-base, limited	Hydrogen	Calomel
Acid-base, limited	Antimony	Calomel
Acid-base, nonaqueous	Glass	Calomel
Redox Reactions		
Redox, inorganic	Platinum	Calomel
Redox, inorganic	Platinum	Tungsten
Redox, organic	Platinum	Nickel *
Iodimetry	Platinum	Tungsten
Precipitation Reactions		
Silver ion	Silver	Mercurous sulfate
Halogen ions	Silver	Mercurous sulfate
Sulfate ion	Carbon	Tungsten
Heavy metals	Heavy metal	Calomel

* I. A. Atanasiu and A. I. Velculescu, *Bull. Soc. Chim. România, 18A*, 53 (1937).

14.8 Apparatus for potentiometric titrations. While redox titrations may be carried out with the same techniques and apparatus as potentiometric acid-base titrations, there are certain simplifications which are advantageous. The usual redox reactions come to equilibrium instantaneously with sufficient agitation, and the response of the platinum indicator electrode is equally rapid. On the other hand, because of the effect of pH and other factors on the absolute potential of the system, there is little information to be obtained from plotting a titration curve. Therefore the equivalence point is obtained by titrating to the sharp break in potential shown by the redox system.

The simplest titrimeter for redox titrations is shown in Fig. 14.5. The balancing potentiometer may be a linear-wire-wound radio control, and the sensitivity control a standard radio-volume control. A Federal anticapacity switch is recommended rather than the ordinary toggle type, and the galvanometer should be a pointer type with a sensitivity of about 0.2 μa per mm. In operation, the electrodes are mounted in the beaker containing the solution to be titrated, the sensitivity reduced by the control, the titrimeter turned on, and the galvanometer brought to zero by adjusting the balancing potentiometer. The sensitivity is then increased to a point suitable for the titration, the galvanometer again brought to zero, and the titration begun. The approach of the equivalence point is indicated by a slight drift of the galvanometer, and the equivalence point by a sudden needle deflection of several millimeters. The correct sensitivity setting is determined previously by trial, a good value being one where a galvanometer deflection of 5 to 10 mm at the equivalence point is caused by one drop of titrant. A higher sensitivity frequently

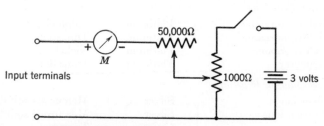

Fig. 14.5   Simple potentiometer circuit

causes annoying drift of the galvanometer needle during the titration.

Either a student-grade or a precision potentiometer may be operated in the same way. However, unless actual potential measurements are desired, they offer no advantage over the simple system described.

Many electronic titrators have been developed, the simplest being that of Garman and Droz [3] for a meter type and that of Serfass [4] for an electron-ray tube type. Commercial instruments are available, and their convenience and improved appearance may well balance the saving made by constructing such apparatus. The chief advantage of the electronic units is that the amplification allows the use of a less sensitive and more rugged meter.

The circuit of Garman and Droz [3] (Fig. 14.6) is available as the Leitz electrotitrator. The single-tube circuit is extremely simple, and the low current drain allows battery operation without frequent battery replacement. The diagram shows the values for the various components. These may be standard radio parts, but a few substitutions increase the dependability and ease of operation of the titrimeter. R_1 should be a Beckman "Helipot," a multirevolution con-

[3] R. L. Garman and M. E. Droz, *Ind. Eng. Chem., Anal. Ed.*, 11, 398 (1939).
[4] E. J. Serfass, *ibid.*, 12, 536 (1940).

trol which allows easier setting. The switch should be a Federal anticapacity switch to prevent jarring the titrimeter as a toggle switch does. The meter may be left off the panel, terminals being provided for external connection to a common-pointer-type galvanometer having a sensitivity of 1 to 5 μa per mm, or a 50-μa meter may be mounted permanently.

The Fisher Titrimeter shown in Fig. 14.7 is based on a circuit similar to that of Smith and Sullivan [5] and Serfass.[4] The elec-

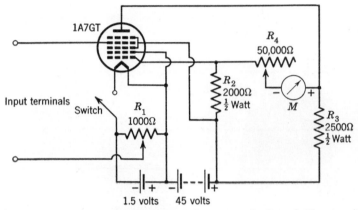

Fig. 14.6   Garman and Droz titrator (Courtesy *Analytical Chemistry*)

tron-ray tube used in this titrimeter is familiar as a tuning indicator for radios. In operation, the opening or closing of the shadow angle on the tube replaces the motion of the meter needle. The electric circuit is simple and the electron-ray tube, unlike a sensitive meter, is not damaged by an extreme electrical unbalance of the titrimeter.

Both the Garman and Droz and the Serfass circuits are suitable for determining the equivalence point by the single-deflection method. If the measurement of potential after increments of titrant have been added is necessary, a pH meter as an electronic potentiometer is recommended. These instruments may be operated as titrators with suitable electrodes, and their millivolt scales allow direct reading without previous calibration.

The Precision-Dow dual recordomatic titrator is an automatic instrument which records potentiometric-titration curves. This instrument consists of four essential components, a dual automatic reagent-feeding unit, an electronic-control system, a recording potentiometer,

[5] G. F. Smith and V. R. Sullivan, *J. Soc. Chem. Ind.*, 56, 104 T (1937).

and a vacuum-tube bridge-type voltmeter. This instrument automatically controls the speed of reagent feeding and automatically plots a complete, permanent record of the titration curve.

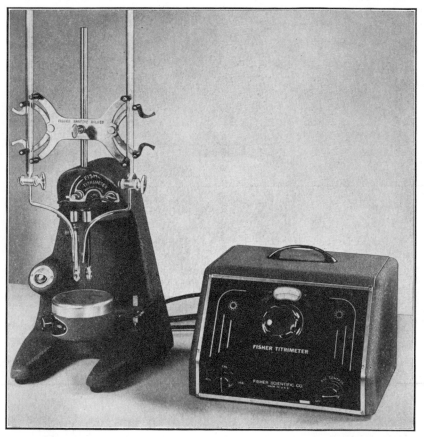

Fig. 14.7 Fisher Titrimeter (Courtesy Fisher Scientific Company)

Another automatic dual titrimeter is the Beckman automatic titrator. This instrument performs all types of potentiometric titrations automatically, stopping the liquid flow at the equivalence point.

Bibliography

Books

W. Hiltner, *Ausführung potentiometrischer Analyse,* Julius Springer, Berlin (1935).

I. M. Kolthoff and N. H. Furman, *Potentiometric Titrations,* 2nd ed., John Wiley, New York (1931).

I. M. Kolthoff and H. A. Laitinen, *pH and Electro Titrations,* 2nd ed., John Wiley, New York (1941).

J. S. Fritz, *Acid-Base Titrations in Nonaqueous Solvents,* G. Frederick Smith Chemical Co., Columbus, Ohio (1952).

Review Articles

N. H. Furman, *Ind. Eng. Chem., Anal. Ed., 2,* 213 (1930).

Ind. Eng. Chem., Anal. Ed., 14, 367 (1942).

N. H. Furman, *Anal. Chem., 22,* 33 (1950).

Other Articles

D. R. Clippinger and C. W. Foulk, Electrometric Indicators with the Dead Stop Endpoint System, *Ind. Eng. Chem., Anal. Ed., 11,* 216 (1939).

L. Lykken, P. Porter, H. D. Ruliffson, and F. D. Tuemmler, Potentiometric Determination of Acidity in Highly Colored Materials, *Ind. Eng. Chem., Anal. Ed., 16,* 219 (1944).

J. A. Riddick, Acid-Base Titrations in Nonaqueous Solvents, *Anal. Chem., 24,* 41 (1952).

Conductance Measurement

In our discussion of potentiometric titrations we showed how the concentration of certain ions in solution determined the potential of our electrodes. For example, in the titration of ferrous ions with ceric ions, the potential at the start of the titration was dependent upon the ratio of ferric to ferrous ions, and, after the equivalence point was passed, upon the ratio of ceric to cerous ions. In contrast to this, the conductivity of a solution is dependent continually upon all the ions present in a solution.

Conductance measurements are valuable for analysis not only for determining the equivalence point of a titration but also for determining the composition of binary mixtures, such as a single salt dissolved in water, or for determining the total electrolyte content as a check on the purity of distilled water. However, the nonspecific nature of conductance measurements has limited their application.

15.1 Electrolytic conductance. Solutions of electrolytes conduct an electric current by the migration of ions under the influence of an electric field. For example, if we place a solution of copper chloride in the conductivity cell shown in Fig. 15.1 and apply a d-c potential, we would find that a given ion would migrate to the electrode of opposite sign. The positive copper ions would migrate to the negative electrode, and the chloride ions would migrate to the positive electrode. Upon reaching the negative electrode the copper ions would take on electrons while at the positive electrode the chloride ions would release electrons. This exchange of electrons would complete the electric circuit and allow the current to flow as long as there was an impressed emf on the solution.

If we measured the impressed emf, the current flowing, and the resistance of the solution, we would find adherence to Ohm's law,

$$E = IR$$

where E = the emf in volts, I = the current in amperes, and R = the resistance in ohms.

The reciprocal of resistance $(1/R)$ is called the conductance C and is measured in mhos (reciprocal ohms). The standard unit of conductance is specific conductance k, which is the conductance in mhos of one cubic centimeter of solution between two electrodes one centimeter square and one centimeter apart.

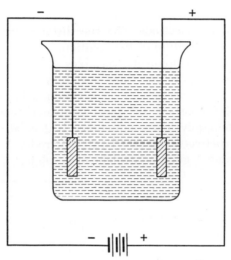

Fig. 15.1 Simple electrolysis cell

To determine the specific conductance it is not necessary to make cells with these exact specifications. By measuring the conductance of a solution of known specific conductance k, we can obtain a cell constant q. For example, a 0.0200 M solution of potassium chloride with a specific conductance k at 25° C of 0.00277 mho is convenient for obtaining the cell constant as follows:

(1) $k = 1/r$ where r is the resistance of 1 cm³ of solution, and

(2) $k - q/R$ where q is the cell constant, and R is the measured resistance.

If we measure R in an unknown cell filled with 0.0200 M potassium chloride solution,

(3) $q = 0.00277\ R$.

Now that q is known, for any unknown solution we can obtain the specific conductance by measuring R and substituting in equation 2.

In other words, the cell constant is simply a constant by which the measured conductance is multiplied to give the specific conductance. The constants for practical cells have numerical values which vary from 0.1 for use with poorly conducting liquids like distilled water to 20 for highly dissociated electrolytes like sodium hydroxide.

If we studied the variables concerned in the passage of current through a solution containing an electrolyte, we would find that the conductance of this solution depended upon (1) the number of ions present, (2) the charge on the ions, (3) the ion mobility, i.e. the ability of each kind of ion to conduct an electric current, (4) the effective area of the electrode, (5) the distance between the electrodes, (6) the temperature of the solution.

In conductance measurements, variables 4 to 6 are normally kept constant, so that only the first three variables are of major concern. In order to compare electrolytes on a common basis and maintain variables 1 and 2 constant, the term equivalent conductance Λ is introduced. The equivalent conductance is defined as the conductance measured between the two large electrodes 1 cm apart of a solution containing 1 gram equivalent of a solute,

$$\Lambda = kV$$

where k = the specific conductance and V = the volume in cubic centimeters containing 1 gram equivalent weight.

Table 15.1 contains the equivalent conductances of some strong electrolytes at 25° C.

TABLE 15.1

Equivalent Conductances of Strong Electrolytes at 25° C, mhos

Elec-trolyte	Concentration, equiv. per liter							
	0	0.0005	0.001	0.005	0.01	0.02	0.05	0.1
KCl *†	149.86	147.81	146.95	143.55	141.27	138.34	133.37	128.96
HCl *‡	426.16	422.74	421.36	415.80	412.00	407.24	399.09	391.32
NaCl †§	126.45	124.50	123.74	120.65	118.51	115.76	111.06	106.74

* T. Shedlovsky, *J. Am. Chem. Soc.*, *54*, 1411 (1932).

† H. E. Gunning and A. R. Gordon, *J. Chem. Phys.*, *10*, 126 (1942).

‡ B. B. Owen and F. H. Sweeton, *J. Am. Chem. Soc.*, *63*, 2811 (1941).

§ T. Shedlovsky, A. S. Brown, and D. A. MacInnes, *Trans. Electrochem. Soc.*, *66*, 165 (1934).

From Table 15.1 it is evident that the equivalent conductance increases as the concentration is decreased. This variation of equivalent conductance with concentration can be explained by the same interionic forces which necessitated the introduction of the concept of activity in Chapter 12. As the solution is progressively diluted, the ions become so far apart that they do not influence one another, and the equivalent conductance approaches a limiting value known as Λ_0, or the equivalent conductance at "infinite dilution." In order to determine Λ_0 values from the data in Table 15.1, the Λ values should be plotted against the square root of the concentration, and the resulting straight line extrapolated to zero concentration.

15.2 Ion mobility. If the equivalent conductances at infinite dilution, Λ_0 values are compared for pairs of salts having a common ion, certain regularities are noticed. For example as shown in Table 15.2 the difference in conductance of sodium and potassium salts of

TABLE 15.2

Equivalent Conductances at Infinite Dilution at 18° C, mhos

Salt	Λ_0	Salt	Λ_0	Difference
KNO_3	126.3	$NaNO_3$	105.2	21.1
KCl	130.0	$NaCl$	108.9	21.1
$\frac{1}{2}K_2SO_4$	133.0	$\frac{1}{2}Na_2SO_4$	111.9	21.1

the same anion is independent of the nature of the anion. F. W. Kohlrausch explained this regularity by assuming that each ion contributes a fixed amount to the total conductance of the electrolyte, irrespective of the other ion with which it is combined in the salt. From this rule of the independent migration of ions, we obtain

$$\Lambda_0 = l_+ + l_-$$

where l_+ = the ion mobility (or ion conductance) of the cation, l_- = the ion mobility (or ion conductance) of the anion.

It is impossible to measure directly the conductivity of a single ionic species, but, since the total conductivity is the sum of the conductance of the individual ions, the measurement of several selected substances allows us to calculate the conductance of the ion species. Table 15.3 gives the ionic mobilities at infinite dilution for the common ions, and from these we may qualitatively predict the change in conductivity which will appear during a titration.

It is apparent that the ion mobility is a function of the charge on the ion. The ion mobility is also a function of the effective size of the ion. The effective size varies with the number of molecules of water associated with each ion; for example, the lithium ion has a

TABLE 15.3

Ion Mobilities at Infinite Dilution at 25° C, mhos *

Cation	l_+	Anion	l_-
H^+	349.8	OH^-	197.6
Li^+	38.69	Cl^-	76.34
Na^+	50.11	Br^-	78.3
K^+	73.52	I^-	76.8
NH_4^+	73.4	NO_3^-	71.44
$\frac{1}{2}Mg^{++}$	53.06	$\frac{1}{2}C_2O_4^=$	24.0
$\frac{1}{2}Ca^{++}$	59.50	$\frac{1}{2}SO_4^=$	80.0
$\frac{1}{3}La^{+++}$	69.5	$\frac{1}{3}Fe(CN)_6^\equiv$	101.0

* For a more complete list, see B. E. Conway, *Electrochemical Data*, p. 145, Elsevier Publishing Co., New York (1952).

lower mobility than the sodium ion because it is associated with more water molecules in solution. In inspecting Table 15.3 it is important to notice that the ion mobilities of the H^+ and OH^- ions are much higher than those of the other ions listed. Conductimetric titrations are based upon the fact that the mobilities of most ions vary considerably from one another, particularly H^+ and OH^- ions. It is for this reason that the conductance changes during the course of a titration so that an equivalence point can be detected.

15.3 Conductimetric titrations. It has been shown that many variables affect the measurement of conductance but that it is experimentally feasible to control these variables so that the ion mobilities will be the governing one. If we titrate hydrochloric acid with sodium hydroxide,

$$HCl + NaOH \rightleftarrows NaCl + H_2O$$

an inspection of the equation and the ion mobilities involved shows that the conductivity of the solution will decrease as we approach the equivalent point. The mobile H^+ ions react with the OH^- ions added to form essentially undissociated water molecules. The net effect is the substitution of Na^+ ($l_+ = 50$) for H^+ ($l_+ = 350$) so that the conductivity decreases. After all the H^+ ions have reacted and the equivalent point has been passed, the addition of excess sodium hydroxide with the highly mobile OH^- ion causes a steep rise in the conductivity. A plot of conductance ($1/R$ values) against the volume of NaOH added would appear as shown in Fig. 15.2. The equivalence point is the volume at which the two arms of the curve intersect, as indicated in Fig. 15.2. The titration curve may

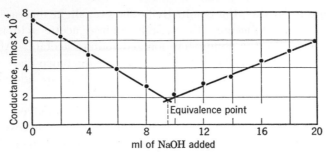

Fig. 15.2   Titration curve of a strong acid with a strong base

assume other shapes, depending upon the particular reaction being studied.   Figure 15.3 shows some of the possible forms for acid-base titrations.

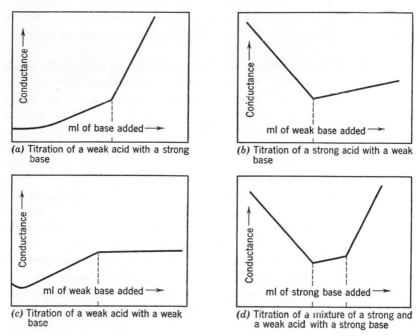

(a) Titration of a weak acid with a strong base

(b) Titration of a strong acid with a weak base

(c) Titration of a weak acid with a weak base

(d) Titration of a mixture of a strong and a weak acid with a strong base

Fig. 15.3   Characteristic conductimetric titration curves for acid-base reactions

The shape of these curves can be explained by considering the ion mobilities involved, the ionization constants of the reactants, and the hydrolysis of the salt formed during the titration.   In curve a, the titration of a weak acid such as acetic acid with a strong base such as sodium hydroxide, the conductivity shows a slight increase to the equivalence point because the weakly ionized acetic acid is gradually replaced by the completely ionized sodium acetate. After the equivalence point has been reached, the conductance rises steeply as the excess Na^+ and the highly mobile OH^- ions are added to the solution.

In curve b the highly mobile hydrogen ion is removed to form water, and, after the equivalence point, the addition of excess weakly ionized base causes a negligible increase in the conductance.

In curve c, the titration of a weak base such as ammonia with acetic acid, the initial conductivity is low and shows a gradual increase as the ionized salt is formed. After the equivalence point has been reached the excess ammonia does not cause much change in conductivity because its ionization is repressed by the presence of the ammonium salt (common ion effect). Occasionally in the titration of weak acids and weak bases, ethanol is added to decrease the ionization of the acid and base to yield a sharper angle at the endpoint.

In curve d, the titration of a mixture of a strong acid and a weak acid with a strong base, the strong acid is neutralized first and the conductivity decreases. After the first equivalence point, the weak acid is neutralized and the conductivity rises slowly until the second equivalence point, where it rises sharply. This method is an important illustration of an analysis that cannot be performed satisfactorily by other electrometric methods and has practical value for the determination of small amounts of mineral acids in vinegar.

Conductimetric titrations are also applicable to replacement reactions and to precipitation and complex-formation reactions. Figure 15.4 shows the titration of 0.1 N sodium acetate with hydrochloric acid and the titration of lithium chloride with silver nitrate.

Conductimetric titrations are best applied to those precipitation reactions that yield reasonably insoluble compounds of constant composition which precipitate rapidly. In order to obtain a sharp angle in the titration curve it is advisable to select an ion with a lower mobility than the ion that it replaces. For example, in the titration of a soluble silver salt such as silver nitrate, the chloride of lithium ($l_+ = 38.69$) would be preferable to sodium ($l_+ = 50.11$) which in turn would be preferable to potassium ($l_+ = 73.52$). Likewise, the larger the mobility of the anion of the reagent which reacts with the cation to be determined, the sharper the angle will be. For example, in the titration of silver nitrate, lithium chloride ($l_- = 76.34$) would be preferable to lithium oxalate ($l_- = 24.0$).   It is common practice in such precipitation reactions to reduce the solubility and to increase the rate of precipitation by the addition of alcohol.

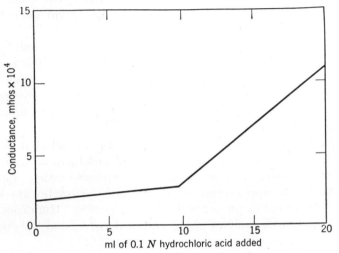

Fig. 15.4*a*   Titration curve for a replacement reaction

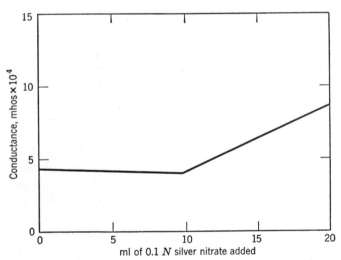

Fig. 15.4*b*   Titration curve for a precipitation reaction (LiCl with AgNO₃)

In carrying out conductimetric titrations it is not necessary to measure the actual conductance, as only relative values are required. Nor is it necessary in analytical work to determine the cell constant and calculate specific conductance values. As a further simplification the volume change during the titration is kept small by using a reagent approximately ten times more concentrated than the substance being titrated. If this is done, the two arms of the curve are linear, and careful measurements near the equivalence point do not need to be taken.

In fact, conductimetric plots of conductance against milliliters of reagent frequently show curvature in the vicinity of the endpoint because of hydrolysis or solubility of the precipitate. One of the main advantages of conductimetric titrations is that such titrations can be performed rapidly on samples of unknown composition without fear of missing the equivalence point.

As a general rule, conductimetric titrations are selected in place of potentiometric titrations in cases where considerable hydrolysis, solubility, or dissociation of the reaction product occurs. But they are restricted to applications where foreign electrolytes are known to be either absent or present in low concentration. High concentrations of foreign electrolytes give a flattened curve, and the endpoint is difficult or impossible to distinguish accurately.

15.4   Apparatus for conductimetric titrations. Erratic conductance measurements were obtained by early investigators because the measurements were made with direct current. These erratic measurements were caused by *polarization* of the electrodes which results with direct current because the ions attracted to an electrode become so concentrated that their collective electric charge almost equals that of the electrodes. When such a condition exists, it becomes exceedingly difficult for an ion to reach the electrode because of the mutual repulsion of ions of like charge. Inasmuch as the charge of the ionic field surrounding the electrode nearly equals the electrode charge, the resulting potential is very low, and additional ions of opposite charge are not attracted from the solution. Kohlrausch showed that polarization effects could best be eliminated by employing a rapidly alternating current of low intensity. In general this system has been followed. However, the difficulty of electrode polarization in d-c measurements has been overcome by Andrews and Martin [1] by using calomel electrodes and a low current density. Taylor and Furman [2] have obtained reproducible conductance curves with direct current by passing a constant direct current across a

[1] L. V. Andrews and W. E. Martin, *J. Am. Chem. Soc.*, 60, 871 (1938).
[2] R. P. Taylor and N. H. Furman, *Anal. Chem.*, 24, 1931 (1952).

solution through a pair of platinum primary electrodes, and measuring the voltage drop across a pair of tungsten secondary electrodes. The voltage drop is inversely proportional to the conductance of the solution. Although this method is of theoretical interest, it offers no obvious advantages over the classical system of Kohlrausch which is illustrated in Fig. 15.5.

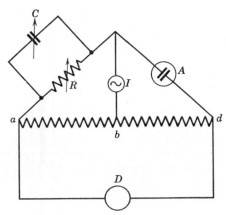

Fig. 15.5   Experimental measurement of conductance

In making conductance measurements, the resistance of the solution of the electrolyte in the conductivity cell A forms one arm of the familiar Wheatstone bridge. I is the source of alternating current (approximately 1000 cps), ad is a calibrated slide wire of uniform resistance, and D is the current detector. The variable resistance R and the two arms ab and bd of the Wheatstone bridge are adjusted (the latter by varying the position of the contact b) until no current can be detected by D. Then, the resistances are related by the simple proportion,

$$A/R = bd/ab$$

Since the resistance R is known and the ratio of ab to bd can be measured, the resistance of the cell A is readily calculated. In practice the resistance of R should be such that the bridge is balanced about at the midpoint of the slide wire ad, so that the error in the setting of R will cause the least error in the final result. For electrolytes of low conductance, it is advisable to compensate for the capacity of

A with the variable condenser *C* in order to obtain a sharp balance point.

The most satisfactory source of alternating current is a vacuum-tube oscillator. Induction coils are not nearly so satisfactory because they do not give a symmetrical sine wave, and some electrode polarization may occur.

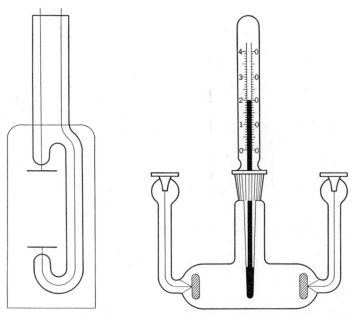

Fig. 15.6   Two types of conductivity cells

Earphones, a loudspeaker with an amplifier, or an a-c galvanometer are commonly employed to measure the balance of the Wheatstone-bridge circuit. If available, an oscilloscope is preferable to these three detectors because it allows separate compensation for capacitance effects.

The conductivity cells are of varying types (Fig. 15.6). The electrodes should be coated with platinum black by electrolyzing them in 3% chloroplatinic acid containing a trace of lead acetate until a thin coating has been deposited. Since insoluble coatings on the electrode will affect the sensitivity of conductivity measurements, the electrodes should be stored in distilled water. The sensitivity of a coated electrode can frequently be restored by immersion in 10% nitric or hydrochloric acid solution for 2 minutes followed by a rinse

with distilled water. If no improvement is noted after such a procedure, the electrodes should be briefly dipped in aqua regia to remove
the original plating and then replated.

A typical laboratory setup for a conductimetric titration with commercially available components is shown in Fig. 15.7. The compo-

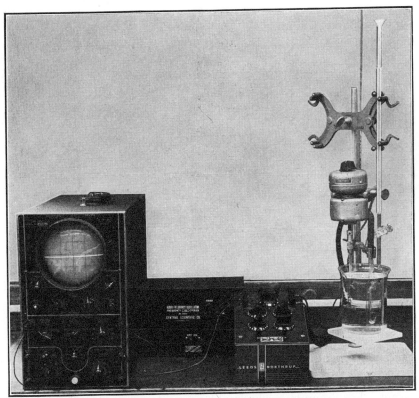

Fig. 15.7   Apparatus for conductimetric titrations

nents are a Central Scientific audio-frequency oscillator, a Leeds and
Northrup resistance bridge and a DuMont cathode-ray oscilloscope.

It is necessary to compensate for temperature changes because the
mobility of most ions increases approximately 2% for a 1° C increase
in temperature. For this reason precise conductance measurements
require that the temperature be maintained to 0.01° C. However,
in the usual conductimetric titration, adequate results can be obtained without placing the conductivity cell in a thermostat, provided

reasonable care is taken to insure that there is no abrupt temperature change during the titration.

15.5 Applications. In the discussion in the previous section we have indicated the application of conductimetric titrations to acid-base, complex-formation, and precipitation-type reactions. An excellent list of many specific examples of the above types can be found in the text of Kolthoff and Laitinen.[3]

It should be mentioned that an important industrial application involves the continuous recording of conductance values for solutions

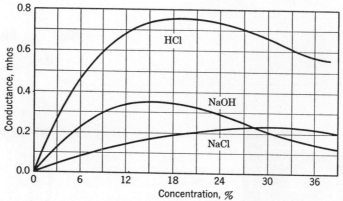

Fig. 15.8   Three typical curves of specific conductance versus concentration (Courtesy Minneapolis-Honeywell Company)

of electrolytes in order to check the concentration of the electrolyte in solution. Figure 15.8 shows curves of specific conductance for three strong electrolytes plotted against concentration. From these curves it is obvious that only in certain ranges can the specific conductance values be used to determine the concentration of electrolyte present. For example, for hydrochloric acid, measurements made in the concentration range of 0 to 15% are suitable for process control, but, at 18% where the curve reaches a maximum, the measurements are of little values because decreasing conductivity values might indicate either decreasing or increasing concentration.

In concluding this chapter on conductivity it should be pointed out that the method is limited because all ions contribute to the conductance, and often in analytical work we must deal with solutions of relatively unknown compositions. However, the importance

[3] I. M. Kolthoff and H. A. Laitinen, *pH and Electro Titrations*, 2nd ed., pp. 134–35, John Wiley, New York (1941).

of conductance measurements in systems involving considerable hydrolysis or dissociation of the reaction product or for checking the purity of distilled water should not be underestimated.

Bibliography

H. T. S. Britton, *Conductometric Analysis*, D. Van Nostrand, New York (1934).

CHAPTER 16

Polarography

We have shown the analytical value of electrode-potential measurements, where it was specifically required that no current flow during the measurement. In conductance analysis, there was a flow of current, but the measurements were not specific for a particular ion. In polarography, the measurement of current flow can be a specific property, as we measure the current due to ion diffusion and subsequent electrolysis. This unique type of analysis was initiated by Heyrovsky at Charles University at Prague in 1922. It has since become widely accepted as both a qualitative and quantitative method.

16.1 Current-voltage curves. With the simple apparatus shown in Fig. 16.1, the voltage applied to the electrodes may be gradually increased by means of the potentiometer, and the current flow measured with a galvanometer. If the solution contains a single reducible ion species, such as Cd^{++} and the cathode is very small, a curve similar to that shown in Fig. 16.2 will be obtained.

As the applied voltage is increased, the current will rise gradually until the decomposition potential is reached. This decomposition potential for the reaction $(Cd^{++} + 2e \rightarrow Cd)$ is a function of $E°$ for the reaction and the Cd^{++} concentration. The current will show a sharp increase and then level off. The current increase (diffusion current) is caused by diffusion of the Cd^{++} ions to the electrode where they are plated out, and the leveling-off limiting current appears when complete concentration polarization occurs.

If two reducible ions such as cadmium and zinc are present, and their decomposition potentials are sufficiently separated, a curve similar to Fig. 16.3 will be obtained. The diffusion current for the second ion is the difference between the first and the total diffusion currents. Under ideal conditions as many as six elements may be determined from the current-voltage curve.

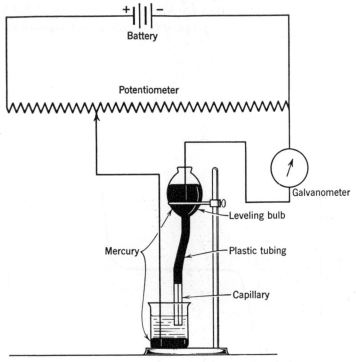

Fig. 16.1 Simple circuit for polarographic analysis

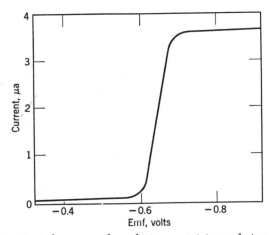

Fig. 16.2 Polarogram of a solution containing cadmium ions

Such current-voltage curves are known as polarograms, and instruments used to obtain such curves are known as polarographs.

16.2   The diffusion current.   The diffusion current in the curve of Fig. 16.2 may be explained on the basis of electrolysis and the consequent concentration polarization.   Until the decomposition potential of the reducible ion is reached, its concentration is uniform throughout the solution.   However, at the decomposition potential, the

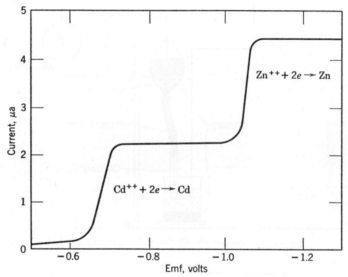

Fig. 16.3   Polarogram of a solution containing cadmium and zinc ions

ions will begin to plate out on the drop, lowering the concentration at the solution–mercury interface.   The concentration gradient established will cause ions to diffuse from the body of the solution into the interface at a rate proportional to the concentration difference, and the current will increase sharply.   As the voltage is increased, a point will be reached at which the effective concentration at the interface is reduced to zero, and the diffusion rate becomes constant and proportional to the ion concentration in the body of the solution.

Any further increase in applied voltage will not change the diffusion rate or the value of the diffusion or limiting current until the decomposition potential of a second reducible substance is reached, where the same process is repeated.

The illustrations of Fig. 16.4 may serve to clarify the process.   In contrast to electrolysis in which deposition of an element occurs, polarographic electrolysis leaves the concentration of the element being determined essentially unchanged because the electrolysis is conducted for a short time with a minute indicator electrode.   This

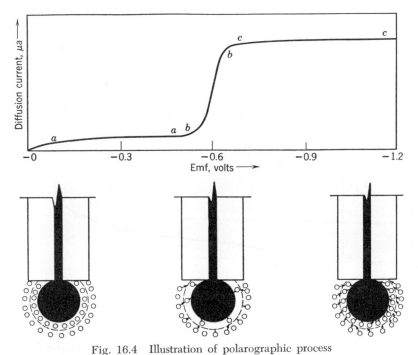

Fig. 16.4   Illustration of polarographic process

(a)   (b)   (c)

(a) Decomposition potential of Cd++ not reached.   Small increase in current caused by residual current

(b) Decomposition potential reached.   Cd++ ions plate into drop lowering the concentration at the solution–mercury interface.   The concentration gradient established causes Cd++ ions to diffuse from the body of the solution into the interface at a rate proportional to the concentration difference and the current increases sharply.

(c) Current levels off as the number of Cd++ ions plating into drop equals the maximum number of Cd++ ions furnished by diffusion from the body of the solution

is a unique advantage of the polarographic method because, if necessary, numerous rechecks can be made, and the solution is available virtually unchanged for further measurements.

16.3   The migration and residual currents.   The preceding section has assumed that the measured current has been only that carried by the diffusing ions.   This is not the case, and allowance must be made for other currents flowing simultaneously with the diffusion current. Reducible ions are supplied to the electrode surface by electric forces, which attract positive ions to the negative mercury drop, as well as by diffusive forces. Thus, if the solution being measured contained only cadmium ions, the limiting current obtained would be a sum of both a *migration current,* i.e. the migration of cadmium ions under the influence of the electric-potential difference between the mercury surface and the solution, and the diffusion current. In the discussion on conductance in the previous chapter, it

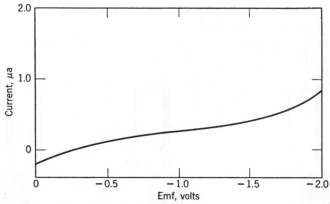

Fig. 16.5   Typical residual-current curve

was pointed out that the current through a solution is carried by all the ions present. This is true, whether or not the ions take part in any reactions at the electrodes. The fraction of the total current carried by a particular ion species is dependent upon its concentration relative to that of the other ions present as well as upon its electric charge and its mobility. If we therefore add to the solution of cadmium ions a large excess of an *inert electrolyte,* such as potassium chloride, which is not reduced or oxidized in the potential region under consideration, the migration current will be carried almost entirely by the inert electrolyte. The limiting current obtained with the dropping mercury electrode will then be solely the diffusion current for the cadmium ions.

In addition to the migration current, another current, the *residual current* must be considered. If we were to obtain a polarogram for a solution containing only an inert electrolyte and no ions reducible in the potential range covered, we would obtain a curve similar to that shown in Fig. 16.5.

It will be noted that, as the voltage is increased, there is a small but definite increase in the current. With the dropping mercury electrode each new drop acquires a charge sufficient to raise it to the applied potential, and consequently a continuous current flows. This current is called the *residual current,* and is compensated for by measuring standard and unknown samples under the same condi-

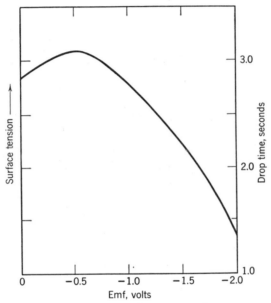

Fig. 16.6   Electrocapillary curve of mercury

tions or is corrected for by determining it in the manner described and subtracting it from the over-all diffusion current.

16.4   The electrocapillary curve of mercury. The variation of the surface tension of mercury with the applied potential is shown in Fig. 16.6. This curve is known as the *electrocapillary curve* of mercury. The point at which the surface tension is at a maximum is known as the *electrocapillary maximum.* This curve is important in polarographic work because the drop time is closely related to the surface tension of mercury (see Fig. 16.6). The surface tension is dependent upon the presence of capillary-active substances as well as upon the applied potential so that the electrocapillary maximum may be shifted to more positive or negative values by such capillary-active substances.

The shape of the electrocapillary curve is explained on a similar basis as the residual current. As each drop of mercury is formed, it acquires a small charge. As has been pointed out, this charging or residual current depends upon the applied potential. However, at −0.52 volt versus the saturated calomel electrode (the *isoelectric point of mercury*) the mercury is uncharged and the surface tension is at a maximum. On either side of the electrocapillary maximum the surface tension of mercury is decreased because of electrostatic repulsion between the charges at the mercury surface.

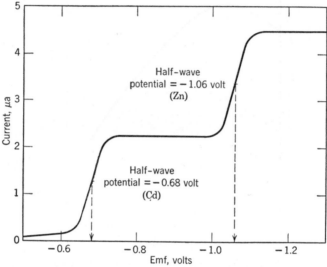

Fig. 16.7 Polarogram with half-wave potentials of cadmium and zinc indicated

16.5 Half-wave potentials. In Fig. 16.7 the half-wave potentials of cadmium and zinc ions are designated. The half-wave potential is the polarographic reduction or oxidation potential at the midpoint of a polarographic wave where the current is equal to one-half its limiting value. Half-wave potentials are used rather than decomposition potentials because the latter vary with concentration. Half-wave potentials are usually independent of the concentration and have exact thermodynamic significance. They are related to standard electrode potentials ($E°$ values) and are reported with reference to the saturated or normal calomel electrode, which in turn are referred to the standard hydrogen electrode.

Half-wave potentials, like standard electrode potentials, are a function of the molecular form of the reducible or oxidizable material.

Half-wave potentials can therefore be shifted by the addition of complexing agents or by varying the pH of the solution. In cases where it is necessary to determine two substances simultaneously and their half-wave potentials overlap, it is sometimes possible to separate the waves by adding complexing agents or by varying the pH of the solution. For example, in acid solution, tin and antimony have half-wave potentials of -0.47 and -0.20 volt, respectively, but in alkaline solution the half-wave potential for tin is -1.1 volts and for antimony -1.8 volts. In determining these elements simultaneously an alkaline medium would therefore be selected.

In general, substances will not interfere with one another if the half-wave potentials are separated by 0.3 volt or more. This is true when the two are present in approximately equimolar quantities. When the concentration of one is ten or more times the other, a greater separation in the half-wave potentials is required.

A list of half-wave potentials for the common elements is given in Appendix E. More complete lists, which include organic compounds are available from E. H. Sargent Company, Chicago, Ill.

16.6 The Ilkovic equation. Ilkovic first derived the following theoretical equation for the diffusion current obtained with the dropping mercury electrode,

$$i_d = 607nD^{1/2}m^{2/3}t^{1/6}c$$

where i_d = the average current during the life of the drop in microamperes, n = the number of Faradays of electricity required per mole of the electrode reaction, D = the diffusion coefficient of the reducible or oxidizable substance in square centimeters per second, m = the rate of mercury flow from the dropping electrode capillary in milligrams per second, t = the time required for each drop of mercury to form in seconds, and c = the concentration of the electroactive substance in millimoles per milliliter.

In the usual polarographic analysis, all the above factors are kept constant except c so that the equation simplifies to the form

$$i_d = Kc$$

where the constant K includes all of the factors in the previous equation.

The linear relation between the diffusion current and the concentration is shown by Fig. 16.8 which is plotted from the data of Meites and Meites.[1] In their data, id/c is constant to within $\pm 0.17\%$ over

---

[1] L. Meites and T. Meites, *J. Am. Chem. Soc.*, 72, 3686 (1950).

a concentration range of cadmium of 630-fold. However, this is an ideal example, for it is more often found in actual practice that the relationship is not exactly linear. In such cases empirical curves are prepared to obtain the concentration from the diffusion current.

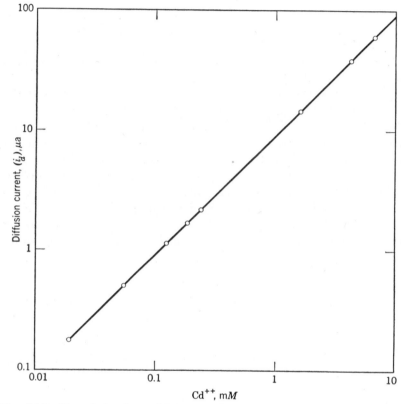

Fig. 16.8 Plot of the data of Meites and Meites (reference 1) showing the linear relation between diffusion current and concentration

It is important to know the variables concerned in the Ilkovic equation so that care can be taken to maintain these variables not only constant but within the optimum limits. Although temperature is not given in equation 1 as a variable, D, m, and t vary with the temperature. To obtain results reproducible to $\pm 1\%$, it is necessary to maintain the temperature within $\pm 0.5°$ C.

The optimum drop time is from 2 to 5 seconds. It is important to remember that the drop time is a function of the applied voltage (see Fig. 16.6) when determining the drop time. The height of the mercury column should be between 30 and 60 cm. In selecting a capillary it should be emphasized that the drop time varies directly with the length of the capillary but inversely with the radius to the third power. Hence, the radius of the capillary is more important than the length in determining the drop time. As a general guide, with a height of mercury 30 to 60 cm, drop times from 2 to 5 seconds can be obtained with capillaries 5 to 10 cm long with an internal diameter between 0.04 and 0.09 mm.

16.7 Electrodes. In general, the indicator or polarizable electrode in the polarographic method is either a dropping mercury electrode for reduction reactions or a platinum electrode, which may be either stationary or rotating, for oxidation reactions. Polarographic waves that involve reductions are termed *cathodic waves* and those that involve oxidation are termed *anodic waves*. By convention, diffusion currents for reduction reactions are given a positive sign and for oxidation reactions a negative sign.

The dropping mercury electrode is the best electrode for reduction reactions because the overvoltage * of hydrogen on mercury is exceptionally high, and hence many metals may be reduced before the reaction $H^+ + e \rightarrow \frac{1}{2}H_2$ occurs. Determinations, therefore, can be successfully carried out in acid medium. The dropping mercury electrode has many other advantages. It yields a smooth, reproducible surface, which is continually renewed. Since mercury amalgamates with many metals, the potential at which these metals plate into the drop is lower than with a noble-metal electrode. And finally diffusion currents obtained with the dropping mercury electrode are very steady and reproducible. The main disadvantage of the dropping mercury electrode is that at relatively small positive potentials (approximately $+0.2$ volt versus the saturated calomel electrode) anodic dissolution of the mercury occurs,

$$Hg \rightarrow Hg^+ + e$$

For this reason, for anodic waves a platinum or other noble-metal electrode is selected. The limitation of such electrodes in the direction of positive potential is the evolution of oxygen gas which occurs at $+1.0$ volt versus the saturated calomel electrode. Analytical re-

---

* In the electrolysis of aqueous solutions, the potential where hydrogen gas is liberated is considerably more negative than 0.00 volt, the standard $E°$ value for the hydrogen gas–hydrogen ion half-cell. The difference between the potential at which hydrogen is actually evolved and the standard $E°$ value is the overvoltage of hydrogen.

sults obtained with stationary electrodes are not nearly so reproducible as for the dropping mercury electrode, the precision being
only $\pm 5\%$ in favorable cases.   In addition it is necessary to wait for
at least 2 minutes at each value of the applied voltage until a steady
diffusion current is obtained.   This disadvantage can be eliminated
by rotating the electrode.   Since the overvoltage of hydrogen on
platinum is small, the evolution of hydrogen interferes with many
reductions.

A pool of mercury is often the nonpolarizable reference electrode
in the cell illustrated in Fig. 16.9.   This cell has inlet tubes for bub-

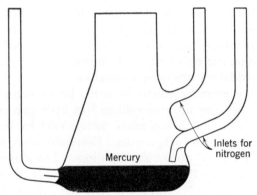

Fig. 16.9   Erlenmeyer-style polarographic cell according to Heyrovsky

bling nitrogen through the solution before the polarogram is obtained
and then over the solution while the polarogram is being obtained.
Nitrogen is bubbled through the solution to remove dissolved oxygen,
which must be removed because oxygen produces a double cathodic
wave, the first wave being caused by the formation of H_2O_2 and the
second wave by the formation of H_2O from the H_2O_2.   For ordinary
work commercial tank nitrogen is adequate for removing dissolved
oxygen.

In place of a pool of mercury, a better reference electrode is the
saturated calomel cell.   This is conveniently made one side of the
H-type cell designed by Lingane and illustrated in Fig. 16.10.   This
particular cell has two distinct advantages over the cell previously
shown.   First, it furnishes a constant-reference emf, so that half-
wave potentials can be accurately measured.   Second, it is more
economical in the quantity of mercury used per sample.   In view of
the known hazard of mercury as a cumulative poison, any device

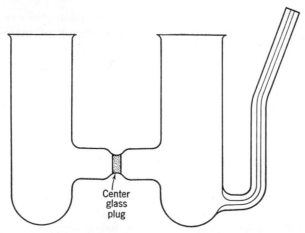

Fig. 16.10 H-type polarographic cell according to Lingane and Laitinen

such as this H-type cell, which reduces mercury handling and spillage to a minimum, is most desirable. A micro H-type cell for the polarographic analysis of small amounts of solution has been described by Meites and Meites.[2]

16.8 Current maxima and suppression. Frequently during the course of obtaining a polarogram the curve obtained is not like the one shown in Fig. 16.2 but resembles that shown in Fig. 16.11.

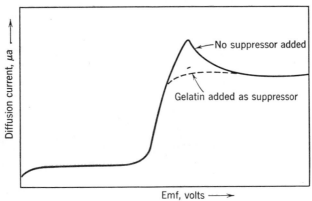

Fig. 16.11 Polarogram showing a maximum and its suppression

Such an abnormal hump on the wave is known as a *maximum*. For such a maximum to occur, an extra supply of reducible or oxidizable

[2] T. Meites and L. Meites, *Anal. Chem.*, 23, 1893 (1951).

ion over that furnished by the normal diffusion process must be reaching the electrode surface. The occurrence of maximum has been attributed to the stirring effect of the mercury drop.[3] Maxima vary in their shape and height and apparently depend upon the charge and concentration of the inert electrolyte present, the concentration of the electroactive material and the characteristics of the capillary. It is frequently noted that, in obtaining a polarogram of several elements, only one of the elements will yield a curve with a maximum, and occasionally we have found that changing the capillary will eliminate the maximum. The simplest way to eliminate maxima is to add gelatin to make approximately a 0.01% solution. Such a substance which suppresses maxima is often termed a *maximum suppressor*. Indicators such as methyl red or bromthymol blue also act as maximum suppressors. In using suppressors, the same amounts should be added to both the standard and unknown samples, and the amount should be kept low, as otherwise the over-all wave height will be reduced with a consequent loss in sensitivity.

It has been reported recently to us from one laboratory that maximum free curves are obtained with mercury from polyethylene bottles in contrast to those from ceramic bottles. No published data have appeared, however, to substantiate this statement.

16.9 Apparatus. The equipment available for polarographic analysis can be classified into two types, manual and recording. With the manual polarograph, it is necessary to take point-by-point current readings at each given applied voltage in order to obtain a complete polarogram. In instructional work such a procedure may have some merit. In routine work, however, it is only necessary to make two readings per wave to obtain the diffusion current. For example, as shown in Fig. 16.12 it is only necessary to measure the diffusion current at A, B, C, and D to obtain the wave heights for the copper and zinc. This is known as the *increment method* and has been successfully applied to routine analysis.

A simple circuit for a manual polarograph was shown in Fig. 16.1. A Leeds and Northrup student-type potentiometer or the Fisher potentiometer is adequate for this circuit. As a null-point indicator a Leeds and Northrup or Rubicon galvanometer (see Fig. 3.11) is quite convenient. A galvanometer should be selected that has a period three to four times the drop time because the diffusion current oscillates as the mercury drop grows and falls. If necessary, the galvanometer can be overdamped by putting a suitable resistance,

---

[3] N. J. Antweiler, Z. *Elektrochem.*, *43*, 596 (1937); *44*, 719, 888 (1938).

which is smaller than the critical resistance, across the terminals of the galvanometer.

Copeland and Griffith [4] have described an easily constructed manual polarograph which has a circuit similar to one previously given by Kolthoff and Lingane.[5]

The first commercially available manual polarograph was the Fisher Elecdropode, shown in Fig. 16.13. Other units are the model-III manual polarograph manufactured by E. H. Sargent, and the

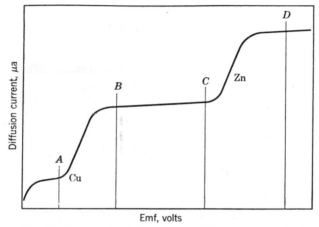

Fig. 16.12   Graphical illustration of increment method

model-R1 Patwin electropolarizer available from the General Scientific Equipment Company. All three units have the galvanometer built in the instrument and are equipped with galvanometer shunt switches so that the proper galvanometer sensitivity can be obtained. These instruments are also well suited for amperometric titrations, which will be discussed in the next chapter.

Two types of recording polarographs are available from E. H. Sargent. The Sargent model-XXI polarograph provides a continuous, visible record of the current-voltage curve on a recording potentiometer. The applied emf is varied at a constant rate by a rotating bridge and contactor. The current passing through the polarographic cell is measured as the IR drop across a known resistance in series with the cell, and is plotted by the recording potentiometer. The

[4] L. C. Copeland and F. S. Griffith, *Anal. Chem.*, 22, 1269 (1950).

[5] I. M. Kolthoff and J. J. Lingane, *Polarography*, Vols. I and II, Interscience, New York (1952).

Sargent-Heyrovsky polarograph model XII is an electrically driven instrument, utilizing a galvanometer for current measurement and recording the polarogram photographically. A motor-driven voltage

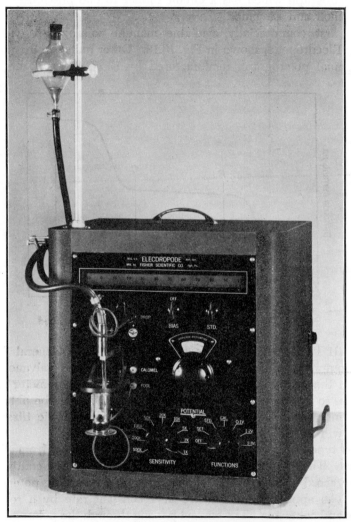

Fig. 16.13 Fisher Elecdropode (Courtesy Fisher Scientific Company)

divider applies a unidirectional voltage change, through either anodic or cathodic ranges, to the dropping mercury electrode. Voltage ranges up to approximately 4.5 volts may be selected by a continuously variable potentiometer and are measured by an integral voltmeter. The current passing through the cell is measured by a sensitive galvanometer. A line image of the light reflected from the galvanometer mirror is passed through a mirror system to provide the customary projection distance and is then divided, one half being directed to a scale for visual observation and the other half passing through the camera slit to record the polarogram.

The polarogram is recorded on a 150×250-mm sheet of photographic paper held on a cylindrical camera drum, driven by an extention of the voltage-divider drive shaft. Since the voltage divider and camera are driven by the same shaft, the voltage axis of the polarogram is linear and independent of any variations in motor speed.

The Leeds and Northrup Company manufactures the Electrochemograph type-E automatic recording polarograph. A null-balance current-measuring system is applied to the dropping mercury electrode. The polarographic current I produces a voltage drop across the detector. This voltage is amplified and impressed upon one winding of the two-phase balancing motor, which advances the slide wire until the potentiometer current equals I. The system remains at balance until a further change in I occurs, and the unbalance voltage produces a compensating motion of the motor to reposition the slide-wire arm and restore balance.

An excellent "polarographic scanner" has been described by Müller.[6] This unit may be assembled from standard mechanical components available from Servomechanisms Inc.[†] A reversible synchronous motor is coupled to a 50-ohm Helipot potentiometer which acts as the polarographic bridge. The applied voltage is indicated directly by a revolution counter coupled to the Helipot. A standard 0- to 2.5-mv Brown recording potentiometer records the current in terms of the IR drop across a standard resistance in series with the cell.

Another polarograph which yields visible recorded polarograms has been described by Lykken, Pompeo and Weaver.[7]

An ingenious oscillographic polarograph has been developed by Snowden and Page.[8] This type of instrument is particularly valuable for studying reaction rates involving substances that can be oxidized

[6] R. H. Müller, *Anal. Chem.*, 22, 76 (1950).

[†] Address, Old Country and Glen Cove Road, Mineola, N. Y.

[7] L. Lykken, D. J. Pompeo, and J. R. Weaver, *Ind. Eng. Chem., Anal. Ed.*, 17, 724 (1945).

[8] F. C. Snowden and H. T. Page, *Anal. Chem.*, 22, 969 (1950).

or reduced at the dropping mercury electrode, as the complete polarogram is continuously visible as a trace on the oscilloscope screen.

16.10 Applications. The tremendous growth of the polarographic literature reflects an increasing interest not only in the theoretical aspects of polarography but also in the practical value of the method in chemical analysis. The early analytical applications were mostly in the inorganic field, but at the present time the growth in the organic field is even more spectacular.

The lower limit of determination for the common ions is about $10^{-5}\ M$ when interfering ions are absent.

Excellent examples of the determination of the different elements are given by Heyrovsky.[9] An outstanding performance of the polarograph in the analytical field is in the analysis of zinc-base [10] or magnesium-base [11] alloys. The highly negative half-wave potentials of these matrix elements allow the determination of copper, cadmium, tin, lead, and other more positive elements.

Occasionally it is easier to determine an element indirectly, a good example being aluminum. Aluminum yields a fairly well-defined wave at -1.7 volts, but it is necessary to adjust the pH of the solution very carefully to prevent the succeeding discharge of hydrogen from overlapping the diffusion current of aluminum. For this reason the determination of aluminum is more accurately and readily carried out by the reduction of an aluminum di-*o*-hydroxyazo complex.[12] This latter method can be viewed as an inorganic-organic application.

In the strictly organic field most of the work has been done in mixtures of water and organic solvents. The nonaqueous solvents most often used are methanol, ethanol, glycerine, acetic acid, formamide, and benzene. In nonaqueous media the waves are lower and in some cases more drawn out than those obtained for the same concentration of oxidizable or reducible substance in water. For a supporting or inert electrolyte the tetraalkyl ammonium salts are the most valuable because they make possible the investigation of compounds reduced at potentials more negative than those of the alkali metals. However, sodium, potassium, and ammonium chlorides are also employed as inert electrolytes.

[9] J. Heyrovsky, *Physical Methods in Chemical Analysis* (W. G. Berl, editor), Vol. II, pp. 23–42, Academic Press, New York (1951).

[10] R. C. Hawkings and H. G. Thode, *Ind. Eng. Chem., Anal. Ed.*, 16, 71 (1944).

[11] H. C. Gull, *J. Soc. Chem. Ind. London*, 56, 177 (1937).

[12] H. H. Willard and J. A. Dean, *Anal. Chem.*, 22, 1264 (1950).

As a brief indication of what can be done in the organic field certain members of the following classes of compounds have been successfully analyzed: aldehydes, ketones, organic halides, nitro compounds, nitroso compounds, disulfides, heterocyclics, and unsaturated hydrocarbons. For example, aromatic and cyclic ketones are not reduced in ammonium chloride solution; however the aliphatic ketones, acetone and methyl ethyl ketone are reduced and can be determined polarographically in tetramethyl ammonium iodide solution with an accuracy of 5%. Aldehydes such as formaldehyde and acetaldehyde do not interfere. Phenones such as benzophenone and acetophenone give two waves. With benzophenone the first wave represents the formation of benzopinacol, while the second wave represents the formation of benzhydrol. Both aliphatic and aromatic ketones conjugated with a double bond or another ketone group are reducible; thus benzil is reduced to benzoin.

Other applications in the organic field include studies on differences in the ease of reduction of *cis-trans* isomers, the effect of hydrogen bonding or resonance on half-wave potentials, and reaction rate studies. For readers interested in the organic field, the articles of Wawzonek,[13] Elving and Tang,[14] and English [15] are especially recommended.

Bibliography

Books

J. Heyrovsky, *Polarographie,* Springer-Verlag, Wein (1941).

Leeds and Northrup Co., *Bibliography of the Dropping Mercury Electrode,* Philadelphia (1950).

O. H. Müller, *The Polarographic Method of Analysis,* 2nd ed., Chemical Education Publishing Co., Easton, Pa. (1951).

E. H. Sargent and Co., *Bibliography of Polarographic Literature,* Chicago (1946).

Review Articles

J. J. Lingane, Interpretation of the Polarographic Waves of Complex Metal Ions, *Chem. Rev.,* 29, 1 (1941).

J. J. Lingane, Polarographic Theory, Instrumentation and Methodology, *Anal. Chem.,* 21, 45 (1949); 23, 86 (1951).

[13] S. Wawzonek, *ibid., 21,* 61 (1949); *22,* 30 (1950); *24,* 32 (1952).

[14] P. J. Elving and C. S. Tang, *ibid., 23,* 341 (1951).

[15] F. L. English, *ibid., 23,* 344 (1951).

CHAPTER 17

Amperometric Titrations

The basic principles of the polarographic method apply to ampero-metric titrations. The main difference is that the voltage is not varied but is kept fixed during the course of the titration. The diffusion current measured at the polarizable electrode is plotted against the volume of the titrating solution added. The endpoint of the titration is taken as the intersection of the two straight lines whose slopes are determined by the change in the diffusion current before and after the equivalence point, respectively.

Amperometric titrations are not limited to substances yielding diffusion currents, for often a substance that cannot be determined polarographically can be determined by reaction with a reagent yielding a diffusion current. Usually amperometric titrations involve the determination of a single constituent rather than several con-stituents as is often done in polarography.

17.1 Principle of the method. It has been stated that in the course of an amperometric titration the voltage is kept constant. The reason becomes more obvious if we consider the actual case of the titration of sulfate ion with lead ion. From the tables of half-wave potentials in Appendix E we find that in acid solution the reaction $Pb^{++} + 2e \rightarrow Pb$ occurs at the dropping mercury electrode at -0.46 volt. A polarogram of a solution containing lead ions and an inert electrolyte such as potassium nitrate would appear as in Fig. 17.1. The height of the wave is governed by the concentration of the lead ions. From this polarogram it is apparent that at a potential more negative than -0.46 volt, referred to the normal calomel electrode, the reduction of lead ion will occur. In the case of sulfate ion at these potentials no electrode reaction occurs, and so, if we have a beaker containing sulfate solution and a dropping mer-cury electrode at a potential more negative than -0.46 volt, there will be no diffusion current. As lead ions are added, lead sulfate will precipitate, and no diffusion current will be obtained until the endpoint is reached.   As soon as there is an excess of lead ions, a diffusion current will result from the reaction $Pb^{++} + 2e \rightarrow Pb$.   As

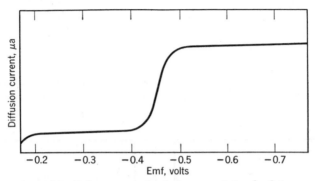

Fig. 17.1   Polarogram of solution containing lead ions

more lead ions are added, the diffusion current will increase.   A plot of the diffusion current versus milliliters of the lead solution added will appear as in Fig. 17.2.

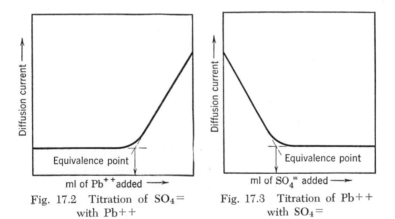

Fig. 17.2   Titration of $SO_4^=$ Fig. 17.3   Titration of Pb^{++}
with Pb^{++} with $SO_4^=$

As indicated in Fig. 17.2, the endpoint is obtained by drawing two straight lines through the series of points obtained and dropping a perpendicular to the abscissa.   For precise results the diffusion current should be corrected for the change in volume from each addition of reagent by the following formula:

$$i_d = i(V + v)/V$$

where i_d = the true diffusion current, i = the measured current, V = the original volume in milliliters, and v = the milliliters of reagent added.

In this type of titration, however, as in conductimetric titrations, the correction for volume change can be neglected if the reagent being added is approximately ten times more concentrated than the material being titrated. For the sake of simplicity, this latter procedure is normally followed.

17.2 Typical titration curves. From the previous discussion it should be realized that the titration curves obtained may have shapes other than that shown in Fig. 17.2. For example, in the lead sulfate

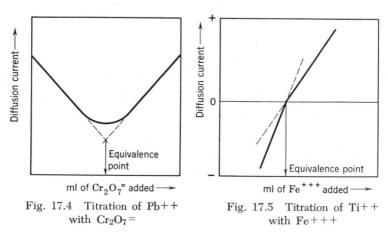

Fig. 17.4   Titration of Pb++ with Cr_2O_7 =

Fig. 17.5   Titration of Ti++ with Fe+++

precipitation, if we reverse the procedure from that previously described and add sulfate ions to a lead solution, the titration curve will appear as in Fig. 17.3.

At the start of the titration the diffusion current will be large because of the high concentration of lead ions, but, as sulfate ions are added, the lead ions are removed from solution as lead sulfate and the diffusion current decreases. At the equivalence point all the lead ions are effectively removed from solution, and the diffusion current remains constant as additional sulfate is added.

If we were to titrate a solution of lead acetate or nitrate with sodium or potassium dichromate at a potential of -1.2 volts we would obtain a curve similar to that shown in Fig. 17.4.

In this case both the lead and chromium ions are reduced at the potential applied, and both ions yield diffusion currents proportional to their respective concentrations. Once all the lead ions are removed from solution, the excess chromium ions present yield an increase in diffusion current.

The final type of curve shown in Fig. 17.5 is obtained in the amperometric titration of titanous ions in tartrate solution with ferric ions at a potential of -0.3 volt. At the start of the titration, the diffusion current is negative because of the reaction $Ti^{++++} \rightarrow Ti^{+++++} + e$. At the equivalence point the diffusion current (when corrected for the residual current) is zero. Then as the excess ferric ions are added to the solution a positive diffusion current is obtained because of the reaction

$$Fe^{+++} + e \rightarrow Fe^{++}$$

at the dropping mercury electrode. The equivalence point is more difficult to obtain in this case because the titration curve is approximately a straight line. The slight change in slope at the equivalence point is caused by the difference in the diffusion coefficients (see Section 16.6) of the titanous and ferric ions. This type of curve is typical of that obtained when the material being titrated gives an anodic wave at the same potential at which the reagent being added gives a cathodic wave. The titration of iodide ion with mercuric ion yields a similar titration curve.

In performing amperometric titrations the techniques of polarography still apply. For example, an inert electrolyte must be added to take care of the migration current. Gelatin is added both as a maximum suppressor and to prevent depolarization of colloidal precipitates. Before the titration is started, nitrogen is bubbled through the solution for 10 minutes to remove dissolved oxygen, and for 2 minutes between each addition of the titrating reagent to stir the solution. The titrations are conveniently performed in a modified H-type cell which has one side larger than the other to accommodate both the dropping mercury electrode and the tip of a microburet.

Similar to conductometric titrations alcohol or acetone is often added to reduce the solubility of the precipitate formed.

17.3 Apparatus. Amperometric titrations may be performed with any of the polarographs described in Chapter 16, although the manual instruments are easier to operate as titrators. Titration at a constant voltage, however, allows construction of the very simple titrator shown in Fig. 17.6. The potentiometer, for example a Helipot, has a calibrated dial showing the fraction of the battery voltage applied to the cell, and an inexpensive, low-resistance voltmeter may be used to measure the actual battery voltage. Galvanometer sensi-

tivity may be varied by a series rheostat. If desired, a condenser
(about 1000 μf, 6 volts) may be placed across the galvanometer to
reduce the fluctuations caused by the charging current.

In operation, the required voltage is applied to the titration cell
and the galvanometer sensitivity set. This is done by adjusting to
about full scale with the solution to be titrated if the titration is of
the type shown in Figs. 17.3 or 17.4, or with a few milliliters of the

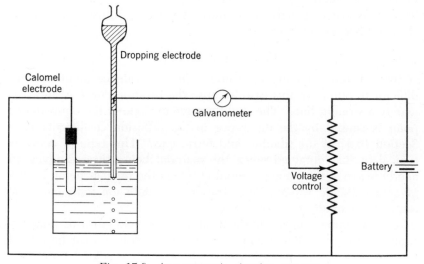

Fig. 17.6 Amperometric titration apparatus

titrant in the cell if the titration is of the type shown in Fig. 17.2.
This procedure will give full-scale galvanometer deflections for the
titration.

The drop time and other variables in the Ilkovic equation are not
critical, provided they remain constant during each titration. Many
requirements of polarography, such as temperature control, may be
relaxed, since only relative diffusion currents are needed. Reproducibility from titration to titration is not necessary.

17.4 Applications. One of the earliest applications of amperometric titrations involved the determination of sulfate. Sulfate cannot be determined accurately by potentiometric methods because of
the lack of a completely suitable indicator electrode, and the conductometric method is unsatisfactory where foreign electrolytes are
present. However, amperometric titrations of sulfate yield excellent

results, the accuracy being 0.2% in the titration of 0.01 M solutions.[1]

Another interesting application is the titration of fluoride ion with thorium or lanthanum nitrate.[2]

In addition to precipitation reactions amperometric titrations have been extensively applied to oxidation-reduction reactions and to determinations involving organic reagents or compounds. Many specific applications are given in the text of Kolthoff and Lingane,[3] and the most current developments are covered in the review articles of Laitinen.[4]

[1] I. M. Kolthoff and Y. D. Pan, *J. Am. Chem. Soc.*, *62*, 3332 (1940).

[2] A. Langer, *Ind. Eng. Chem., Anal. Ed.*, *12*, 511 (1940).

[3] I. M. Kolthoff and J. J. Lingane, *Polarography*, Vol. II, Interscience, New York (1952).

[4] H. A. Laitinen, *Anal. Chem.*, *21*, 66 (1949); *24*, 46 (1952).

CHAPTER 18

High-Frequency Methods

Many substances absorb electromagnetic radiation in the range from one-tenth to several hundred megacycles per second. This absorption covers a very broad band of frequencies and is therefore a non-specific property; there is no high-frequency absorption spectrum similar to that found in the ultraviolet, visible, or infrared regions. However, the degree of absorption is characteristic for many compounds, and it may be used in a limited way for the quantitative analysis of pure organic liquids. When combined with a specific chemical reaction, the absorption of high-frequency radiation may be an endpoint indicator for titrations.

18.1 Electrical properties of liquids. For many years, cells similar to the two shown in Fig. 15.6 have been used to study the electrical properties of liquids. If a potential is placed across the electrodes, the resistance of the liquid will determine the current flow through the external circuit. This resistance may be measured directly by application of Ohm's law, or the cell may be one arm of a bridge (Chapter 15). The resistance (or its reciprocal, the conductance) of the liquid is one of its electrical properties. Usually, simple conductance measurements are made with a d-c or low-frequency (10 to 300 kc) a-c potential source.

Low-conductance liquids act as a dielectric or insulating medium, and the electrodes and liquid form a condenser which will allow the flow of alternating current. Again the dielectric properties of the liquid may be measured by either a direct or a bridge method. The dielectric constant, which is the ratio of the capacitance of a cell filled with the substance to that of the cell in air, is one of the many properties available for characterizing organic liquids and for determining the composition of many binary mixtures.

In all cases, both conductive and capacitive effects are present, although one may be very small compared to the other. Therefore, bridges designed for the accurate measurement of conductance or dielectric constant must be capable of balancing both effects.

18.2 High-frequency effects. As the frequency of the applied potential is increased, the impedance (apparent resistance to flow of alternating current) of the condenser formed by the electrodes

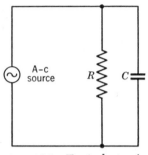

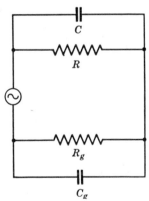

Fig. 18.1 Equivalent cir-
cuit of cell

Fig. 18.2 High-frequency cell

and the liquid is decreased. The resistance remains constant, but the capacitative reactance (capacitative equivalent of resistance) decreases. This results in a greater flow of current through the cell. The equivalent circuit of such a cell may be shown as in Fig. 18.1, where C is the capacitance and R the resistance.

At high enough frequencies, >100 kc per second, ordinary insulators may not prevent the flow of current. In fact, the usual cell for high-frequency measurements has the electrodes outside the glass cell walls (Fig. 18.2). Such a cell therefore is three capacitors in series, two having glass as a dielectric and one having the liquid as dielectric. The equivalent circuit for such an arrangement is shown in Fig. 18.3, where C_g is the cell-wall capacitance and C the solution capacitance. Such a system is too difficult to analyze electrically for direct conductance or dielectric measurements, but it

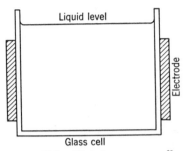

Fig. 18.3 Equivalent cir-
cuit of high-frequency cell

is suitable for relative measurements on pure liquids or solutions.

18.3 Generation of high frequencies. The usual method of producing frequencies above a few thousand cycles per second is the electronic oscillator. The heart of the oscillator is the tank circuit (Fig. 18.4) which regulates the frequency produced. The combination of inductance L and capacitance C has a natural frequency at which the impedance to a circulating current is at a minimum. In fact if there were no resistance R in the circuit, the oscillations would be self-sustaining, like a frictionless mechanism. However, since perpetual, nonrandom motion is no more possible for electrons than mechanical devices, it is necessary to supply energy to the tank circuit to overcome losses and thus maintain oscillations. The energy

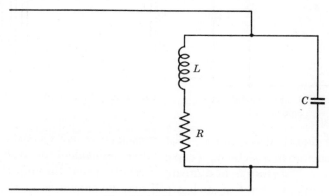

Fig. 18.4 Tank circuit

must be supplied as an electric current of the proper frequency and must be in phase with the circulating current. This may be done if a circuit similar to Fig. 18.5 is used. A portion of the voltage appearing across the terminals of the tank circuit is fed into the input of an electronic amplifier. The amplifier output is then fed in proper phase to the input of the tank circuit. It is apparent that by the adjustment of the feedback ratio, and the amount of amplification, any loss in the tank circuit may be compensated for.

Besides the resistive losses in the tank circuit, it is possible to withdraw power from the tank. This power withdrawal, or loading, may be continued until the amplifier circuit can no longer make up both losses and the oscillator goes out of oscillation. The circuit will resume oscillation as soon as the overload is removed.

18.4 Coupling of the sample to the oscillator. In an earlier section, the cells for the measurement of conductivity and dielectric constant were described. Similar cells may be used at high frequencies, but it is possible to simplify the apparatus considerably if we take advantage of the ability of high frequencies to pass through glass and other insulators.   Thus the common methods of coupling the sample to the oscillator are indirect, the liquid acting to modify the characteristics of L or C in the oscillator tank circuit.

If the cell is a test tube placed inside the wire coil forming the tank inductance, the dielectric and conductive properties of the liquid will modify the coil inductance.   Both properties essentially effect the leakage of high-frequency current from one turn of the

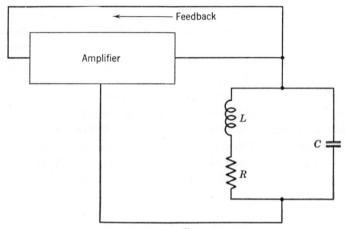

Fig. 18.5   Oscillator circuit

coil to the next.   As a result, the resistance of the coil may be affected as well as the inductance.   These changes may be measured either as a frequency shift or as a change in power dissipation in the tank.

If the liquid is made the dielectric in the tank condenser, similar results will be obtained.   Capacitance or resistance of the condenser will be modified by the presence of the liquid, and the changes will appear as a frequency shift or change in tank power dissipation.

In comparing different organic compounds by either method of coupling the liquid to the tank circuit, the predominant effect is the difference in dielectric constant of the compounds.   In the case of aqueous solutions of electrolytes, there has been some difference in opinion regarding the relative effect of dielectric and conductance. The leading groups in the field, however, are coming to realize that conductance is the controlling factor except at extreme dilutions. Though it may seem that it would be a simple matter to prove the relative effect of the two factors, the high-frequency equipment used by the analyst has not been adaptable to fundamental measurements, and electrical analysis of the existing equipment is too difficult.   At this time, no clear relationship has been shown between fundamental physical properties and the quantities measured by different high-frequency apparatus. Therefore the present methods are completely empirical.

18.5   Practical high-frequency measurements. It is possible with high-frequency measurements to distinguish between organic liquids. Qualitative analysis by this method is limited, just as refractive-index measurement for example, by the fact that the high-frequency response is not specific and many compounds or mixtures could give the same response. However, if the number of possible liquids is limited, high-frequency measurements may distinguish among this small number of substances. The most accurate method, since the organic liquids are poor conductors, is the measurement of frequency shift. The systems described in the literature [1-3] compare the frequency of the oscillator modified by the sample with a standard oscillator or other fixed frequency. West, Burkhalter, and Broussard [1] measured the frequency shift by a heterodyne beat method similar to the method for dielectric measurements. The sample, in a 50-ml test tube, loads the tank inductance. With an initial fre-

TABLE 18.1

Beat-Frequency Change Induced by Various Organic Compounds

Compound	Beat-Frequency Change, cps	Compound	Beat-Frequency Change, cps
n-Pentane	660	Diethyl ketone	3922
n-Hexane	681	Methyl n-amyl ketone	3062
n-Heptane	697	Acetophenone	4014
Methanol	5560	Benzene	810
Ethanol	4763	Toluene	830
n-Propyl alcohol	4288	Bromobenzene	1675
Isopropyl alcohol	4117	Aniline	2040
n-Butyl alcohol	3895	Nitrobenzene	5720
Isobutyl alcohol	3906		
sec-Butyl alcohol	3658	Acetic acid	2190
tert-Butyl alcohol	2998	Propionic acid	1242
n-Amyl alcohol	2031	Butyric acid	1094
tert-Amyl alcohol	2938	Caproic acid	1005
n-Octyl alcohol	2550		
		Methyl acetate	2135
Acetone	4397	Methyl n-propionate	1890
Methyl ethyl ketone	4103	Methyl n-butyrate	1687

[1] P. W. West, T. S. Burkhalter, and L. Broussard, *Anal. Chem.*, 22, 469 (1950).
[2] O. A. Nance, T. S. Burkhalter, and P. H. Monaghan, *ibid.*, 24, 214 (1952).
[3] P. J. Elving, D. G. Flom, and A. I. Coleman, *ibid.*, 24, 198 (1952).

quency of 4 Mc the frequency shifts shown in Table 18.1 were obtained.

The earliest instruments for high-frequency measurements were based on power absorption by the liquid. The first high-frequency titrator, developed by Jensen and Parrack,[4] measured the change in

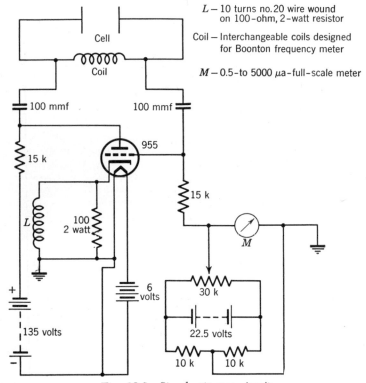

L — 10 turns no. 20 wire wound on 100-ohm, 2-watt resistor

Coil — Interchangeable coils designed for Boonton frequency meter

M — 0.5-to 5000 μa-full-scale meter

Fig. 18.6   Simple titrator circuit

plate current of the oscillator tube during the course of the titration. The sample was held in a test tube inserted in the tank coil, and with an initial frequency of 15 to 20 Mc the authors obtained titration curves very similar to those found with conductimetric titrations.

Anderson, Bettis, and Revinson [5] coupled the liquid by making it the dielectric in the tank condenser and measured the oscillator grid current. Their design was simplified by Revinson and Harley,[6] and the circuit diagram of the simplified unit is shown in Fig. 18.6. In

[4] F. W. Jensen and A. L. Parrack, *Ind. Eng. Chem., Anal. Ed., 18,* 595 (1946).
[5] K. Anderson, E. S. Bettis, and D. Revinson, *Anal. Chem., 22,* 743 (1950).
[6] D. Revinson and J. H. Harley, presented 119th meeting, Am. Chem. Soc., Cleveland, Ohio (Apr. 1952).

order to evaluate some of the instrument variables, the loading effect of sodium chloride at several frequencies was measured (Fig. 18.7). The shape of these curves explain the variation in shape of the titra-

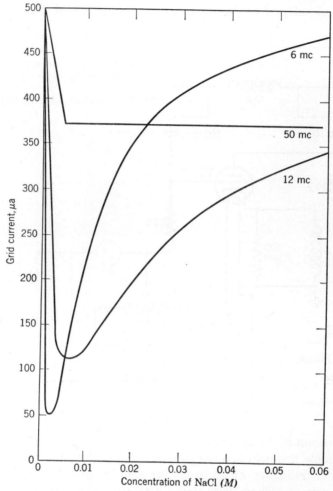

Fig. 18.7   Loading effect of sodium chloride

tion curves found at different salt concentrations.[5]   For example, at 12 Mc, if the original solution were very dilute, an increase in loading would cause a decrease in grid current whereas above 0.01 M solution the grid current would show an increase. At a certain critical concentration a reversal in grid current would take place. The initial decrease in grid current is probably a conductance and dielectric effect, while the major change after the grid current minimum is due to conductance change. These conclusions were later confirmed by Hall [7] and by Blaedel, et al.[8] The most thorough analysis of the electrical variables involved in high-frequency titrimetry is that of Reilley and McCurdy.[9] They demonstrated that, in spite of the complexity of the system, it is possible to predict the general

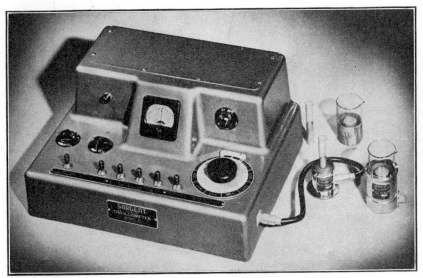

Fig. 18.8   Sargent model-V oscillometer (Courtesy of E. H. Sargent & Company)

shape of loading and titration curves for the different types of instruments based purely on low-frequency conductance data.

The only commercial unit available at this time is the Sargent model-V oscillometer (Fig. 18.8). This instrument operates at 5 Mc and comes equipped with a small cell for measurements on organic liquids and a large cell for titrations. As in all of the present designs, the recommended maximum electrolyte concentrations for titrations is 0.01 N. The measuring device is a calibrated variable capacitor placed in parallel with the solution cell. This method enables the instrument to measure the dielectric of poor conductors

[7] J. L. Hall, *Anal. Chem.*, 24, 1236 (1952).

[8] W. J. Blaedel, H. V. Malmstadt, D. L. Petitjean, and W. K. Anderson, *ibid.*, 1240 (1952).

[9] C. N. Reilley and W. H. McCurdy, Jr., *ibid.*, 25, 86 (1953).

as well as the endpoint in titrations of aqueous solutions. An electrical analysis of the system is given in the manufacturers' literature. Hall and Gibson [10] have described a titrator assembled from commercial components.

Considerable work remains to be done to extend high-frequency methods to concentrated (over 0.1 N) aqueous solutions. Improve-

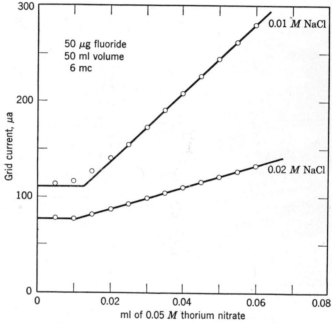

Fig. 18.9   High-frequency titration curves

ments in the transfer efficiency of the high-frequency energy have been made by raising the initial frequency [11] and by improvements in cell design or coupling.

18.6   Applications of high-frequency methods.   High-frequency absorption by organic liquids may be a qualitative tool for pure compounds or a quantitative tool for analysis of binary mixtures. The apparatus required is relatively complex, approaching a good bridge for dielectric measurements. The requirements can be relaxed if the need for high stability is reduced by standardization of the equipment when each sample is run.

[10] J. L. Hall and J. A. Gibson, Jr., *ibid.*, *23*, 966 (1951).
[11] W. J. Blaedel and H. V. Malmstadt, *ibid.*, *22*, 734 (1950).

Application to inorganic materials, especially aqueous solutions, is chiefly to titration procedures. Figure 18.9 shows the titration curves obtained for the thorium fluoride complex.[6] It is apparent from Fig. 18.7 that the slope of the 6-Mc curve is less at higher concentrations of sodium chloride. This is shown by the relative slopes of the two titration curves given in Fig. 18.9.

The comparison of direct-reading and differential response of titrators has been made by Blaedel and Malmstadt.[12] The differential response is more sensitive, but the titrator is quite complex, and a constant-flow buret is required.

[12] *Ibid.*, *24*, 450, 455 (1952).

CHAPTER 19

X-Ray Analysis

For analytical purposes, there are three important X-ray methods: X-ray powder-diffraction analysis, X-ray emission-spectral analysis, which is being supplemented by X-ray fluorescent analysis, and X-ray absorption analysis. The composition of a chemical substance can be established by all three methods, and by X-ray diffraction analysis the structure can also be established. For this reason X-ray diffraction measurements have been more important to the chemist than the other two types.

19.1 Production of X rays. In Fig. 2.2 the position of X rays in the electromagnetic spectrum was shown. Their main characteristic is their high energy and correspondingly small wavelength, approximately 1 A. X rays are produced by bombarding a metal target in an evacuated tube with electrons of high velocity. The target is maintained at a high positive potential with respect to the electron source (cathode), to accelerate the electrons to the required high velocity. X-ray tubes are of two main types: the gas-discharge tube and the hot-cathode tube.

The gas-discharge tube is generally a metal tube maintained at a pressure of 0.01 mm of mercury with air entering the tube through a controlled leak. The positive ions present in the gas are attracted to an aluminum cathode and liberate electrons which then bombard the target anode. Gas-discharge tubes have the advantages that the target material can be changed readily and that the long-wave X rays which are produced are not lost by absorption by a glass envelope. However, these tubes must be continuously evacuated and checked while in operation.

The hot-cathode tube may be either permanently sealed or demountable so that the target material can be varied. A permanently sealed (Coolidge-type) tube is shown in Fig. 19.1. This tube consists of a gas bulb at high vacuum with a tungsten-filament cathode and a metal target (anticathode or anode) sealed into opposite ends of the tube. Electrons emitted from the heated tungsten filament are accelerated by a 30-to-40-kv potential and attracted to the metal target. The X rays produced are emitted through beryllium windows. Since the bulk of the energy carried by the electrons is converted into heat upon striking the target, the target material must have a high melting point (molybdenum, chromium, or tungsten)

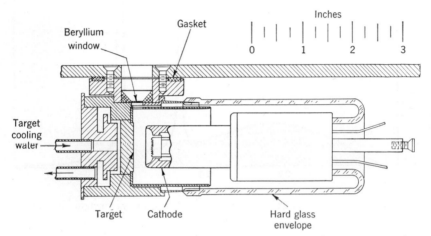

Fig. 19.1   Coolidge-type X-ray tube (Courtesy General Electric Company)

or else be an excellent conductor (silver or copper). In addition, the target is normally water-cooled.

19.2   X-ray spectra.   The radiation emitted by the target is of two types:

1. A continuous spectrum (sometimes called white or general radiation). The distribution of various wavelengths and their intensities in this spectrum depend mainly upon the high voltage applied to the tube.

2. A characteristic X-ray emission spectrum consisting of a few sharp lines. Each line has a specific wavelength which depends only upon the target material, provided the voltage is above a certain minimum value characteristic also of the target material. Figure 19.2 shows a plot of the intensity of X rays against wavelength for a tube containing molybdenum as a target. The two sharp peaks shown in Fig. 19.2 constitute the characteristic X-ray emission spectrum of molybdenum. These peaks can be explained with the structural concept of the atom. The impact of the high-velocity electron

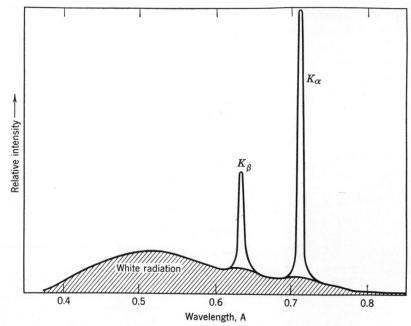

Fig. 19.2   Relative intensity of X rays plotted against wavelength for molybdenum

with the target material expels an electron from one of the lower
quantum levels of the atom. This vacant space is then filled by an
electron jumping from an upper energy level.   In this transition a

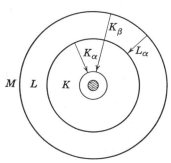

Fig. 19.3   Electronic transitions
associated with the production
of characteristic X-ray spectra

photon is emitted. This photon contains the energy that the original electron lost in approaching the nucleus.
If E_1 is the initial energy of the electron and E_2 the final energy, then the
frequency of the emitted line is given
by $h\nu = E_1 - E_2$. The corollary with
emission spectroscopy discussed in
previous chapters is rather obvious,
the main difference being the relatively large energy difference involved
in X-ray spectra. If the electron initially removed is from the K quantum
level and the electron jumps from the
L level, the radiation is called K_a, and, if the transition occurs from
the M to the K level, K_β, etc. These transitions are illustrated in

Fig. 19.3. The K series consists of three lines, a very close doublet $K_{\alpha 1}$, and $K_{\alpha 2}$, and a K_β line. Normally the doublet cannot be resolved, and for most practical work, the wavelength of the unresolved doublet (designated K_α) is used. Table 19.1 contains a list of the wavelengths for the targets available in commercial X-ray tubes.

TABLE 19.1

Characteristic Wavelengths for Different Target Materials *

Target Metal	$K_{\alpha 1}$	$K_{\alpha 2}$	K_α	K_β	Absorption Edge	Min. Voltage, kv
Tungsten	0.20904	0.21388	0.2106	0.18458	0.1793	69.30
Silver	0.55941	0.56381	0.5609	0.49701	0.4855	25.50
Molybdenum	0.70926	0.71354	0.7107	0.63225	0.6197	20.00
Copper	1.54050	1.54434	1.5418	1.39217	1.3802	8.86
Nickel	1.65783	1.66168	1.6951	1.50008	1.4869	8.29
Cobalt	1.78890	1.79279	1.7902	1.62073	1.6072	7.71
Iron	1.93597	1.93991	1.9373	1.75654	1.7429	7.10
Chromium	2.28962	2.29352	2.2909	2.08479	2.0701	5.98

* The values given are in angstrom units (A). Much of the published data is in kX units, where a kX unit was evaluated on the basis that the spacing of the cleavage planes in calcite was 3.02945 A. Recent measurements have shown that this value is closer to 3.03560 A. The factor to convert from kX units to angstroms is $1 kX$ unit = 1.00202 A.

For X-ray emission analysis the sample to be analyzed must be made the target, and the resulting spectra obtained. Although the method is applicable to elements of atomic number greater than 10 and to quantitative as well as to qualitative analysis, the tedious nature of the method has limited its application.

19.3 Absorption of X rays. The absorption of X rays is governed by an exponential law similar to Beer's law for the absorption of radiant energy. Thus, the absorption of a monochromatic X-ray beam is given by

$$I = I_0 e^{-\mu l} \tag{1}$$

where I = intensity of the transmitted beam, I_0 = intensity of the incident beam, μ = linear-absorption coefficient in cm^{-1}, and l = absorber thickness in centimeters. Equation 1 can be converted into the following equivalent form involving common logarithms:

$$\log (I_0/I) = \mu l/2.303 \tag{2}$$

For calculations involving absorption, the mass-absorption coefficient μ_m is a more practical quantity than the linear absorption coefficient. The mass-absorption coefficient is obtained by dividing the linear-absorption coefficient by ρ, the density of the absorber,

$$\mu_m = \mu/\rho \quad (\text{cm}^2 \text{ per gram})$$

The mass-absorption coefficients for all the elements are tabulated in handbooks and in many reference works.

When the μ_m value for a given wavelength and the grams per square centimeter of sample are known, the absorption can be calculated. The grams per square centimeter for a given sample can be found from (a) the thickness and density (cm $\times$ grams/cm³), (b) the length, mass, and volume (cm $\times$ grams $\times$ 1/cm³), (c) the mass and cross-sectional area (grams $\times$ 1/cm²).

If the μ_m values for a given element such as zirconium are plotted against wavelength, a curve similar to Fig. 19.4 is obtained. The

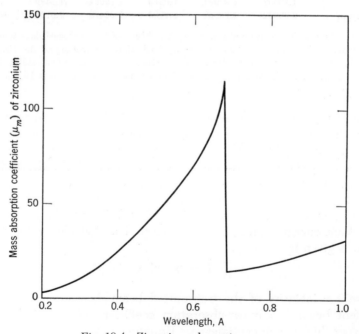

Fig. 19.4   Zirconium absorption curve

discontinuity in this curve is called an absorption edge and can be explained in the same manner as the production of X-ray spectra.

In order to produce the K series of spectra it is necessary to dislodge a K electron by either bombardment with high-velocity electrons or by absorption of X radiation. However, the quantum of energy of exciting radiation must exceed the energy required to dislodge the K electron. As the wavelength of the exciting radiation is decreased, energy of the quantum (hc/v) reaches a value sufficient to dislodge a K electron. At this wavelength, the absorption of the zirconium (Fig. 19.4) increases rapidly because practically all of the energy of the exciting radiation is absorbed in dislodging the K electron. At the same time, characteristic K radiation of the zirconium is emitted when an L or M electron replaces the one dislodged. Because this radiation is always of longer wavelength than the exciting radiation, it is called *fluorescent radiation*. Essentially then, the fluorescent spectrum emitted by an element is identical with its X-ray emission spectrum, and the difference lies in the method of producing the spectrum. In X-ray fluorescence analysis, the element is a secondary target in the path of an X-ray beam produced from a primary target. In X-ray emission analysis the element is the primary target for a beam of high-velocity electrons. The fluorescent method of analysis will be discussed in more detail in a subsequent section.

A knowledge of the absorption-edge effects enables us to choose X-ray filters and select the proper X-ray target. An element with the proper absorption edge will act as a filter in a X-ray beam so that essentially monochromatic radiation can be obtained. For example, as shown in Fig. 19.5, a thin film of zirconium will filter out the K_β line from a molybdenum target while a thin film of nickel foil will filter out the K_β line from a copper target. For molybdenum the wavelength of the resulting X-ray beam would be that of K_α line or 0.7107 A whereas for copper the wavelength would be 1.5418 A (see Table 19.1). Table 19.2 lists the filters that should be selected for a given target material.

TABLE 19.2

Appropriate Filters for Different Target Materials

Target	Filter
Silver	Rhodium or palladium
Molybdenum	Zirconium
Copper	Nickel
Nickel	Cobalt
Cobalt	Iron (as iron oxide)
Iron	Manganese (as manganese oxide)
Chromium	Vanadium (as vanadic acid)

In choosing the thickness of the filter it must be remembered that the K_α intensity is reduced as well as the K_β intensity. So the choice is dependent upon how monochromatic the radiation must be, with some consideration being given to the exposure time needed. A 0.003-inch-thick zirconium foil in the path of molybdenum radiation will transmit slightly less than half of the K_α radiation and give a K_α-to-K_β ratio of 300 to 1.

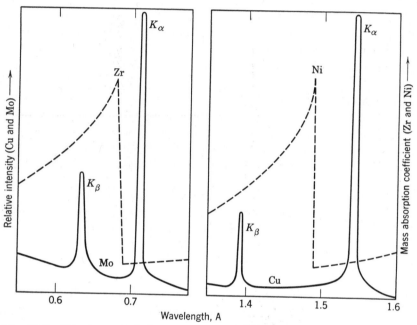

Fig. 19.5 Filtering action of zirconium on molybdenum radiation and of nickel on copper radiation

Second, absorption edge effects are important in the selection of the proper type of radiation for a given sample. For example, if the wavelength of the exciting radiation is overlapped by the absorption edges of the elements present in the sample, the resulting diffracted beam will be weak and the background from the fluorescent radiation will be intense. In making measurements of samples containing iron (absorption edge 1.74 A) Cr K_α radiation (2.29 A) is suitable whereas Cu K_α radiation (1.54 A) is not.

19.4 Measurement of X rays. For purposes of generalization it should be realized that in X-ray spectrometry, as in absorption spectroscopy, the essential components of an instrument are a source, a monochromator, and a receptor. The source is the X-ray tube, and the monochromator is usually a thin-metal foil in diffraction analysis or a crystal of mica, quartz, lithium fluoride, or rocksalt in fluorescent analysis. As a receptor for measuring X rays, there are four major devices: the photographic emulsion, the ionization chamber, the Geiger counter, and the photoelectric X-ray detector.

Although the photographic emulsion is still widely used for reasons of economy and simplicity, it suffers from the limitations that were discussed in Chapter 10. Although these limitations were discussed in conjunction with the ultraviolet and visible regions, they also apply to the X-ray region of the spectrum. For example, the emulsion response varies with the wavelength, particularly at the absorption edges of the silver and the bromide that compose part of the emulsion. For X-ray diffraction work a fast film such as Eastman Kodak No-Screen or type K is used. The type-K film is faster than the No-Screen and requires a shorter exposure time. However, it also yields a higher background, and so the selection of a suitable film is a compromise between these two factors. These films are developed in Kodak rapid X-ray developer * for 5 minutes at 20° C with 5 seconds agitation per minute, rinsed, and fixed in acid fixer with occasional agitation for 15 minutes. If the development time is increased to 8 minutes there is a speed increase of 15% for the No-Screen film and 10% for the type K. The main disadvantage of film for measuring X rays is the long exposures required, the time varying from 2 to even 20 hours in extreme cases.

For this reason, receptors capable of converting X-ray beams directly into electric currents proportional to the beam intensities have been developed. Historically, the ionization chamber was the first of these, but it has been abandoned in favor of the Geiger counter and the photoelectric X-ray detector. The Geiger counter consists essentially of a gas-filled tube having a cylindrical cathode with an axial wire at 200 to 1500 volts positive potential with respect to the cylinder. The construction, characteristics, and operation of Geiger counters are described in more detail in Chapter 21. The photoelectric X-ray detector is simply a photomultiplier tube with a phosphor to convert X radiation to visible light. This tube has been quite successfully applied to X-ray absorption analysis while the Geiger counters are almost universally used in the field of X-ray spectrometry.

* Kodak D-19 is a suitable substitute.

19.5   X-ray diffraction analysis.   At the present time X-ray diffraction analysis is the most important method that the chemist has for the identification of crystalline substances.   X-ray diffraction patterns are characteristic of the crystal form and spacing and thus of chemical compounds rather than of the elements or chemical groups, and so many analytical problems can only be solved by X-ray diffraction methods.

In Chapter 8, in the discussion of diffraction gratings, it was pointed out that a plane grating acts to diffract ordinary light.   In a similar manner a crystal diffracts X rays, since the spacings are of the same order as the wavelength of X rays.   The three-dimensional crystal acts like a series of plane gratings placed one above the other. Since the height as well as the width between the lines is involved, the diffraction law differs from that for plane gratings given in Chapter 8.

When a beam of monochromatic X rays strikes the planes of atoms in a crystal, interference phenomena occur, and the reinforced beams are diffracted from the crystal in specific directions (see Fig. 19.6).

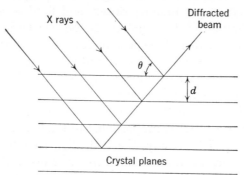

Fig. 19.6   Diffraction of X rays by the planes of a crystal

The relationship among the wavelength of the X rays, the incident angle of the X rays, and the interatomic distance is given by Bragg's law,

$$n\lambda = 2d \sin \theta$$

where n = the order of the diffraction (i.e. $n = 1, 2, 3 \cdots$),[†] λ = the wavelength of the X rays, θ = the incident angle and one-half the

[†] Since $\sin \theta$ cannot exceed 1, $n\lambda$ can never be greater than $2d$, and so the values of n are limited.

angle of scattering, d = the distance between atomic planes in the crystal in angstroms.

In the case of a single crystal, the diffracted X rays will consist of a few specific beams, but with a powder composed of randomly

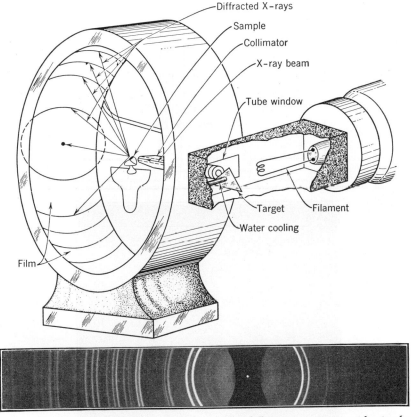

Fig. 19.7   Arrangement for obtaining powder-diffraction patterns with circular camera.   A typical pattern is shown

oriented crystals the diffracted radiation will consist of a series of concentric cones with their common apex at the sample.   When recorded on photographic film, these cones are projected as arcs with a cylindrical camera arrangement (Fig. 19.7) or as circles with a Laue or flat cassette camera (Fig. 19.8).

Some consideration should be given to the manner of mounting the samples in Figs. 19.7 and 19.8.   With the circular camera the powder is formed into a wedge so that the edge of the wedge bisects

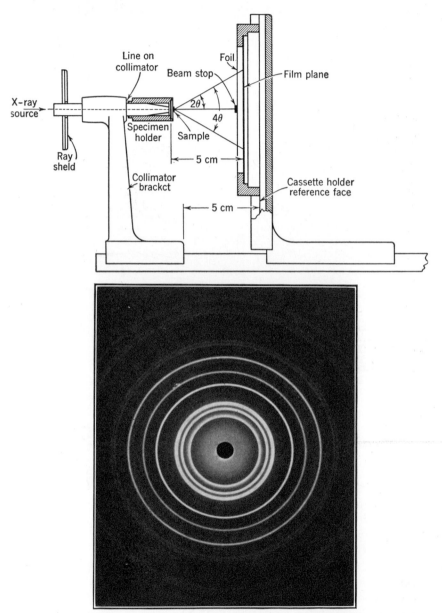

Fig. 19.8 Arrangement for obtaining powder-diffraction patterns with a flat cassette assembly. A typical pattern is shown (Courtesy General Electric Company)

the X-ray beam.   Alternatively, thin-walled glass or plastic capillaries may serve as sample holders, or the powder may be extruded
in the form of a rod from a narrow tube and held in the beam with
the tube as a support.

With the Laue camera, the best method is to press the powder
into a small hole in a disk of Celluloid and glue the Celluloid to the
specimen holder.   For liquids, cells with extremely thin glass windows (Pyrex blown thin enough to show interference colors) are
most suitable.   If the glass is too thick, halos will be apparent on the
film with a resulting loss in detail of the diffraction pattern.

It is necessary to collimate the X-ray beam so that sharp diffraction
patterns may be obtained.   The diameter of the collimator passing
the X-ray beam varies from 0.005 to 0.030 inch.   The choice of collimator is a compromise between the sharpness of the pattern desired and the exposure time.   Normally a 0.020-inch collimator is
chosen.   The cameras shown in Fig. 19.7 and Fig. 19.8 are covered
with thin metal foil (aluminum, nickel, or zirconium depending upon
the type of radiation) to make the cameras light-tight.   This foil
can be cemented in place readily with a thin rubber cement soluble
in naphtha.   A lead button is cemented to the center of the foil to
absorb the primary X-ray beam.

The circular camera diameter is often 57.3 mm or 114.6 mm so that
1 or 2 mm, respectively, measured between corresponding lines represents 1° for 2θ.   The General Electric XRD powder camera has
an effective film diameter of 143.2 mm, and so the θ angle in degrees
on a processed film of normal shrinkage can be obtained by multiplying by 2 the distance in centimeters between corresponding lines on
opposite sides of the central spot.   With the flat cassette camera, the
sample-to-plate distance is normally 5 cm.   With this distance, 2θ
values are obtained by finding in a table of trigonometric functions
the angle whose tangent is the diameter in decimeters of the given
circle in the pattern (see Fig. 19.8).   Then, with the basic equation
$n\lambda = 2d \sin \theta$, the d values of interplanar spacings can be calculated
since the wavelength is known and n is assumed to be 1.   Tables [1,2]

[1] Tables for Conversion of X-ray Diffraction Angles to Interplanar Spacings,
Publication AMS10, Supt. Documents, Govt. Printing Office, Washington 25,
D. C. (contains spacings for angles from 0° to 90° 2θ in intervals of 0.01° for
molybdenum, copper, nickel, cobalt, iron, and chromium.   Also for copper and
iron from 0° to 180° 2θ in intervals of 0.02°).

[2] Tables of Interplanar Spacings for Angle 2θ, Directions No. 11710, General
Electric X-ray Corp., Milwaukee, Wis. (contains spacings for angles from 0°
to 180° 2θ in intervals of 0.10° for silver, molybdenum, copper, nickel, cobalt,
iron, and chromium).

of interplanar spacings (d values) for angle 2θ are available for the most common types of radiation. A very small portion of three of these tables is given in Table 19.3 for purposes of illustration.

TABLE 19.3

Interplanar Spacings (d values) for Angle 2θ

	Type of Radiation		
2θ, degrees	$MoK_{\alpha 1} =$ 0.70926 A	$FeK_{\alpha 1} =$ 1.93597 A	$CrK_{\alpha 1} =$ 2.28962 A
20.00	2.0422	5.5744	6.5927
60.00	0.70926	1.9360	2.2896
100.00	0.46294	1.2636	1.4944
140.00	0.37739	1.0301	1.2183

An even more rapid method involves measurement with transparent X-ray diffraction scales.‡ Each set of 5 or 6 scales is printed on one sheet of transparent Vinylite and is for one particular radiation and one camera diameter.

The scales of each set are slightly different in length and cover a total range of 1% in film length. The scales are graduated in both directions from the low- and high-angle centers, to permit easy positioning of the film on the scale that fits it best. This compensates for film shrinkage and variations in length. The d values are then read directly in angstroms. The scales are available for camera diameters of 57.3, 114.6 and 143.2 mm.

Occasionally, in powder-diffraction work, it is necessary to calibrate a circular camera or check the sample to plate distance for a flat cassette camera. This is easily done with compounds of accurately known d spacings such as sodium chloride or cadmium oxide.

From the X-ray diffraction patterns shown in Fig. 19.7 and 19.8 it will be noticed that more lines are apparent in the film obtained from the circular camera. These lines correspond to the larger diffracted angles or to the short spacings in the sample (see Table 19.3). Since for approximately equal sample to film distances for the circular and the flat camera, short spacings are only obtained with the circular camera, most diffraction patterns are obtained in this manner.

In attempting to obtain the d values accurately for the long spacings (i.e. small values for 2θ) a target material with a K_a of long

‡ Available from Nelson P. Nies, 1495 Coolidge Ave., Pasadena 7, Calif.

wavelength should be chosen, such as chromium. In this way the error of visual measurement of the film will be minimized. This is particularly true in working with organic compounds.[3]

The most valuable application of X-ray diffraction is the comparison of a pattern of an unknown sample with a standard pattern. In this instance, as in infrared spectroscopy, a large library of known compounds is needed. In a classical paper, Hanawalt, Rinn, and

				2598			
d	2.70	2.34	1.65	d in A $= 0.708$	$\frac{I}{I_1}$	d in A $= 0.708$	$\frac{I}{I_1}$
$\frac{I}{I_1}$	1.00	1.00	1.00				
I	100	100	100				
CdO				2.70	1.00	0.830	0.02
				2.34	1.00	0.793	0.15
				1.65	1.00	0.782	0.10
				1.412	0.75		
				1.352	0.30		
				1.171	0.15		
				1.075	0.30		
				1.047	0.40		
			$Z =$	0.957	0.25		
				0.902	0.18		
$a_o =$	$b_o =$	$c_o =$					
$A =$	$C =$						
$D =$							
$n =$	$\omega =$	$\epsilon =$					

Fig. 19.9   ASTM card for cadmium oxide (Courtesy American Society for Testing Materials)

Frevel[4] described a system for applying the powder-diffraction method to chemical analysis. In this paper they tabulated Bragg spacings (d values) and relative intensities for 1000 compounds. Shortly thereafter the American Society for Testing Materials published a set of index cards for Hanawalt's list of compounds plus additional ones. Two supplements have subsequently been published so that more than 3000 compounds have now been indexed. A typical ASTM card for cadmium oxide is shown in Fig. 19.9. These cards are indexed and cross-indexed according to the three most intense lines. In using this file, the three strongest spacings of the unknown are obtained and compared with similar values in the file. When a probable card is found, the other lines of the pat-

[3] F. W. Matthews and J. H. Michell, *Ind. Eng. Chem., Anal. Ed.*, **18**, 662 (1946).

[4] J. D. Hanawalt, H. W. Rinn, and L. K. Frevel, *ibid.*, **10**, 457 (1938).

tern are compared to insure positive identification. The ASTM file is also available on edge punch cards.

For mixtures consisting of two or more components the identification becomes increasingly difficult. From the sample history and additional information such as a qualitative chemical analysis, the identification can normally be made.

In addition to the determination of unknown samples, X-ray diffraction is valuble for checking the purity of a material. For example, as shown in Fig. 19.10, there is a linear relationship between the

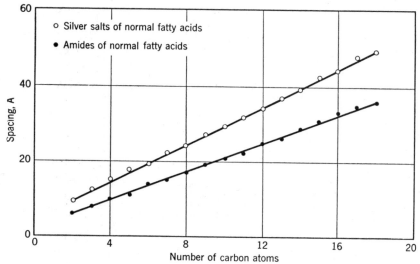

Fig. 19.10   Long spacings of the silver salts and amides of normal fatty acids plotted against number of carbon atoms

long spacing and the number of carbon atoms in the chain for the silver salts and the amides of the straight-chain fatty acids.[5] A similar relationship holds for other straight-chain organic compounds, such as the acids, alcohols, iodides, dicarboxylic acids, and the methyl and ethyl esters of the aliphatic acids.[6] Many substances can exist in different crystalline modifications, and X-ray diffraction is the best method of determining the crystalline modification present.

Commercial units for X-ray diffraction measurements are available

[5] F. W. Matthews, G. G. Warren, and J. H. Michell, *Anal. Chem.*, 22, 514 (1950).

[6] F. Francis, F. J. E. Collins, and S. H. Piper, *Proc. Roy. Soc. London*, A158, 691 (1937).

from General Electric X-Ray Corporation, North American Philips Company, Picker X-Ray Corporation, and Hayes Scientific Appliances. A General Electric XRD-4 X-ray diffraction unit is shown in

Fig. 19.11   General Electric XRD-4 diffraction unit (Courtesy General Electric Company)

Fig. 19.11. Both a circular camera and a flat cassette camera can be seen mounted near the X-ray tube.

The present trend in commercial units is to replace the cameras with Geiger-counter goniometers which can automatically scan the X-ray diffraction pattern of a specimen material. The pattern is obtained on a recorder chart. These units are equally valuable for fluorescence analysis.

19.6   X-ray fluorescence analysis.[7-10] In contrast to X-ray diffraction, which yields precise data about crystal structure, X-ray fluorescence analysis provides precise qualitative and quantitative data about the elements present. The range of concentration is 0.25 to 100% with the optimum range being 5 to 50%. Difficult analyses of both solids and liquids are possible, and the samples are normally

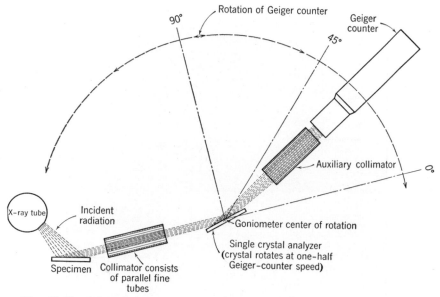

Fig. 19.12   Schematic diagram of fluorescent analysis unit (Courtesy North-American Phillips Company)

not destroyed or affected by the analysis. Very small specimens may be handled successfully.

A diagram of a basic fluorescence analysis unit is shown in Fig. 19.12. The target in the X-ray tube is usually tungsten because of the short wavelength and correspondingly high energy of its X-ray spectrum (see Table 19.1). The beam of X rays produces the characteristic X-ray spectra of the elements present in the sample. These fluorescent X-rays are passed through a collimator, and the nearly parallel beams of the radiation strike an analyzing crystal. The

[7] H. Friedman and L. S. Birks, *Rev. Sci. Instruments, 19,* 323 (1948).

[8] F. Behr, *Steel, 130,* 70 (1952).

[9] P. K. Koh and B. Caugherty, *J. Applied Phys., 23,* 427 (1952).

[10] J. Buhler, *Wire and Wire Products,* 570 (1952).

TABLE 19.4

Characteristic Secondary X-Ray Spectra

These data are estimated to the nearest 0.5° of angle 2θ from a chart published in 1952 by the North American Philips Company. The K_α and K_β angles are shown for three analyzing crystals.

Values of Angle 2θ

Atomic Number	Symbol	Mica (Reflecting) K_α	K_β	Quartz K_α	K_β	Rocksalt K_α	K_β
50	Sn					9.0	10.0
49	In					9.5	10.5
48	Cd					9.5	11.0
47	Ag					10.0	11.5
46	Pd					10.5	12.0
45	Rh					11.0	12.5
44	Ru					11.5	13.5
43	Ma					....	....
42	Mo					12.5	14.5
41	Nb					13.5	15.5
40	Zr					14.5	16.0
39	Y					15.0	17.0
38	Sr			10.0	11.5	16.0	18.0
37	Rb			11.0	12.0	17.0	19.0
36	Kr			11.5	13.0	17.5	20.0
35	Br			12.5	14.0	19.0	21.0
34	Se			13.5	15.0	20.0	22.5
33	As			14.0	15.5	21.5	24.0
32	Ge			15.0	16.5	23.0	25.5
31	Ga			16.0	18.0	24.5	26.5
30	Zn			17.5	19.0	26.5	29.5
29	Cu			18.5	20.5	28.5	31.5
28	Ni			20.0	22.0	30.5	34.0
27	Co			21.5	24.0	33.5	37.0
26	Fe	10.0	11.0	23.5	26.0	36.5	40.0
25	Mn	11.0	12.0	26.0	28.0	39.5	43.5
24	Cr	12.0	13.0	28.0	30.5	43.5	48.0
23	V	13.0	14.5	30.5	33.5	48.0	52.5
22	Ti	14.5	16.0	34.0	37.0	53.0	58.0
21	Sc	16.0	17.5	37.5	41.0	59.0	65.0
20	Ca	17.5	19.0	41.5	45.0	66.0	73.0
19	K	19.5	21.5	47.0	51.0	75.5	84.0
18	A	....	....	....	....	....	....
17	Cl	25.5	27.5	60.5	66.0	102.0	113.5
16	S	29.0	31.0	71.0	76.0	126.0	144.0
15	P	33.5	36.0	83.0	90.0		
14	Si	39.5	41.5	102.5	111.0		
13	Al	46.5	49.0	134.0	148.0		
12	Mg	56.5	59.0				
11	Na	70.5	73.0				

crystal acts as a diffraction grating and by proper positioning reflects each of the individual radiations at a specific angle. Long wavelengths of X radiation are dispersed to higher angles while the shorter wavelengths are dispersed to lower angles. The intensity of the resulting radiation is measured with a Geiger counter which is arranged together with its angulating mechanism on a goniometer. As an indication of the qualitative work possible, the characteristic radiations of elements 11 to 50 are shown in Table 19.4. As is ap-

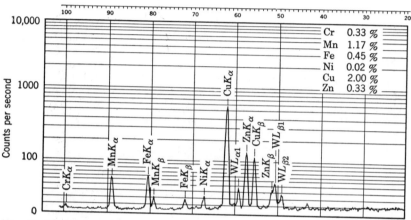

Fig. 19.13   Fluorescent spectrum of an aluminum alloy obtained on a General Electric XRD-3 unit (Courtesy General Electric Company)

parent from this table, the analyzing crystal selected is dependent upon the element to be determined.

For measurement, the specimens may be in a variety of forms. An open-faced level holder serves for either liquids or powders with the powder being pressed to give a flat surface. A thin transparent membrane cover is sealed over this holder if the vapor state must be studied. Metal samples as foils $\frac{1}{16}$ to $\frac{1}{4}$ inch thick may be placed in the specimen holder. If the metal specimen cannot be cut or deformed, the face may be irradiated in the holder.

For quantitative analyses the spectrogoniometer is set at a specific angle corresponding to the element to be analyzed. The intensity of the radiation is accurately measured with a Geiger counter. Standard samples, similar to those to be analyzed, of known chemical content must be available to obtain calibration curves. A typical fluorescence analysis chart of an aluminum alloy is shown in Fig. 19.13, and a calibration curve for the determination of copper in this alloy is shown in Fig. 19.14.

It is necessary to have suitable standards because of the many variables involved in fluorescence analysis. These variables include the geometrical setup, the amount of the element present and its

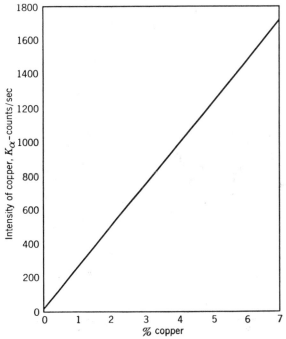

Fig. 19.14   Calibration curve for the determination of copper in an aluminum alloy (Courtesy General Electric Company)

excitation efficiency, the absorption effects of other elements and particularly the major element in the sample, air absorption, the reflecting plane spacing (d value) of the diffraction crystal, the voltage and current applied to the X-ray tube, and the characteristics of the Geiger counter. For reproducible quantitative analysis, these variables must be controlled.§ Although the accuracy of quantitative analysis varies with the nature of the specimen components, under optimum conditions it is in the order of $\frac{1}{2}$ of 1% of the amount present. Impurities can be detected in the parts per million range.

§ For a detailed discussion of these variables, consult the reference by F. Behr previously cited.

An entire unit for fluorescence analysis, available from North American Philips Company, is shown in Fig. 19.15. The complete assembly consists of three components, a basic X-ray diffraction

Fig. 19.15   North-American Phillips Company X-ray spectrograph (Courtesy North-American Phillips Company)

unit, a wide-range Geiger-counter goniometer, and an electronic-circuit panel with a strip-chart recorder. The output of the Geiger counter can be fed into the strip-chart recorder for normal qualitative or quantitative analysis or into a count register when extreme precision is required. A complete assembly is also available from the General Electric X-Ray Corporation. The General Electric fluorescent X-ray spectrometer has a tungsten target tube with a larger focal spot and a larger window than the conventional diffraction tubes and consequently can be operated at a higher current rating to yield higher X-ray intensities. A curved, focusing mica crystal acts as an analyzer.

19.7 X-ray absorption analysis.[11-13] Although X-ray fluorescence analysis has been discussed in the previous section, it is often listed with X-ray absorption analysis because X-ray fluorescence depends upon absorbed X rays to excite the emitted line whose intensity is measured. For comparison then with the truly absorptometric methods this discussion will also include reference to X-ray fluorescence analysis.

The three truly absorptometric methods are based on the absorption-edge effect, the absorption of a monochromatic X-ray beam, and the absorption of a polychromatic X-ray beam. The exponential law governing the absorption of X rays has already been discussed, and a characteristic curve showing the variation of the mass-absorption coefficient of zirconium with wavelength was plotted in Fig. 19.4. From a similar curve for lead shown in Fig. 19.16, it can be seen that the absorption of X rays is continuous over certain regions and then shows sudden characteristic discontinuities. Since these discontinuities (absorption edges) are characteristic of an element, the element can be qualitatively identified by this method.

From Fig. 19.16 and Table 19.5 the four absorptometric methods can be compared.[14]

1. In the X-ray fluorescence method, energy of wavelengths below 1 A excites the L line, whose intensity is measured.

2. In the absorption-edge method, absorbance measurements are taken at wavelengths above and below an absorption edge. Extrapolation to the edge gives the change in absorbance from which the amount of the corresponding element is calculated. Several absorbance measurements are necessary, although a modification[15] of this method requires only two absorbance measurements.

3. In the monochromatic X-ray beam method, an absorbance measurement is made at a single wavelength, preferably one shorter

[11] H. A. Liebhafsky, *Anal. Chem.*, 21, 17 (1949); 22, 15 (1950); 24, 16 (1952).

[12] P. D. Zemany, E. H. Winslow, G. S. Poellmitz, and H. A. Liebhafsky, *ibid.*, 21, 493 (1949).

[13] H. A. Liebhafsky, *Ann. N. Y. Acad. Sci.*, 53, 997 (1951).

[14] H. A. Liebhafsky and E. H. Winslow, *ASTM Bull. 167* (July 1950).

[15] A. Engstrom, *Rev. Sci. Instruments, 18*, 681 (1947).

than an absorption edge of the element or elements being determined. This method is nonspecific because any element absorbing X rays at this wavelength will contribute to the absorbance.

4. In the polychromatic X-ray beam method, an absorbance measurement is made with a beam consisting of a range of wavelengths.

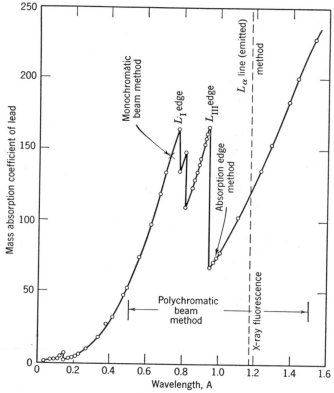

Fig. 19.16   Relationship of various analytical methods to fundamental X-ray data for lead (Courtesy American Society for Testing Materials)

This method is nonspecific, and the polychromatic nature of the beam can cause complications.

Of these four methods, the X-ray fluorescence method has already been discussed in detail.

Absorption-edge measurements as just described for both qualitative and quantitative analysis were initially carried out by Glocker and Frohnmayer [16] with photographic methods. With a similar pro-

[16] R. Glocker and W. Frohnmayer, *Ann. Physik*, 76, 369 (1925).

TABLE 19.5

Comparison of X-Ray Absorption Methods

Name	Type	Specific	Intensity Measured	Preferred Detector	Extreme Voltage Stabilization
X-ray fluorescence	Spectrophotometric	Yes	Low	Geiger counter	Desirable
Absorption edge	Spectrophotometric	Yes	Low	Geiger counter	Desirable
Absorptometry (monochromatic)	Spectrophotometric	No	Low	Geiger counter	Desirable
Absorptometry (polychromatic)	Photometric	No	Can be high	Multiplier phototube	Sometimes mandatory

cedure Andrews [17] determined iron in beryllium with an ionization chamber as an X-ray detector. More recently Frevel and North have designed the Dow automatic X-ray absorption spectrometer so that either absorption-edge measurements or measurements with a monochromatic X-ray beam can be made.

Analysis with a monochromatic X-ray beam simplifies the interpretation of results, but the low-beam intensity is a serious limitation.

Analysis with a polychromatic X-ray beam is more important at the present time because the high-beam intensity means that the apparatus can be constructed more readily. It has been shown that a polychromatic X-ray beam can be converted into an electric current by a photomultiplier tube coated with a phosphor. This current is proportional to the intensity of the X-ray beam striking the phosphor and can be amplified and measured with a suitable micro- or milliammeter. The current readings therefore measure the extent to which a sample in an X-ray beam reduces the beam intensity. For example, for absorption analysis the law governing the absorption of monochromatic X rays is written as

$$\log (I_0/I) = \mu_m m / 2.303 a$$

where I_0 and I are the intensities of the X-ray beam on entering and leaving the sample of m grams. μ_m is the mass-absorption coefficient and a is the area of the sample in square centimeters. With a photometer, the equation becomes

$$\log i_0/i = \mu_m m / 2.303 a$$

where i_0 and i are the output currents for intensities I_0 and I, respectively. Although this law is for monochromatic radiation, it

[17] C. L. Andrews, *Phys. Rev.*, *54*, 994 (1938).

still holds if the "effective" wavelength of a polychromatic beam is constant.[18]   Figure 19.17 shows a schematic diagram of the initial

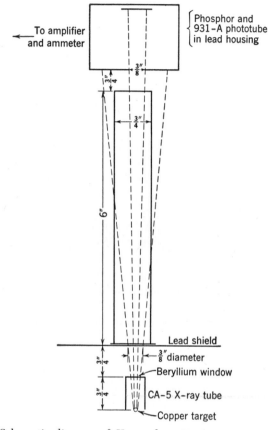

To amplifier and ammeter

{ Phosphor and 931–A phototube in lead housing

Lead shield

$\frac{3}{8}$″ diameter

Beryllium window

CA–5 X–ray tube

Copper target

Fig. 19.17   Schematic diagram of X-ray absorption apparatus.   The sample is placed in the 6-inch-long glass cell (Courtesy *Analytical Chemistry*)

X-ray absorption apparatus designed by Liebhafsky, Winslow, and co-workers.[19, 20]

In this direct method of measuring X-ray absorption with a multiplier phototube, the intensity of the X-ray beam was adjusted to a

[18] G. L. Clark, *Applied X-Rays*, 3rd ed., Chaps. VII and VIII, McGraw-Hill, New York (1940).

[19] H. A. Liebhafsky and E. H. Winslow, *Gen. Elec. Rev.*, 48, no. 4, 36 (1945).

[20] H. A. Liebhafsky, H. M. Smith, H. E. Tanis, and E. H. Winslow, *Anal. Chem.*, 19, 861, 866 (1947).

standard initial value by varying the X-ray tube voltage and current until the desired output current was obtained with a standard thickness of aluminum in the beam, the voltage across the detector and amplifier setting being fixed. The output currents obtained with known weights of sample in the beam were then plotted to give a calibration curve so that unknown samples could be analyzed.

The direct method, however, has two serious sources of error. The output current varies as the 24th power of the primary voltage across the X-ray tube and as the 5th power of the voltage across the multiplier phototube. For this reason a comparative method in which there is rapid commutation in the X-ray beam from the unknown to a suitable standard was devised.[12] The same principle has been used in the General Electric X-ray photometer developed by Michel and Rich.[21] This photometer has a chopper on the X-ray beam so that the rate of synchronous commutation between the standard and sample is 30 times per second. This unit operates satisfactorily on the ordinary unregulated 110-volt a-c supply.

A few of the many applications of the X-ray photometer include determination of tetraethyllead content of gasoline, sulfur content of oil, halogen content of halogenated hydrocarbon polymers, additives in lubricating oil, ash content of coal, and measurement of sample thickness.

In addition, it should be realized that the Norelco and G.E. XRD-3 units previously described can be used not only for fluorescence analysis but for all types of absorption analysis as well.

Bibliography

Books

A. H. Compton and S. K. Allison, *X-Rays in Theory and Experiment*, 2nd ed., D. Van Nostrand, New York (1935).

N. F. M. Henry, H. Lipson, and W. A. Wooster, *The Interpretation of X-Ray Diffraction Photographs*, MacMillan, London (1951).

H. Hirst, *X-Rays in Research and Industry*, Chemical Publishing Co., Brooklyn (1943).

W. T. Sproull, *X-Rays in Practice*, McGraw-Hill, New York (1946).

J. M. Robertson, *Organic Crystals and Molecules*, Cornell University Press, Ithaca (1953).

Articles

Symposium on X-Rays as an Analytical Tool, *Anal. Chem.*, 25, 688–748 (1953).

[21] T. C. Michel and T. A. Rich, *Gen. Elec. Rev.*, 50, 45 (1947).

CHAPTER 20

Mass Spectrometry

If a beam of electrons is passed through a tube containing a gas at very low pressures, positively charged ions of the gas are formed. A beam of these positively charged ions will normally travel in a straight line but, if subjected to an electric or a magnetic field, will be deflected in the form of a parabola. If the beam consists of positive ions of different masses, a series of parabolic paths will be obtained.

In 1919, Aston designed a positive-ray deflection apparatus based on these principles. In this instrument the electric and magnetic fields were so arranged that all particles of the same mass were brought to a focus so as to produce a fine line. These lines were recorded on a photographic plate. Since each line was characteristic of the presence of atoms or molecules of one particular mass, the over-all picture was called a *mass spectrum*, and the instrument was called a *mass spectrograph*. In place of a photographic plate, present-day instruments have sensitive electrometers to record the positive ion currents for each particular mass. The nonphotographic instruments are called *mass spectrometers*.

20.1 Mass-spectrometer development. A year before Aston finished his mass spectrograph, A. J. Dempster constructed an instrument that could determine not only the relative masses but also the relative proportions of the positive ions present.

A schematic diagram of this instrument is shown in Fig. 20.1. The substance to be analyzed is vaporized by heating it electrically. The atoms or molecules in the vapor are then subjected to bombardment by electrons emitted from a hot filament. Some of the positive ions formed pass through S_1 and are then accelerated by a potential difference V of 1000 volts or more maintained between the plates P_1 and P_2. The ions pass through the slit S_2 with the same kinetic energy, and hence the lighter ions have less momentum than the heavy ones. The ions move perpendicular to the magnetic field in semicircular paths with radii proportional to their respective momenta or masses. By varying V the ions of any desired mass can be made to pass through the slit S_3 to a collector plate. The positive ion currents are measured with a suitable electrometer. The main feature of this mass spectrometer is that it gives *direction focusing;* i.e., charged particles of the same mass coming out of the slit S_2 in different directions are all brought to a focus at S_3.

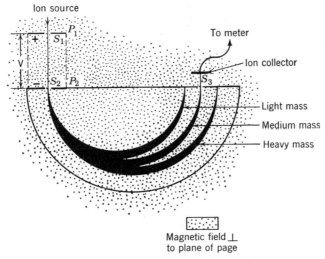

Fig. 20.1 Dempster mass spectrometer

In 1932 Bainbridge designed a mass spectrometer with *velocity focusing.* This spectrometer employed the combined action of crossed electric and magnetic fields (see Fig. 20.2). The beam of positive ions is directed through the slits S_1 and S_2 into crossed electric and magnetic fields. With the slit openings S_1 and S_2 in a straight line the combined fields act as a velocity filter since the two forces, electric and magnetic, are in opposite directions, and one of these forces, the magnetic, depends upon the velocity of the charged particle. Hence, a constant-energy ion beam entering such crossed fields is dispersed into its component parts. Those component mass beams that do not have the critical velocity are deflected to one side. The net result is that all ions leaving the slit S_3 have the same velocity.

Present-day commercial instruments have both direction and velocity focusing and are, for convenience, divided into two types, the

Dempster 180° or π-radian spectrometer (Figs. 20.1 and 20.2) and the 60° sector type * shown in Fig. 20.3. The sector type is based on the idea of Barber,[1] who pointed out that, if the central beam of

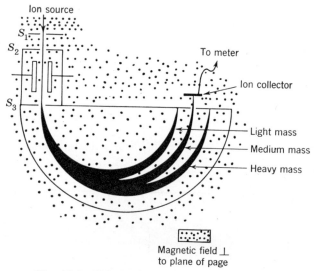

Fig. 20.2   Velocity-focusing mass spectrometer

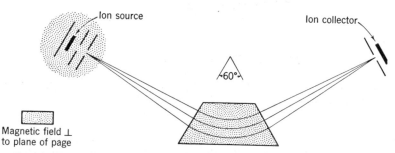

Fig. 20.3   Schematic diagram of a 60° sector-type mass spectrometer

a diverging group of ions enters and leaves a uniform magnetic field normal to the pole edges, the ions come to a focus on a line extended from the source through the center of curvature of the central beam.

As can be seen from a comparison of Figs. 20.1 and 20.3 the main difference between the 180° and the 60° sector type is that the source in the 60° sector type lies outside and some distance from the analyzer

---

* Occasionally the sector-type spectrometer has a 90° deflection.
[1] N. F. Barber, *Proc. Leeds Phil. Soc.*, 2, 427 (1933).

magnetic field. To maintain a well-defined electron beam in the ion source, a small source magnet is needed with the sector-type instrument. However, the sector-type instrument requires a much smaller analyzer magnet than the 180° type.

The equation relating the variables concerned in the deflection of a positive ion of a given mass for both types of spectrometers is given by

$$m/e = H^2 r^2 / 2V$$

where m = the mass in grams, e = the charge in abcoulombs, H = the magnetic field strength in gausses, r = the radius of curvature in centimeters, and V = the potential difference of the electric field in abvolts. This gives all quantities in consistent electromagnetic units.

In addition to conventional mass spectrometers whose design is based on the above equation, Goudsmit and coworkers [2,3] have constructed a magnetic-time-of-flight mass spectrometer. This instrument is based on the cyclotron principle that for N revolutions in a uniform magnetic field of H gausses, the time of flight T of an ion of atomic weight M is independent of its path and is given by

$$T = 652NM/H \ \mu sec$$

Short bursts of ions, lasting a fraction of a microsecond, are released at the rate of a few hundred per second from a small conventional ion source. After a number of revolutions in the magnetic field the ion burst is collected on a beryllium–copper plate from which electrons are released and which is the first plate of a twelve-stage multiplier.[4] The time-measuring equipment follows the radar principle of Loran [5] navigation receivers. Although primarily designed for precision mass measurements, this instrument has been successfully adapted to conventional analytical problems. The whole mass spectrum is observed continuously on an oscilloscope, and changes in the sample composition are seen instantaneously.

[2] S. A. Goudsmit, *Phys. Rev.*, 74, 622 (1948).

[3] E. E. Hays, P. I. Richards, and S. A. Goudsmit, *ibid.*, 84, 824 (1951); 85, 630 (1952).

[4] L. G. Smith, *Rev. Sci. Instruments*, 22, 166 (1951).

[5] See *Loran*, Vol. 4, of MIT Radiation Lab. Series, McGraw-Hill, New York (1949).

20.2 Commercial mass spectrometers. At the present time the three major manufacturers of mass spectrometers are Consolidated Engineering Corporation, General Electric Company, and Process Industries. As a typical example of a commercial instrument, the

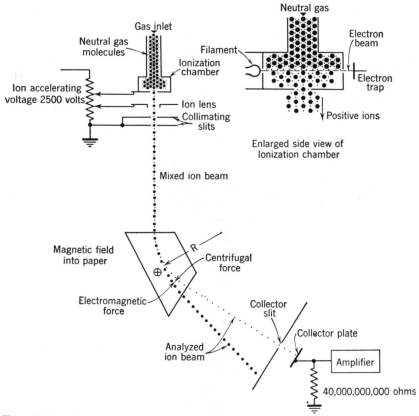

Fig. 20.4   Schematic diagram of General Electric mass spectrometer (Courtesy General Electric Company)

General Electric mass spectrometer will be considered in some detail. Schematic diagrams illustrating the principle of operation of this 60° sector type and its functional components are shown in Figs. 20.4 and 20.5.

The material is analyzed in the following manner.

(*a*) The sample is introduced into the low-vacuum side of the system which is maintained at 10^{-4} to 10^{-5} mm of mercury. The neutral gas molecules pass through a small leak † and into the ion source which is maintained at a pressure of 10^{-6} to 10^{-7} mm. The gas molecules are bombarded with electrons emitted from a heated filament. The direction of the electron stream is controlled by a

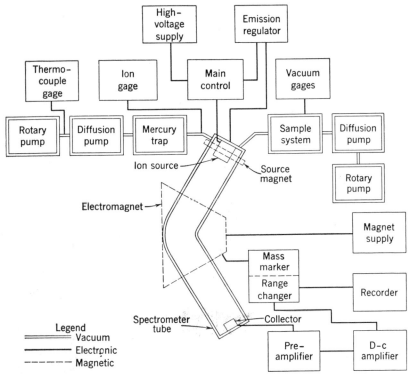

Fig. 20.5 Functional components of the General Electric mass spectrometer (Courtesy General Electric Company)

source magnet and the intensity regulated by the emission regulator. Un-ionized molecules are drawn out of the system by an exhaust pump.

(b) The positive ions are accelerated by a high voltage and focused by an ion lens into a sharp beam.

† Leaks are normally made by punching a small hole through some noble metal such as gold or platinum and then hammering the hole shut. A simpler method involves blowing a thin Pyrex bulb and sealing the thin glass to the end of a piece of glass tubing. By evacuating the tubing and sparking the thin bulb once with a Tesla-type vacuum testing coil a suitable leak is obtained.

(c) The high-velocity ion beam passes through a narrow collimating slit into a region free from electric fields, forming a collimated beam of uniform energy.

(d) The ion beam passes through a strong magnetic field, and ions of different mass follow circular paths of different radii.

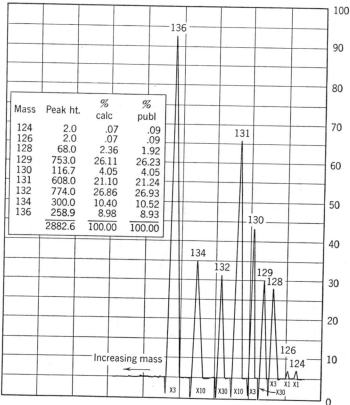

Mass	Peak ht.	% calc	% publ
124	2.0	.07	.09
126	2.0	.07	.09
128	68.0	2.36	1.92
129	753.0	26.11	26.23
130	116.7	4.05	4.05
131	608.0	21.10	21.24
132	774.0	26.86	26.93
134	300.0	10.40	10.52
136	258.9	8.98	8.93
	2882.6	100.00	100.00

Fig. 20.6   Mass spectrum of xenon taken with the General Electric analytical mass spectrometer (Courtesy General Electric Company)

(e) Ions having a particular specific mass pass through a narrow collector slit and strike a collector plate.

(f) The collector plate current is measured, giving an indication of the abundance of the particular mass for which the instrument is adjusted. This abundance is recorded on a strip chart as a peak, and the peak height is directly proportional to the abundance of the mass number present (see Fig. 20.6).

(g) A precollector slit, consisting of a fine-wire electrode, collects some of the ions of a given mass number just before the majority of ions of the same mass number pass through the main slit and are collected. The precollector electrode current activates suitable circuits so that the recorder sensitivity and speed are automatically adjusted for optimum recording of each mass peak.

(h) For a fixed geometrical arrangement of spectrometer tube and collector electrodes, the specific mass is proportional to the square of the magnetic field. By varying the magnet current, the magnetic field is varied, and the mass spectrum from mass 1 to 300 can be continuously scanned.

The complete assembly of the General Electric mass spectrometer is shown in Fig. 20.7.

The Consolidated Engineering Corporation manufactures the model-21-103 mass spectrometer, designed primarily for the qualitative and quantitative analyses of mixtures of gases and liquids. The model 21-201 is designed for isotope-ratio measurements, and the model 21-401 is a combined analytical- and isotope-ratio mass spectrometer.

The model-21-103 mass spectrometer is the 180° type. The ion source is mounted on the 180° ion-segregating tube and lies within the gap of an electromagnet. The recording system consists of an oscillograph recorder with four galvanometers, each operating at a different sensitivity level. Light beams reflected from the galvanometer mirrors record simultaneously on a photographic paper. Special features include direct measurements of sample pressures with an electronic micromanometer, and control of the operating temperature of the ion source within a fraction of a degree. The scope of the instrument is limited mainly by sample volatility. Components to be analyzed must exert sufficient vapor pressure at room temperature to provide a vapor-phase sample at about 50 microns absolute pressure.

The isotope-ratio mass spectrometer model 21-201 is based on the design of A. O. Nier.[6] The instrument, as the name implies is designed for the measurement of the ratio of stable isotopes. The operation of this instrument is shown in Fig. 20.8.

Molecules of gas, at an absolute pressure of about 30 mm mercury are continuously bled through a capillary restriction a into an ion source b where a much lower pressure is maintained to prevent inter-collisions among them. This atmosphere of neutral molecules is bombarded with electrons c from a hot filament to convert them to

[6] A. O. Nier, E. P. Ney, and M. G. Ingraham, Phys. Rev., 70, 116 (1946).

positively charged particles, or ions. The positive ions thus formed are projected into the analyzer tube at high velocity by means of the electric potential maintained between the focusing and collimating

Fig. 20.7   General Electric mass spectrometer (Courtesy General Electric Company)

slits d. In the analyzer tube, the ions are acted upon by a 60° sector magnetic field e in such a manner that ions of different masses are brought to a focus at physically separated positions in the neighborhood of the two ion collectors, f and g. Through proper adjustment of the magnetic field and the accelerating potential, ions of a given specific mass are made to strike the no. 2 collector f, and then ions of lighter and adjacent, or nearly adjacent, mass automatically fall on the no. 1 collector g. The charge on each collector, given up by the ions, is amplified by a discrete amplifier channel. The output of

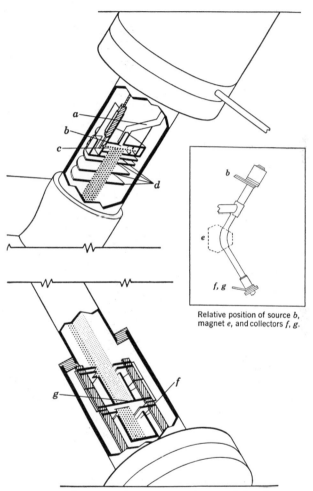

Relative position of source b, magnet e, and collectors f, g.

Fig. 20.8 Schematic diagram of operation of Consolidated-Nier isotope-ratio mass spectrometer model 21-201 (Courtesy Consolidated Engineering Company)

one amplifier is then balanced against the output of the other to an electrical null by attenuating with decade-resistor dials. The numerical value of the ratio of the intensities of the two ion "beams" is obtained directly from these decade dials.

Since the spread between two ion beams at their point of focus decreases with the mass of the ions, the dual collectors are not suitable for the simultaneous collection of hydrogen and deuterium ions. The lowest range in which beams of adjacent mass can be collected

Fig. 20.9   Consolidated model-21-401 spectrometer (Courtesy Consolidated Engineering Company)

simultaneously is in the region of mass 15. However, deuterium can be determined by comparing the intensities of the HD/H_2 ratios with a reference voltage as a standard of comparison.

The Consolidated model 21-401 (Fig. 20.9) is a 180° mass spectrometer with somewhat unusual design. About 160° of the ion path is in the maximum magnetic field, while the ion source and collector ends are at about one-third this field intensity. Spectrum scanning from mass 2 to mass 100 is performed magnetically by motor-driven shunts on a permanent magnet. The spectra are recorded automatically on a strip recorder with the peak magnitudes being anticipated by an auxiliary collector and amplifier to permit automatic alteration of the recorded peaks. Figure 20.10 shows the partial spectrum of *n*-butane as recorded on this instrument. A dual collector is also available for isotope-ratio measurements.

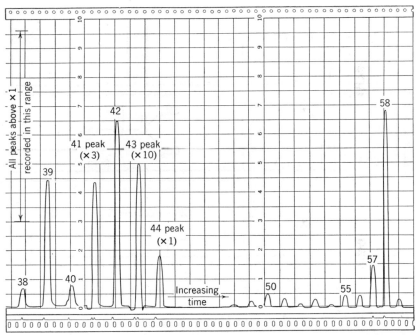

Fig. 20.10   Partial spectrum of *n*-butane obtained on Consolidated model-21-401 mass spectrometer (Courtesy Consolidated Engineering Company)

For the location and measurement of leaks in evacuated or pressure systems, the Consolidated Engineering Corporation manufactures the model-24-101A leak detector. This leak detector is a simplified, portable mass spectrometer sensitive to minute traces of helium. Inert, noncontaminating helium is used as a probe gas in testing either evacuated or pressurized systems. Both visual and audible indicators are available for checking for leaks.

20.3   Variables involved in the production of mass spectra. (*a*) *Molecular Structure.* The molecular structure of an organic compound is the most important variable in determining the relative abundance of ions of a given mass obtained in the mass spectrum. For example, the mass spectra of three related ketones, methyl *n*-propyl, methyl isopropyl, and methyl cyclopropyl ketone are shown in Fig. 20.11. Although each compound has a distinct mass spectrum, there are similarities in the patterns because of similarities in the molecules themselves. Methyl *n*-propyl ketone and methyl isopropyl ketone have very strong peaks at mass 43, whereas the peak

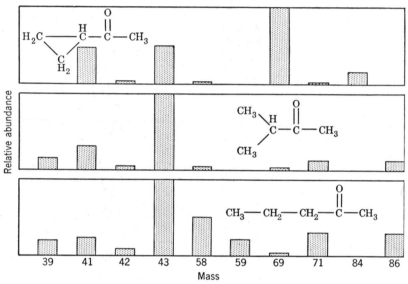

Fig. 20.11   Relative abundance for mass spectra of three ketones

at mass 43 in the cyclopropyl ketone is considerably weaker. The mass of the *n*-propyl or isopropyl radical is 43, and so is the mass of the CH$_3$—C— group. Apparently both groups contribute to the 43 peak in the *n*-propyl and isopropyl ketones but only the CH$_3$—C group can contribute in the cyclopropyl ketone. In contrast, cyclopropyl methyl ketone has strong peaks at masses of the groups. The parent peaks (i.e. the peaks at masses equal to the molecular weight) are apparent at 86 for the *n*-propyl and isopropyl ketones and at 84 for methyl cyclopropyl ketone. A mass spectrum is often a good check on the molecular weight. However, as the molecular weight increases, the parent peaks diminish in intensity, and, for molecules of high molecular weight, the parent peak is often not observed. Although certain peaks can be attributed fairly well to certain groups in the molecule, many others cannot be. Rearrangements often occur in the process of positive ion formation to complicate the pattern further. Attempts to predict a mass spectrum of a given molecule from its molecular structure have not been successful, and the correlations that have been made are largely on an empirical basis. Unlike infrared and Raman spectra, the mass spectrum of an organic compound is not invariant but depends on the conditions under which the spectrum is obtained.

(*b*) *Ionizing Voltage.* The ionizing voltage has a very large effect on the mass spectrum obtained. Figure 20.12 shows the mass spectrum of cyclopropyl *tert*-butyl ketone obtained at various ionizing voltages on Goudsmit's magnetic time-of-flight mass spectrometer. The lower scale shown in Fig. 20.12 is an electronic mass scale which is displayed simultaneously with the ion pulses on the oscilloscope. The height of the pulses represents the relative abundance of a positive ion of that particular mass. In particular, marked changes in the peak intensities are apparent at lower voltages. Peak intensities relative to one another remain fairly consistent above 50 volts. For this reason in the American Petroleum Institute Compilation of Mass Spectral Data the spectra are normally reported at 50 and 70 volts.

The minimum ionizing voltage required to ionize a molecule is known as the *appearance potential.* Occasionally two different positive ions of the same mass but of different appearance potentials may be separated by gradually increasing the ionizing voltage from zero until first one and then the other isomer appears on the recorder. The unusual variation of the positive ion current of H_3O^+ with ionizing voltage enables one to distinguish between the ions H_3O^+ and HOD^+. Figure 20.13 shows the variation of peak height or positive ion current as the ionizing voltage is varied.[7] The curve for HOD^+ was obtained from a 50:50 mixture of H_2O and D_2O and that for H_3O^+ from a mixture of H_2 and H_2O. A practical test for distin-

[7] F. J. Norton, *ibid.*, 85, 154 (1952).

guishing between the ions H_3O^+ and HOD^+ is to measure the ratio of mass-19 positive ion current at 20 volts ionizing potential to that at 70 volts. For H_3O^+ the ratio is 2.0; for HOD^+ the ratio is 0.45.

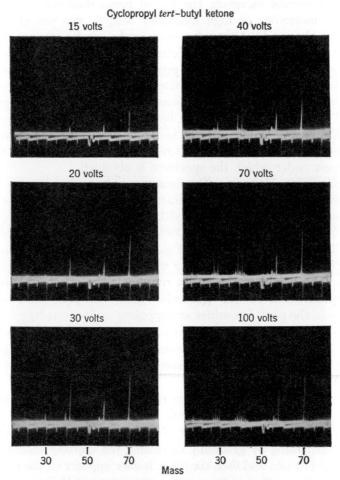

Cyclopropyl _tert_-butyl ketone

Fig. 20.12   Effect of ionizing potential

(_c_) _Kinetic Energy of Ions._ The relative abundances of positive ions of different masses formed by electron impact in the source of a mass spectrometer are not necessarily the same as the relative abundances of these same positive ions received by the collector plate and recorded. The preferential collection of ions of certain masses is called discrimination. One of the consequences of discrimination is that the mass-spectral patterns of molecules or mixtures of isotopes vary with the particular magnetic field and accelerating voltage chosen to focus the various ions on the collector. This is particularly evidenced by the patterns reported in the American Petroleum Institute Research Project 44, Catalogue of Mass Spectral Data. If the patterns obtained with a relatively low accelerating voltage and magnetic scanning are compared with those obtained at higher voltages using electrostatic scanning, differences as large as a factor of two are not uncommon among the lighter fragments.

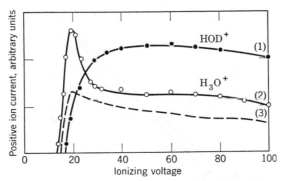

Fig. 20.13   Ionizing efficiency curves for H_3O+ and $HOD+$ (Courtesy *Physical Reviews*)

Discrimination effects are believed to be caused by differences in the initial kinetic energy of the positive ions formed at the source. This initial kinetic energy may be thermal energy acquired from the neutral molecule, or it may be thermal plus some kinetic energy acquired during the rupture of chemical bonds in the ionization process. Variations in the initial velocities of the ions of different masses cause these ions to have different efficiencies in traversing the slit in the ion source. Figure 20.14 shows the variation in ion intensity with ion accelerating voltage for Kr^{84}, A^{40} and He^4 obtained by Schaeffer [8] on a 60° sector-type mass spectrometer. The experimental curves in Fig. 20.14 have been plotted in such a way that at 5000 volts all curves have the same value; i.e., the intensities have been adjusted to make the 5000-volt value the same as the calculated curve. The calculation was made in terms of the geometry

[8] O. A. Schaeffer, AECU-971, U. S. Atomic Energy Commission (Oct. 17, 1951).

of the ion source on the basis that the decrease in intensity as the voltage is lowered is caused by the thermal energy of the ions in the source. It is quite evident that the calculated curve does not approximate the experimental curves except for the region from 4000 to 5000 volts. This indicates that other minor variables, as well as the initial kinetic energy of the ions, cause discrimination. Schaeffer [9]

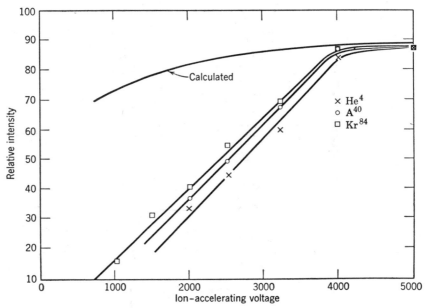

Fig. 20.14   Collected ion current as a function of ion-accelerating voltage
(O. A. Schaeffer, AEC Unclassified Report, AECU-971, October 17, 1951)

has also compared the accuracy of data obtained with magnetic and electrostatic mass scanning by measuring the abundance of the krypton isotopes by both methods. The masses were scanned by varying the magnetic field at different ion-accelerating voltages from 750 to 5000 volts and also by varying the accelerating voltage at constant magnetic field. The data are shown in Table 20.1. As the magnetically scanned results are independent of the ion-accelerating voltage, these results are probably free from voltage discrimination errors. The results of the magnetic scanning agree well with Nier's values,[10] showing that, with magnetic scanning, isotope abundances can be

[9] O. A. Schaeffer, *J. Chem. Phys.*, **18**, 1681 (1950).
[10] A. O. Nier, *Phys. Rev.*, **77**, 789 (1950).

TABLE 20.1

Isotope Abundances of Krypton with Different Scanning Methods

Mass	Magnetic Scanning, volts							Electro-static Scanning [*]
	750	1000	1500	2000	3000	4000	5000	
78	0.350	0.347	0.351	0.353	0.357	0.354	0.358	0.39
80	2.26	2.27	2.27	2.29	2.33	2.32	2.31	2.52
82	11.62	11.63	11.61	11.55	11.55	11.59	11.58	12.03
83	11.51	11.57	11.54	11.47	11.48	11.52	11.51	11.64
84	56.76	56.93	56.96	57.10	56.99	56.90	56.99	56.80
86	17.48	17.25	17.29	17.25	17.30	17.31	17.28	16.62

* Magnetic field such that mass 78 is focused at 1700 volts ion-accelerating potential.

measured directly without resorting to calibrating the instrument with known mixtures.

(*d*) *Other Variables.* The mass spectrum obtained also depends upon the temperature of the molecule during the ionization process. Probably the change in relative abundance with temperature is caused by changes in the number of molecules occupying different vibrational energy levels, which will influence different mechanisms of ionization. The temperature of the ionization chamber should be kept constant to obtain reproducible spectra.

Metastable ions, i.e., positive ions formed at the source which dissociate before reaching the detector, may often cause a diffuse background on the mass spectrum.

Occasionally, in working with relatively nonvolatile compounds, certain masses may be continuously detected for as long as several days. These "memory effects" often can constitute serious errors if proper precautions are not taken in the cleaning and maintenance of the mass spectrometer.

20.4   Applications of the mass spectrometer. It should be apparent from the discussion in the previous section that mass spectra are valuable for qualitative analysis. Again as in infrared, Raman, and X-ray diffraction work, a large library of known spectra is needed. The best compilation of mass spectra has been published by S. M. Rock.[11] This article contains the spectra of 279 compounds with peak intensities indicated only as being in one of the classes: 0–2%, 2–20%, 20–50%, and 50–100% of the base peak (i.e. the strongest peak in the compound). Such an indication of the relative magnitudes of the peaks is sufficient for the usual qualitative identification

[11] S. M. Rock, *Anal. Chem., 23,* 261 (1951).

of hydrocarbons. Mass spectra of hydrocarbons containing 14 to 32 carbon atoms have been published by O'Neal and Wier.[12] The spectra were obtained with a Consolidated Engineering Corporation analytical mass spectrometer modified to provide spectra up to mass 600. The inlet system was heated and, as shown in Fig. 20.15, has a gallium-covered sintered disk in place of the conventional mercury-covered disk for the introduction of liquid samples.

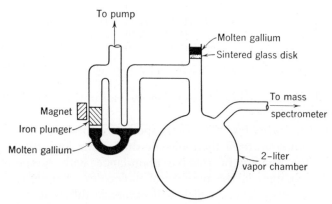

Fig. 20.15   Inlet system used for mass spectra of hydrocarbons (Courtesy *Analytical Chemistry*)

Although mass spectra are very valuable for qualitative analyses, there are a few similar compounds with identical spectra. For example, mass spectra will not distinguish between the positional isomers of trimethyl benzene.

(*a*) *Quantitative Applications.* At the present time the most important application of the mass spectrometer is in the quantitative analysis of complex petroleum fractions. This analysis depends upon the fact that the mass spectrum of a component mixture is a linear superposition of the mass spectrum of each individual component. The problem is very similar to that discussed previously in absorption spectroscopy where the components to be analyzed absorbed at the same wavelength. Again the analysis involves the setting up of a series of simultaneous linear equations. To determine the contribution of each component at a given mass, it is necessary to measure the mass spectrum of each component in order to find the peak height obtained for a given partial pressure of this component. Since the peak heights are directly proportional to the partial pres-

12 M. J. O'Neal, Jr., and T. P. Wier, Jr., *ibid.*, 23, 830 (1951).

sure of the gas, the coefficients determined for the pure component can then be substituted into the series of simultaneous equations. For example, consider the simple case of a mixture composed of the components x, y, and z which are measured at say masses 43, 56, and 70. The equations would be

$$X_{43}p_x + Y_{43}p_y + Z_{43}p_z = H_{43}$$

$$X_{56}p_x + Y_{56}p_y + Z_{56}p_z = H_{56}$$

$$X_{70}p_x + Y_{70}p_y + Z_{70}p_z = H_{70}$$

where p_x, p_y, and p_z represent the partial pressures of x, y, and z in the inlet sample system.

X_{43}, X_{56}, and X_{70} represent the height of the peak at masses 43, 56, and 70 with *unit* pressure of X in the inlet sample system. Y and Z represent the corresponding values for y and z. H_{43}, H_{56}, H_{70} represent the total peak heights at masses 43, 56, and 70.

In order to obtain the coefficients X_{43}, X_{56}, and X_{70}, component X would be put in the system at a known pressure and its mass spectrum recorded. Then,

$$X_{43}p = H'_{43} \quad \text{(measured)}$$

By measuring the peak height H' at mass 43 for the known pressure p, the coefficient X_{43} can be obtained. The other coefficients are obtained in a similar manner. Usually the number of equations to be solved is in the neighborhood of 8 or 10, and for speed an analog computer similar to that described by Berry et al.[13] (commercially available from Consolidated Engineering Corporation) is normally required.

For certain types of mixtures the number of simultaneous equations to be solved can be reduced if certain components of the mixture have characteristic peaks that are not contributed to by the remaining constituents. Another simplification is possible if the ratio of heavy to light isotope peaks are known. In actual practice the analysis of a mixture is often considerably simplified if the mixture is first fractionated into several components by distillation.

(*b*) *Isotope Analysis.* The determination of isotopic ratios is an important application of mass spectrometry as is evidenced by the design of several commercial instruments for such analyses. The

[13] C. E. Berry, D. E. Wilcox, S. M. Rock, and H. W. Washburn, *J. Applied Phys.*, 17, 262 (1946).

availability of a wide variety of stable isotopes from Oak Ridge National Laboratories has increased the use of stable isotopes in tracer experiments. The quantitative analysis of the ratio of uranium isotopes to determine the degree of enrichment is very important in the field of atomic energy.

With the present availability of 99 mole per cent D_2O, experiments with deuterated compounds for the purpose of clarifying reaction mechanisms, or making frequency assignments of optical spectra, have been constantly increasing. Mass spectra are the most suitable way of confirming the structure of such deuterated compounds.

In a sample of $CH_3CH_2CD_2OH$, it was desired to show that the substitution of deuterium was on the carbon atom as indicated. The mass spectra of this alcohol and of normal propanol were obtained. The parent peak of propanol occurs at mass 60 and of $CH_3CH_2CD_2OH$ at 62, showing that there are two deuterium atoms present. In addition, the strongest peak in propanol at 31, which can be attributed only to a CH_2OH group, occurs at 33 in $CH_3CH_2CD_2OH$. Obviously, two possibilities exist, a CHD—OD or a CD_2OH group. Further inspection of the minor peaks of the two alcohols shows that propanol has a fairly strong peak at 59, one mass unit below the parent, while $CH_3CH_2CD_2OH$ has a peak at 60, two mass units below the parent. According to the studies of Friedman and Turkevich [14] on deuterated isopropyl alcohols, a hydrogen atom is removed from the carbon atom adjacent to the oxygen atom, and not from the OH group in the formation of this positive ion fragment. Such evidence supports the choice of a CD_2OH group. However, to prove this point further, the mass spectrum of $CH_3CH_2CH_2OD$ was obtained. The mass spectrum of this compound contains a strong peak at mass 32, and, more important, the strong peak just below the parent mass of 61 is at 60 and not at 59; thus confirming again the observation of Friedman and Turkevich and leading to the definite conclusion that the structure of the first alcohol was CH_3-CH_2CD_2OH. The mass spectra of these alcohols are shown in Fig. 20.16.

The isotope-dilution technique [15,16] is a method of analysis that is a promising adjunct to many phases of research. This technique applies both to elemental analysis and to the determination of indi-

[14] L. Friedman and J. Turkevich, *J. Am. Chem. Soc.*, 74, 1666 (1952).

[15] A. V. Grosse, S. G. Hindin, and A. D. Kirshenbaum, *Anal. Chem.*, 21, 386 (1949).

[16] H. Gest, M. E. Kamen, and J. M. Reiner, *Arch. Biochem.*, XII, 273 (1947).

vidual compounds in complex mixtures. In both cases it involves the addition of measured amounts of a rare isotope to mixtures being analyzed, and subsequent determination of the extent of dilution of the isotope in the mixture. For compounds, the extent of dilution of a compound enriched with a rare isotope is determined. The outstanding advantage of this method is that the element or compound being determined need not be isolated. Similar techniques have

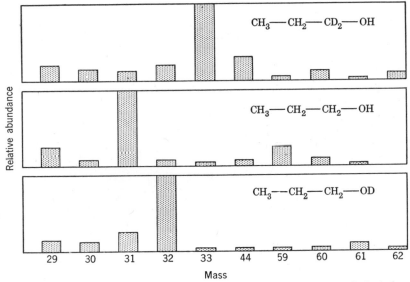

Fig. 20.16   Relative abundance for mass spectra of three *n*-propyl alcohols

been developed with radioactive isotopes and will be discussed in Chapter 21.

(*c*) *Reaction Mechanisms.* A very interesting application of the mass spectrometer to the study of reaction intermediates has been described by Eltenton.[17]   In this work a reaction chamber was coupled to a Dempster-type mass spectrometer in such a way that short-lived intermediates could reach the electron beam. The presence of free radicals was denoted by an increase in the ion current of the corresponding mass. The method has extended more than tenfold the pressure range in which free radicals are detectable, thus bridging the gap between mirror and spectroscopic methods so that low-pressure combustion phenomena may be studied.

[17] G. C. Eltenton, *J. Chem. Phys.*, **15**, 455 (1947).

Leifer and Urey [18] have applied the mass spectrometer to the continuous analysis of the gases formed during the thermal decomposition of dimethyl ether.

In a more recent paper by Bragg, McCarty, and Norton [19] concerning the kinetics of the pyrolysis of diborane, the concentrations of several participant species were followed during the reaction with a mass spectrometer.

(d) *Miscellaneous.* Stevenson [20] has obtained the bond strengths for the C—H bond in methane and ethane and for the C—C bond in ethane and normal butane by combining heats of reaction with appearance potentials measured in a mass spectrometer.

Gorman, Jones, and Hipple [21] have analyzed stainless steels with a spark source and a mass spectrometer. Although the simplicity of the spectra obtained has an advantage over emission spectra, the time-consuming operation of loading solid samples in the vacuum system poses a problem that has as yet not been solved successfully by mass spectrographers.

Bibliography

Books

F. W. Aston, *Mass Spectra and Isotopes,* Longmans, Green, New York and London (1942).

Review Articles

Series of articles in *J. Applied Phys., 13*, 526–569 (1942).
J. A. Hipple and M. Shepherd, *Anal. Chem., 21*, 32 (1949).
M. Shepherd and J. A. Hipple, *ibid., 22*, 23 (1950).
V. H. Dibeler and J. A. Hipple, *ibid., 24*, 27 (1952).

[18] E. Leifer and H. C. Urey, *J. Am. Chem. Soc., 64*, 994 (1942).
[19] J. K. Bragg, L. V. McCarty, and F. J. Norton, *ibid., 73*, 2134 (1951).
[20] D. P. Stevenson, *J. Chem. Phys., 10*, 291 (1942).
[21] J. G. Gorman, E. J. Jones, and J. A. Hipple, *Anal. Chem., 23*, 438 (1951).

CHAPTER 21

Nuclear-Radiation Measurements

For many years the naturally radioactive elements have been detected and determined by measurement of the nuclear radiations which they produce. The small number of these elements and their minor industrial importance left the field to a few specialists, mostly concerned with radium. In more recent years the production of radioactive isotopes of most of the common elements has made the measurement of nuclear radiation a useful method of analysis.

Since the isotopes of an element differ only in their mass, the radioactive isotopes follow the common inactive isotopes in all of their chemical reactions. The radioactivity, however, allows the detection or determination of the active isotope in a simple, convenient manner.

The analytical chemist may use radioactive isotopes as a means of following analytical processes, or he may be called upon to measure the activity of materials used in process development or testing. In either case, he is usually concerned with determining a single radioactive species. This chapter will deal with the determination of the activity of samples of radioactive materials. Other fields, such as beta and gamma spectroscopy and activation analysis, must be left to more specialized texts.

21.1 Characteristics of nuclear radiation. In previous chapters we have considered the emission and absorption of radiant energy in the X-ray, ultraviolet, visible, and infrared regions of the spectrum. These radiations were produced by changes in the energy levels of orbital electrons or changes in molecular states. Both emission and absorption spectra appear only under the influence of external forces, excitation or irradiation. The emission of nuclear radiation, on the contrary, is a spontaneous process. The atomic nucleus, by a series of internal energy transfers, reaches an unstable state and disintegrates, emitting nuclear radiation. The residual atom, called a

351

daughter, may be stable, or it may be unstable and in turn disintegrate.

Some unstable isotopes disintegrate by the loss of alpha particles (helium nuclei) and others by the loss of beta particles (electrons) from the nucleus. As a secondary effect, gamma rays (similar to X rays) may be produced simultaneously with the alpha or beta particles. All three types of nuclear radiation are detectable and are usable in qualitative and quantitative analysis for radioactive isotopes.

The magnitude of the energies involved in the various types of electromagnetic radiation was given in Table 2.2. Although only the gamma rays are electromagnetic radiation, the particulate alpha and beta emission are also spoken of as radiation, and their kinetic energy may be expressed in the same energy units.

TABLE 21.1

Typical Energy of Nuclear Radiation

	Ergs	Mev
Alpha	$6.4 - 12.8 \times 10^{-6}$	4–8
Beta	$0 - 4.8 \times 10^{-6}$	0–3
Gamma	$0 - 3.2 \times 10^{-6}$	0–2

The usual energy units are millions of electron volts (Mev) or thousands of electron volts (Kev), where the electron volt (ev) is defined as the energy acquired by an electron in falling through a potential difference of one volt.

The most interesting and useful characteristic of nuclear disintegrations is their rate of occurrence. All known reactions are simple first order, the rate depending only on the number of atoms of the species present. Mathematically the number remaining at any time may be expressed as

$$N = N_0 e^{-\lambda t}$$

where N = number of atoms present at time t, N_0 = number of atoms present at time zero, λ = disintegration constant (fraction disintegrating per unit time), and t = time. The quantities λ and t must be in consistent units. The differential form of this equation is also of interest.

$$dN/dt = -\lambda N$$

This equation shows that for a given isotope of known λ we can calculate either the disintegration rate or the number of atoms present at any time provided that the other quantity is known.

First-order reactions proceed at such a rate that half the atoms present at any time will react in a certain period of time (dependent on λ). At the end of two such periods, three quarters of the atoms will have reacted, and so on. This period of time is known as the half-life ($T_{\frac{1}{2}}$) for a radioactive species, and is related to λ, since,

$$T_{\frac{1}{2}} = 0.693/\lambda$$

The half-lives of the known isotopes range from a fraction of a microsecond to billions of years.

It is now apparent that we can determine the number of atoms of a known radioactive species if we can measure or count the number of disintegrations occurring in a unit time. This is the important characteristic for quantitative analysis.

Qualitatively, we may characterize a radioactive species by the type of radiation produced, by the energy of the radiation, and by the half-life. Naturally, preliminary chemical separations and reactions are sometimes useful in characterizing the isotope, but the final analysis is by its radioactive properties.

21.2 Alpha emission. Decay of an isotopic species by alpha emission is characteristic of the heaviest natural elements and the transuranic elements. In a practical sense, all the alpha particles from a particular isotope will have a single fixed value of kinetic energy, and almost all of the alpha-particle energies for different isotopes lie within the limits of 4 to 8 Mev. Being a helium nucleus, when the alpha particle is emitted the mass drops four units, while the atomic number is decreased by two. A typical reaction could be expressed *

$$_{90}\mathrm{Ra}^{226} \rightarrow {}_2\mathrm{He}^4 + {}_{88}\mathrm{Rn}^{222}$$

Alpha particles lose their kinetic energy in passage through matter chiefly through interaction with electrons, causing ionization in the absorbing material. Their range in air is only a few centimeters, and in solids such as aluminum it is only a few microns. The dissipation of all this energy in a short distance means that alpha particles have

* In isotope notation, the superscript indicates the atomic weight to the nearest whole number (mass number) while the subscript indicates the atomic number. The latter may be omitted, as it is defined also by the element symbol.

a high specific ionization; that is, a large number of ions are produced in a unit path length.

The electrons produced by the direct action of the alpha particles are called primary electrons and are liberated with sufficient kinetic energy to cause further ionization in the material. Actually, the majority of the ionization produced by an alpha particle is secondary ionization caused by the primary electrons. The average energy required to produce an ion-electron pair is 32.5 ev and includes both primary and secondary ionization.

21.3 Beta emission. Decay by beta emission is characteristic of radioactive elements throughout the periodic table. The electrons produced from a particular isotope will have a continuous distribution of energies from zero up to a fixed maximum energy. The maximum-energy electron is emitted with no energy loss as it leaves the atom, while the others lose part of their energy internally, emerging with less than the maximum energy. The probability of occurrence of the various energies will be reproducible from sample to sample, and the energy distribution will therefore also be reproducible. The average energy will have a fixed value that is approximately one third of the maximum energy.

As an electron, the beta particle has a mass of 1/1840 atomic mass unit and a negative charge of one unit. When a beta particle is emitted, the mass remains essentially unchanged, but the atomic number is increased by one. A typical reaction would be

$$_{91}\text{Pa}^{234} \rightarrow e + {_{92}}\text{U}^{234}$$

Beta particles lose their kinetic energy in passage through matter by the same ionization processes as alpha particles. However, the smaller mass and charge and their higher velocity makes the probability of an interaction within a given path length much less than that for an alpha particle. Beta particles, therefore, have a lower specific ionization than alpha particles. The range of beta particles in air may be over a meter, whereas in aluminum energetic particles may penetrate several millimeters. The proportion of secondary electrons is even higher than with alpha particles, but the average energy loss per ion pair produced is the same, 32.5 ev.

The combination of energy distribution, scattering and other effects results in an absorption that follows approximately an exponential form,

$$I = I_0 e^{-\mu l}$$

where I = transmitted intensity, I_0 = initial intensity, μ = absorption coefficient for the absorber (not an absolute constant, for beta radiation is not monochromatic electromagnetic radiation), and l = absorber thickness.

Since μ is not absolutely constant, it cannot be used as a characteristic of the emitter. However, a plot of log I/I_0 against l is roughly linear, and the curve itself is very characteristic of the particular beta emitter studied.

The thickness of absorber that will just stop the most energetic beta particles emitted by an isotope is called the range and is also characteristic of the isotope.

21.4 Gamma emission. Gamma emission is a secondary effect where the loss of an alpha or beta particle has caused a nuclear disturbance requiring a further loss in energy for stability. Present evidence points to the existence of energy levels within the nucleus, so that a gamma emission corresponds to a transition between two levels. The number of different monochromatic gamma emissions is a function of the available energy levels, and their intensity is a function of the probability of each possible transition. The production of the gamma ray follows the alpha or beta particles so rapidly that we may consider it to be simultaneous.

Three modes of interaction are available for the loss of energy by gamma rays in their passage through matter. The particular mode that predominates is dependent on the energy of the gamma radiation and the atomic number (electron density) of the absorber. The first mode, for low energies and high atomic number absorbers is the photoelectric effect. The gamma photon ejects an electron from an atom of the absorber, any energy in excess of the binding energy being carried by the electron as kinetic energy.

Gamma photons of intermediate energy and absorbers of low atomic number show a mode of absorption called the Compton effect. The gamma energy is lost by several scattering collisions with free or loosely bound electrons which acquire kinetic energy in the process.

High-energy gamma rays in high-atomic-number absorbers lose energy by the mode of pair production. The minimum energy is 1.02 Mev,† and the positron plus electron formed will carry energy

† The requirement of 1.02 Mev is for the creation of two electrons, one positive and one negative. The mass-energy relationship is such that the formation or annihilation of an electron mass involves 0.51 Mev.

in excess of this minimum as kinetic energy. The positron after losing its kinetic energy will interact with any electron, and they will annihilate each other with the formation of two photons with 0.51-Mev energy each. These photons will then lose their energy by the two previous modes.

The net effect of any mode or combination of modes is ionization within the absorber. As in the absorption of alpha and beta radiation, the average energy loss per ion pair formed is 32.5 ev, including both primary and secondary ionization.

Gamma rays are monochromatic electromagnetic radiation and, as such, follow the same absorption laws as visible light, previously described. The range of gamma rays in air may be several meters and the extremely penetrating nature of the radiation is apparent when we consider that $\frac{1}{2}$ inch of lead reduces the gamma radiation from radium to only 50% of the incident value.

21.5 Other emission. Though the emission of alpha, beta, or gamma radiation is the common method of nuclear disintegration, three other effects are worth a brief mention. Positron emission occurs in a few of the artificial radioisotopes, and a typical reaction would be

$$_{15}P^{30} \rightarrow e^+ + {}_{14}Si^{30}$$

Positrons are similar to negative beta particles in energy distribution and ionization effects, but differ in that, after loss of their kinetic energy, they produce annihilation radiation (0.51-Mev gamma) as described in the preceding section.

The transformation shown in the capture of an orbital electron by the nucleus is similar to that of positron emission, for example,

$$_{29}Cu^{64} + e \rightarrow {}_{28}Ni^{64}$$

The most common capture is an orbital electron from the K, or innermost, shell, and the effect is then called K capture. It is detected by the X radiation produced when an outer electron falls into the inner level. The orbital capture may also be accompanied by gamma radiation if the nucleus is left in an excited state by the capture.‡

Another mode of disintegration occurs when a gamma photon leaving the nucleus produces a photoelectron in the decaying atom itself. This is spoken of as internal conversion, and differs from

‡ It should be pointed out again that gamma rays are due to energy-level changes within the nucleus, whereas X rays are due to energy-level changes of orbital electrons in levels near the nucleus.

normal beta emission in that the electrons have discrete energies rather than a continuous spectrum. In any gamma emission a fraction of the photons may cause internal conversion. The probability of such an event depends on the particular isotope, and the fraction of gamma rays causing internal conversion may vary from 0 to 1 for different gamma emitters.

21.6   Principles of radiation measurement. If we consider that our radiation measurement requires absorption of the radiant energy and measurement of the effect produced in the absorber, it is obvious that the different types of emission will cause ionization in air or other gases, producing ion pairs consisting of a positive ion plus an electron. The average energy requirement for air is 32.5 ev, and so a 3-Mev radiation would produce about 9×10^4 ion pairs, regardless of the type of radiation. However, the collection and measurement of this ionization would be very different in the three cases. For alpha particles the ionization would occur in a few centimeters, for gamma rays it would be distributed over several meters, whereas for beta particles it would be intermediate. In a practical instrument, the length of the air path would be limited to perhaps 10 cm maximum. Therefore, while alpha particles would be completely absorbed, only a fraction of the beta and gamma radiation can be absorbed, and fewer ion pairs than the 9×10^4 would be formed in the instrument.

The simplest device for measuring ionization consists of two charged electrodes, which attract the positive ions and electrons, and an external circuit for measuring the current produced. Our 3-Mev radiation, if there were 1000 such disintegrations per second, would give 9×10^7 ion pairs per second, corresponding to a current of about 10^{-11} ampere. This current is definitely measurable, but, if the number of disintegrations per second is reduced markedly, we would be beyond the limit of simple instrumentation. Also, for beta and gamma radiation the number of ion pairs formed in the instrument would be smaller, and therefore the current would be smaller.

Another possible technique is to utilize the individual pulses of current produced by each ionizing event. If the 9×10^4 ion pairs produced by the 3-Mev radiation are collected very rapidly, a small current pulse is produced. This pulse can be amplified electronically and the pulses per unit time counted. The limit to the possible amplification depends on the ability of the instrument to discriminate between the pulses and background noise. The discrimination, in turn, is a function of the noise level in the amplifier itself, the signal-to-noise ratio at the input to the amplifier, and the pulse size and shape. Such a technique is more readily applicable to alpha measurement than to beta and gamma, where the ionization is distributed so widely that only a fraction of the total ion pairs are collected, and the pulse size is small.

Instruments designed to measure either total ionization current or the number of pulses are called ionization chambers. The construction of typical units will be discussed in the section on instruments.

With an ionization chamber of convenient size, beta or gamma radiation is only detectable if the level of activity is high. The pulse

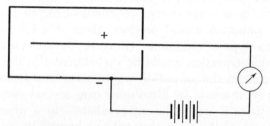

Fig. 21.1   Ionization-chamber schematic

technique is not readily applicable, and a large number of disintegrations is required to produce a measurable total current. The older electroscopes and modern pocket ionization chambers integrate the small currents produced over a long time (several hours) to produce a measurable reading.

It is possible to increase the efficiency of an ionization chamber for beta and gamma radiation by raising the gas pressure. This increases the number of collisions per unit path and brings the total range of the radiation closer to the chamber dimensions. As the pressure is raised, the wall thickness must be made greater, limiting the use of high-pressure chambers to beta emitters which can be placed within the chamber and to gamma radiation.

However, another means of increasing the pulse size is available for beta and gamma counting. If the potential gradient for collecting the ionization is increased, the electrons from the ion pairs may be accelerated sufficiently to cause further ionization in the chamber and produce a larger pulse.

A simple device for measuring ionization is shown in Fig. 21.1. Any ionizing event occurring in the chamber will produce a pulse. The effect of changing the collecting potential on the pulse size obtained is shown in Fig. 21.2. The curve is divided into six parts, with the following characteristics:

A. The pulse size is increasing rapidly with increasing potential.

B. The pulse size remains constant over a considerable range of potential. This is the region selected for ionization chambers.

C. The pulse size increases with increasing potential. In this region the electrons from the radiation ionization are accelerated toward the anode so rapidly that they cause further ionization in the

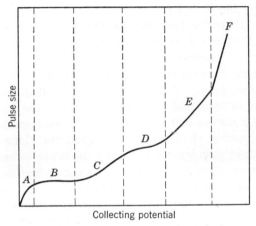

Fig. 21.2   Variation of pulse size with applied potential

chamber gas. Each initial electron is multiplied many times, perhaps 10^6, and the pulse size is dependent on the number of initial ions produced. The pulse size is thus proportional to the specific ionization of the radiation, and a counter operated in this region is known as a proportional counter.

D. In this region, there is no proportionality for events of higher specific ionization, as they tend to saturate and produce equal pulse sizes. The events of lower specific ionization, of course, will give proportional pulses. Counters are not usually operated in the potential range shown.

E. In this region, the amplification is as high as 10^8. The pulse size is still dependent on the applied potential, but is independent of the number of initial ions. At a given potential, any ionizing event, no matter how weak, will produce the same pulse size. This is the Geiger-Müller region, and counters operating in this potential range are known as Geiger-Müller or GM counters.

F. In this region, any ionization in the chamber will start a continuous discharge which will continue until the collecting potential is reduced or removed.

No numerical values are given for the axes of Fig. 21.2, as the relative values depend on the size of the chamber. One thousand volts applied to a 6-inch-diameter cylinder would allow operating in the ionization chamber region, but the same potential applied to a 2-inch-diameter cylinder would give operation in the GM or even the continuous-discharge region. This results from the greater acceleration of electrons by the higher potential gradient existing in the smaller tube. The amplification from the multiplication of electrons at high potential gradient is called gas amplification to distinguish it from the electronic amplification necessary for many counters.

Ionization chambers for the pulse technique are usually filled with argon or similar gases. Oxygen is to be avoided, as it promotes recombination of ions and electrons, reducing the pulse size and flattening the pulse so that it is difficult to distinguish it from the noise. Air-ionization chambers can be used for alpha counting by using a very short path length, but other gases are to be preferred.

Proportional counters are filled with an argon–methane mixture in various ratios of from 1:10 to 1:1. One end of the counter is normally a window whose thickness is adjusted to admit or to exclude alpha particles. Another approach is the windowless counter, the atmosphere being maintained by a continuous gas flow over the sample and through the tube.

The filling gas in GM tubes is modified to aid in quenching the pulse discharge so that the tube may accept another count. Some quenching is caused by the positive gas ions which move very slowly toward the wall (cathode), and thus build up a space charge around the anode. This reduces the potential gradient around the anode and tends to extinguish the discharge. However, as the positive ions approach the cathode, they attract electrons from the electrode and become neutral atoms. Their excess energy is released as ultraviolet radiation which in turn releases photoelectrons from other atoms and maintains the discharge. Modern GM tubes have a small percentage of chlorine or bromine in the argon filling gas to aid in quenching. The halogens have a lower ionization potential and absorb the charge from the argon ions. Only halogen ions approach the cathode, and, when they are neutralized, the photons released are of too low energy to produce photoelectrons with the argon. The energy of the argon ions is thus released in two stages, neither of which is sufficiently energetic to aid in continuing the discharge. Other quenchers have been recommended, but the halogens are to be preferred at the present time.

The ionization of gases is not the only means of detecting radiation. The blackening of film emulsions has been used for many years and is still valuable for radioautographs and personnel monitoring. The early workers with radium measured alpha radiation by visually counting the tiny scintillations produced when the particles struck a zinc sulfide phosphor. Modern scintillation counters include multiplier phototubes for detecting the scintillations, and improvements in phosphors have extended the use of scintillation counters to beta and gamma radiation.

The range of nuclear radiation is much less in solid materials than in air, and a relatively thin section of phosphor will absorb all or most of the available energy. Two criteria exist for a suitable phosphor, first, that it have a high efficiency in transforming radiation into light, and, second, that it be transparent enough to transmit the light to the phototube.

For alpha counting a thin film of activated zinc sulfide fulfills the requirements admirably and will give considerable discrimination against beta and gamma. For beta counting a 1-cm-thick section of a single crystal of sodium iodide or of anthracene or stilbene will stop all but the most energetic beta particles and is transparent to its own scintillations. The discrimination against gamma radiation is not absolute, but, as will be described later, any gamma component can be determined and subtracted. For gamma counting a large enough single crystal is expensive and difficult to obtain. Liquid phosphors, solutions of stilbene, anthracene, or naphthalene in aromatic solvents are quite efficient and inexpensive, as they can be mounted in plastic or other containers of any desired size.

21.7 Instrumental characteristics. Depending on the application of a particular instrument, the following characteristics are of varying importance: (a) high stability, (b) low-background counting rate, (c) high geometry, (d) high counting efficiency, (e) high counting speed.

High stability aids in obtaining both precision and accuracy by relative freedom from spurious counts. It is inherent in the counting detector and electronic circuitry. The recent improvements in instrumentation have made stability less of a problem than formerly, and it is a property that is readily determined by repetitive counting of a sample or a standard.

Low-background counting rates are desirable for measuring low-activity samples. The actual values vary from a few counts per hour for alpha counters, up to 50 counts per minute for some GM beta counters. The maintenance of low background requires that the counter be readily decontaminated.

The radiation from any source presents a wave front that is roughly spherical, and the geometry is the fraction of this sphere that is intercepted by the detector. It is possible, with multiple detectors or with the source inside the detector, to obtain 100% or so-called 360° geometry, but, with a single external detector, the maximum geometry is usually 50%. This may be increased a few per cent by back-scatter of the radiation from the source backing. In practice, a value of 40% for alpha scintillation counters and 25% from GM beta counters is considered normal. The geometry decreases rapidly as the source-detector distance is increased, and as the source area–detector area ratio is increased.

Counting efficiency is inherent in the detector, depending mainly on the proportion of the energy reaching the detector that is absorbed and utilized. It may be modified when an attempt is made to discriminate against unwanted radiation; for example, a detector window thick enough to cut out alpha radiation will also absorb some of the low-energy beta particles present.

In practical measurements, it is difficult to separate the effects of geometry and counting efficiency. For this reason, an instrument is usually calibrated by determining an over-all efficiency. This is done by measuring a standard of known disintegration rate and reporting the results as counts per disintegration (c/d).

Since our instruments do not measure disintegration rates but rather counting rates, the necessity for repeated checking with calibration standards cannot be overemphasized. All contributing factors such as type and energy of the radiation and the geometrical relationship of source and detector must be made as nearly alike as possible for sample and standard.

For high counting speed, that is, the ability of a counter to accept and register closely spaced pulses, it is necessary that the counter recover rapidly after each count. The same resolving time must be maintained in the subsequent circuits as well. It is possible to correct for the loss of counts by coincidence of pulses by running high-activity standards and preparing a calibration curve.

21.8 Practical instrumentation. For alpha counting the best instruments are the ionization chamber, the alpha scintillation counter, and the gas-flow proportional counter. These instruments can maintain low-background counting rates and high efficiencies. The lower limits of alpha counting depend very largely on the time available for counting. The statistics of low-level counting operations are determined by the background counting rate, as well as the net sample counting rate, and by the counting time. As a practical limit, where the background counting rate is 0.1 c/m, a one-hour count will give a standard deviation of about 70% for a sample of 0.1 net c/m and 14% for a sample of 1.0 net c/m.

The upper limit for alpha counting is determined by the ability of the sensitive element to resolve closely spaced counts. This resolving time is of the order of a few microseconds for good counters, and several hundred thousand counts per minute can be readily handled. The problem of measuring very high alpha activity is not ordinarily encountered.

A simple ionization chamber for measuring radioactive gases is manufactured by the Applied Physics Corporation for use with their vibrating reed electrometer. This instrument is capable of measuring currents as low as 10^{-16} ampere. The range from 10^{-16} to 10^{-12} ampere is determined by the rate of charge of a fixed condenser, while higher currents are determined by the voltage drop across a fixed resistor. The input to the electrometer is a condenser, one plate of which is vibrated at 450 cps. This produces an alternating current which is amplified, rectified, and fed back to the input to give a null effect. The over-all design results in an electrometer which is exceptionally stable.

An alpha scintillation counter for small samples (up to $1\frac{1}{8}$ inches diameter) has been described in the literature,[1] and the Tracerlab model-P-12 alpha scintillation counter is somewhat similar to the probe described, except that a thin light-tight window has been added.

For beta counting, the scintillation counters, gas-flow proportional counters, and the standard Geiger-Müller tube are applicable. The GM tube has the advantage that above a certain threshold energy any beta particle entering the tube will cause a pulse and consequently register a count. The scintillation and gas-flow counters are both proportional counters; that is, by suitable adjustment of the operating voltages, the counters can be made to respond to different beta-

[1] R. T. Graveson, H. J. DiGiovanni, and H. D. LeVine, U. S. Atomic Energy Commission Report NYO-1523.

particle energies.   This may be advantageous in discriminating against unwanted isotopes but causes difficulties in that operating conditions must be fixed within very small tolerances.

The background counting rate for beta counters is seldom below 10 c/m, even when an attempt is made to shield against external radiation.   This higher-background count, contrasted to that of alpha counters is caused by (a) the greater range of beta particles in materials for counter construction (surface cleaning or coating is not sufficient), (b) the sensitivity of any beta counter to gamma radiation which penetrates normal shielding, (c) the effect of cosmic radiation, which also penetrates any shield.

A high-background counting rate makes it difficult to evaluate samples having low activity.   With a 10-c/m background, and a one-hour count for both background and sample, a sample of 1.0 net c/m would show a standard deviation of about 60%, and a 10-c/m sample would show about 7%.

The upper limit of beta counting is greater than that for alpha counting because of the shorter resolving times for the GM tube and for the small pulses developed in proportional-type counters. The development of fast counters for beta work has resulted in instruments that can handle over a million counts per minute.   Such high-speed counting is not necessary in ordinary chemical procedures, as suitable aliquot portions may be taken for analysis.

A GM tube for beta counting is constructed with a thin mica window at one end, as contrasted to the cylindrical glass or metal tubes used for gamma counting.   The thickness of the end window varies from about 1.5 to 6.0 mg per cm^2, depending on the manufacturer and type.   The voltage requirements also vary, the range being approximately 600 to 1200 volts as a threshold voltage for counting.   The flat portion of the Geiger region should extend for 150 to 200 volts and have a slope of not more than 5% per 100 volts.

The efficiency of any of the counting devices mentioned is very low for gamma radiation.   For example, a GM tube ordinarily is about 1% as efficient for gamma as for energetic beta radiation.   This of course results from the long path required to dissipate the gamma energy.   Some work has been done with proportional counters, but GM tubes and scintillation counters are more generally used.   The use of large volumes of solutions for gamma phosphors has been an important development in the scintillation counting field.   Thick-walled GM tubes can be used to discriminate against beta particles, and the equipment using these tubes is much more rugged than thin-window beta-sensitive tubes. The background counting rates for gamma measurements are approximately the same as those obtained for beta measurements, and the upper and lower useful counting rates are also equivalent.

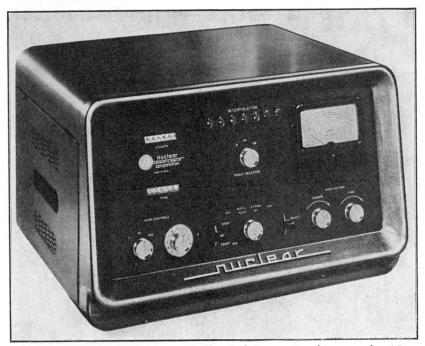

Fig. 21.3 Nuclear Instrument and Chemical Corporation binary scaler (Courtesy Nuclear Instrument & Chemical Corporation)

The pulses produced in the sensitive element of a counter cannot be followed with any mechanical system above a few hundred counts per minute. For higher-counting rates a scaler is required to transmit only a known fraction of the pulses to the mechanical register. The common units employ binary systems: that is, scalers transmitting every second, fourth, eighth, etc. pulse to the register, or a decade system transmitting every tenth, hundredth, etc. pulse to the register. The commercial scalers ordinarily incorporate a high-voltage supply for the counter, the scaling circuits, the mechanical register, a timer and accessory equipment to shut off the instrument at a predetermined count or a predetermined time. In order to obtain constant precision in counting work, a fixed total net count is required. If the background is not negligible, it will be necessary to change the total count in order to compensate for the different cumulative background count obtained in different counting periods.

Fig. 21.4 Lead shield showing counting shelves (Courtesy Technical Associates)

A binary-system scale of 64 scaler produced by Nuclear Instrument and Chemical Corporation is shown in Fig. 21.3. This scaler is designed for a GM tube and includes a regulated high-voltage supply for the tube. It requires an accessory timer which can be plugged into the scaler to indicate elapsed time for any number of counts. A predetermined count may be set in multiples of 10, 100 and 1000 of the 16, 32, and 64 scales.

The Radiation Counter Laboratories Mark 13, model-10 decade scaler is a typical unit. Direct-reading scales of 10, 100, or 1000 are fed into a mechanical register. This scaler is also designed for GM-tube use and has a regulated high-voltage power supply included.

The timer is built into the scaler, and preset timing or preset counting is available if specified at the time of purchase.

For counting many samples, it is desirable to shield the GM tube from as much of the background radiation as possible. The Technical Associates LS-6, shown in Fig. 21.4, is a convenient shield, as it

Fig. 21.5 Beta-gamma survey meter (Courtesy Nuclear Instrument & Chemical Corporation)

has provision for mounting an end-window GM tube and for holding the sample at various fixed distances from the tube face.

Instruments designed for field operation must sacrifice some of the features described for the sake of portability. Usually, the sensitivity to low counting rates is not needed for instruments designed to check personnel exposure or laboratory contamination. Therefore, scaling circuits are not required, and electronic amplification is held to a minimum. This reduction in electronic tubes permits battery operation and complete portability.

The Nuclear Instrument and Chemical Corporation model 2610A (Fig. 21.5) is a typical beta-gamma survey meter. The probe contains a GM tube sensitive to beta particles with energies above 0.2 Mev and to gamma radiation. A shield on the probe allows discrimination between the two radiations.

This instrument and GM survey meters in general are count-rate meters; that is, individual counts are not registered, but only the rate

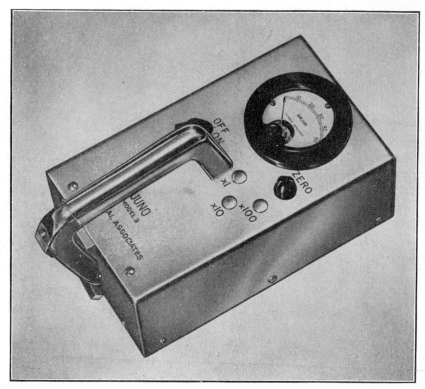

Fig. 21.6   Alpha-beta-gamma survey meter (Courtesy Technical Associates)

at which counts are received. This is done by using a condenser to collect and integrate the current pulses. The charge acquired by the condenser leaks off through a fixed resistance, allowing the resistor-condenser combination to maintain a voltage across it proportional to the rate at which the pulses are received.

If alpha contamination must be measured, a total current-ionization chamber type of instrument must be used. The alpha-beta-gamma "Juno" survey meter (Fig. 21.6) of Technical Associates has an ionization chamber area of 100 cm² and self-contained shields for cutting out alpha or alpha and beta particles.

21.9 Counting statistics. On the basis of statistical theory, a counting operation may be carried out to any degree of accuracy or precision desired. This requires perfect stability of the instrument background and efficiency and applies only to the counting process itself. In practical radiochemical measurements, however, the time available for counting is limited, and it becomes necessary to evaluate the precision of measurement.

The standard deviation of any single counting measurement is estimated as the square root of the total number of counts registered. The precision may be evaluated with the aid of Table 21.2. The

TABLE 21.2

Constants for Evaluating Counting Precision

n	Probability
0.674	0.5
1.0	0.68
1.3	0.80
2.0	0.95
2.6	0.99
3.0	0.997
4.0	0.9999

table shows the probability that the counting error due to the random nature of the disintegrations is less than n times the estimated standard deviation.

If we count our sample long enough to obtain 640 total counts, the standard deviation would be estimated as 25.3 counts. Therefore, the probability is 95% that our true count would lie within the limits of 640 ± 51. If the counting time was 20 minutes, the counting rate would be expressed as 32 ± 2.6 c/m.

For alpha counting the counter background at such a level would be negligible, but for beta counting the background might become important. Suppose a 20-minute background measurement gave 400 counts. The rate would be 20 ± 1.0 c/m. The standard deviation for the sample may be estimated as

$$\sqrt{2.6^2 + 1.0^2} = 2.8 \text{ c/m}$$

and the net count expressed as 12 ± 2.8 c/m.

When the background is negligible, it is apparent that for a constant precision of measurement (constant standard deviation) a fixed total count should be run. When the background is not negligible, the required count may be calculated by the methods shown above.

21.10 Beta and gamma energy measurement. When exact measurement of beta or gamma energies are required, a suitable spectrometer is necessary. However, for practical purposes it is possible to characterize single isotopes or simple mixtures by absorption measurements. If the counting rate is measured with a series of known absorbers in the path of the radiation, it is possible to determine the approximate energy of radiation. The range of absorbers required is zero to complete absorption for beta particles and zero to 90% or more for gamma radiation. The common absorber materials are aluminum or mica for beta, and lead for gamma radiation. Sets of such absorbers are available commercially or they may be prepared readily from pure aluminum sheet (2S grade aluminum) for beta or from pure lead sheet for gamma. If several sheets each of two or three thicknesses are available, the complete range may be readily covered. The absorbers may be calibrated by direct weighing and measurement of their surface area, since the usual units required are milligrams per square centimeter.

The energy of a single gamma component may be readily determined from the slope of the absorption curve. This slope is the absorption coefficient for the particular energy and absorber. Or the half-thickness (absorber thickness which reduces the activity to one half) may be determined and the energy estimated from Fig. 21.7. The desired curve characteristic may best be determined by the method of least squares, using the linear form of the absorption equation

$$\ln A = \ln A_0 - \mu l$$

where A = activity measured with absorber of thickness l, A_0 = activity measured with no absorber, μ = absorption coefficient in square centimeters per gram, and l = absorber thickness in grams per square centimeter.

If two gamma components are present, the absorption curve will show a break as in Fig. 21.8, provided the energies differ by at least a factor of two. The absorption curve of the more energetic component is merely the extrapolated curve, shown as a dotted line in the figure. The absorption curve for the weaker component may be evaluated by subtracting the extrapolated values for the more energetic gamma component from the total activity. The net values are the activities of the weaker component. Similar calculations may be applied to multicomponent systems, but the likelihood of sufficient separation in energies for three or more components is slight.

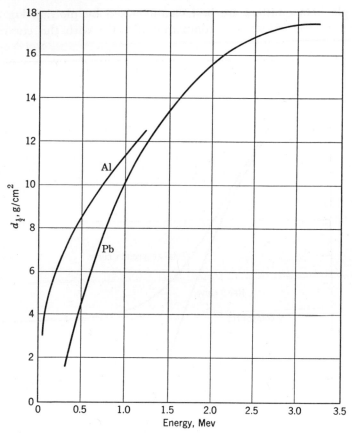

Fig. 21.7   Gamma energy versus half-thickness (Courtesy *Nucleonics*)

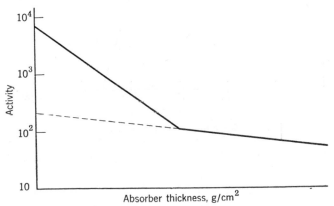

Fig. 21.8   Absorption curve for two gamma components

Single beta emitters are best characterized by plotting $\log A/A_0$ against l (Fig. 21.9) and comparing directly with the curves for

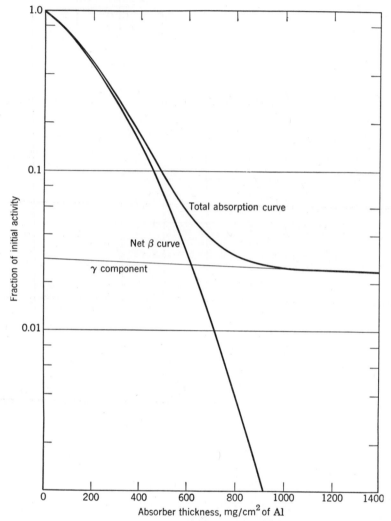

Fig. 21.9   Beta-gamma absorption of Th[234] plus Pa[234]

known isotopes measured under identical conditions. If the proper isotope is not available, the maximum beta energy may be estimated from a Feather [2] analysis. In this method, the absorption curves for

[2] N. Feather, *Proc. Cambridge Phil. Soc.*, *34*, 599 (1938).

the sample and a standard substance such as P^{32}, Pa^{234}, or Bi^{210} are measured under identical conditions. Any fractional activity (A/A_0) for the standard will correspond to a fraction of its known range in the absorbing material. If it is assumed that the same fractional activity for the sample corresponds to the same fraction of the sample range, it is possible to calculate an apparent range for each fraction tested. A plot of apparent range against fraction of range will approach a constant value (Fig. 21.10) as the fraction approaches

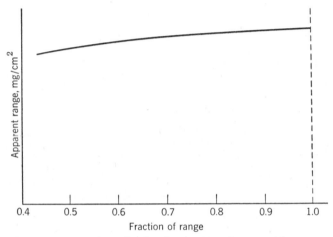

Fig. 21.10   Feather plot for determining beta-particle range

unity. Energies obtained in this way closely approximate spectrometer values and are sufficiently accurate for characterizing an isotope. Figure 21.11 gives the maximum range in aluminum as a function of beta energy. The short range of beta particles makes it necessary to include the counter window thickness and air space between sample and counter as part of each absorber.

In order to make an accurate beta or gamma energy determination, it is necessary to have a moderately high initial activity, preferably a few hundred counts a minute above background as a minimum. Less active samples can be measured, but only with considerable expenditure of counting time.

Alpha-particle energies are all concentrated in a very short range, and the absorption method for characterizing an alpha emitter is difficult. Therefore, alpha energies are usually measured by total absorption in a gas-filled ionization chamber.

Tables of isotopes and their energies are listed in the bibliography, and a short table of a few common isotopes is given in Appendix F.

21.11 Determination of half-life. The half-life of an isotope is a useful characteristic in analysis. Generally emitters may be divided into three general classes: (*a*) The half-life is so long that no appreciable decay occurs in the period available for measurement. (*b*) The half-life has an intermediate value, and a series of counts made

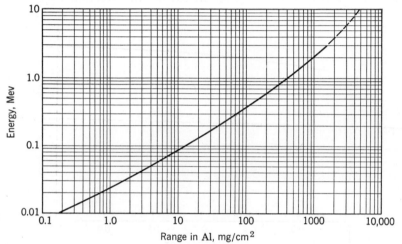

Fig. 21.11   Maximum beta energy versus absorber thickness (Courtesy *Nucleonics*)

over a period of hours or days allows a decay curve to be plotted. (*c*) The half-life is so short that the samples cannot be measured by a simple counting process.

The first class may be evaluated by measuring the amount of the pure isotope in the sample. If the atomic weight is known, the number of atoms present may be calculated and the disintegration constant and half-life calculated from,

$$d/m = \lambda N$$

where d/m is the number of disintegrations per minute.

The quantity of isotope present must be determined by another method of analysis. If more than one isotope is present in the sample, the half-life found will be an effective value for the mixture, and additional information on the system will be necessary before it can be identified.

The second class requires that two or more measurements be made on the sample. The initial activity is related to any subsequent activity by the formula

$$A = A_0 e^{-\lambda t}$$

where A is of course $N\lambda$. To take statistical advantage of several counts, the least-squares method of determining the slope of the line should be followed. This method is best for $T_{1/2}$ values of several minutes to several months. A mixture of isotopes will show a variation of the measured $T_{1/2}$ with time. If the half-lives differ by a factor of two or more, the individual values may be found graphically, by applying the same methods described for separating different energy gamma or beta emission.

The third class is very difficult to handle for individual short-lived isotopes, and considerable ingenuity has been shown in the methods reported in the literature. If the short-lived isotope is the daughter of a longer-lived parent, the coincidence method may be used. In this method, the pulse from the parent decay is delayed electronically for a range of very short times. Some of these delayed pulses will then coincide with the pulses from the daughter decay. If the logarithm of the number of coincidences is plotted against the delay time, a curve is obtained that is directly comparable to a standard decay curve.

21.12 Tracer studies. Artificially produced isotopes are now available for practically every element, and they are of great assistance in the development of analytical methods. Small amounts may be added to a sample before analysis and the effectiveness of separations or the completeness of recovery traced step by step through the complete procedure. Similar techniques are used in the study of organic syntheses and plant and animal metabolism.

For simplicity the tracer isotope should have suitable characteristics of type of emission, energy, and half-life. The most desirable tracers are high-energy beta (over 0.5 Mev) or gamma emitters with half-lives of a few days or longer. Such isotopes allow measurements to be made readily and without excessive haste.

The high energy is desirable because the sample itself acts as an absorber when a count is being taken. Particles or rays originating below the surface must pass through the sample above to reach the counter. In any case rather vigorous standardization of the quantity of sample, the mounting, and the position with respect to the counter is necessary, and, when the sample emits easily absorbed radiation, even more care is required. Alpha and low-energy beta emitters can only be measured readily if it is possible to prepare the sample as a thin layer. Thicker layers of sample can be counted with high-energy beta emitters if the thickness is reproducible, while self-absorption is rarely a problem with gamma emitters.

The handling of short half-life isotopes in tracer studies of all but the simplest reactions is very difficult. Considerable ingenuity and dexterity are required to perform the desired reactions and manipulations and to prepare and count the sample in a short time. If any lengthy chemical operations are involved, the use of short-lived isotopes is impossible. In any case, it is necessary to correct all activities to some arbitrary time in order to compensate for radioactive decay.

No suitable radioactive tracers are available for some common elements, such as oxygen and nitrogen. Most tracer studies with these elements therefore are carried out with nonradioactive isotopes which can be detected by their spectral properties.

21.13 Analytical applications. The major applications of tracer techniques to analytical chemistry have been in the study of separations. Precipitation, ion-exchange, solvent extraction, and electrolytic separations lend themselves readily to radioactivity measurements. The book by Wahl and Bonner listed in the bibliography gives references to many published procedures.

The concept of specific activity of a radioactive material is very important in analytical calculations. For example, we may calculate the specific activity of 53-day Be^7 as 7.8×10^{11} d/m per μg. If we want a lower specific activity, we can mix the Be^7 with a larger amount of Be^9 to dilute the activity. This is particularly necessary if chemical manipulations are to be carried out on the active material, as ordinarily sufficient material must be present to be visible. The added Be^9 is known as a carrier and is merely present to form a usable precipitate or suitable quantity for handling.

A carrier need not always be another isotope of the same element. For example, in the precipitation of radium as the sulfate, there is no inactive radium isotope that can be added, but barium, another member of the alkaline-earth group, is an excellent carrier. Similar methods reduce coprecipitation or adsorption of small amounts of tracers; for example, added barium will reduce the amount of radium adsorbed on glass vessels. In this case, the barium is called a hold-back carrier. The general principle is always the same; micro-

microgram quantities of tracers do not always follow the normal chemical reactions, owing to lack of mass, and carriers must be introduced to raise the mass to the required level.

There are many separations, particularly in the field of organic analysis, in which the final product can be obtained in a pure form, but the yield is variable. Tracers can be added to evaluate the yield in each analysis and thus give a usable method. The technique is known as the isotope-dilution method. A measured amount of the final compound, tagged with a tracer is added to the sample, and the separation is made. Radiometric analysis will determine the percentage recovery of the tagged compound and, therefore, of the chemically identical untagged compound.

21.14 Safety precautions. At the present time it is impossible for an investigator to obtain dangerous quantities of any isotope without proof that he can handle the material without excessive exposure to himself or to others. However, the very nature of radiation, invisible and without immediate effect, tends to invite carelessness on the part of some scientists. No attempt will be made here to discuss specific precautions; the present state of knowledge is well summarized in various handbooks [3] of the National Bureau of Standards, but certain things should be kept in mind.

First, any unnecessary exposure to radiation is foolish, no matter how low the radiation level. Store all sources in suitable shielding, and do not spend unnecessary time in the presence of radioactive material.

Second, radioactive materials, which are harmless externally, such as alpha emitters, may be very dangerous internally. Keep hands and clothing free of radioactive substances. Know how to remove the particular isotope being used from the skin, from clothing, and from work areas. If a spill occurs, get assistance, and clean up all activity immediately. Do not track activity throughout the laboratory and out of the laboratory.

Third, monitor all operations with a suitable survey meter, and monitor all personnel in the laboratory with film badges or pocket chambers as required. Maintain complete personnel records on all exposures.

Fourth, when a new operation is to be performed or unfamiliar equipment is to be used, rehearse with inactive material until the

[3] Natl. Bur. Standards, Handbook 42, Safe Handling of Radioactive Isotopes; Handbook 48, Control and Removal of Radioactive Contamination in Laboratories; Handbook 51, Radiological Monitoring Methods and Instruments.

technique is perfected.   This will not only promote safety but improve the quality of the experimental work as well.

Bibliography

General

R. E. Lapp and H. L. Andrews, *Nuclear Radiation Physics*, Prentice-Hall, New York (1948).

S. Glasstone, *Sourcebook on Atomic Energy*, D. Van Nostrand, New York (1950).

G. Friedlander and J. W. Kennedy, *Introduction to Radiochemistry*, John Wiley, New York (1949).

A. C. Wahl and N. A. Bonner, *Radioactivity Applied to Chemistry*, John Wiley, New York (1951).

E. Rutherford, J. Chadwick, and C. D. Ellis, *Radiations from Radioactive Substances*, Cambridge University Press (1951).

Isotope Tables

E. Segre, U. S. Atomic Energy Commission Report AEF D-2111, *Natl. Bur. Standards Circ. 499* (1948).

Abstracts

Nuclear Science Abstracts, published bimonthly by Technical Information Service, U. S. Atomic Energy Commission, Oak Ridge, Tenn.

CHAPTER 22

Laboratory Experiments

An entire chapter of this book has been devoted to laboratory experiments because it is considered that a text for instrumental analysis would not be complete without a rather extensive laboratory section. No matter how well the theory is presented, a course in instrumental analysis is not adequate unless a large amount of experimental work is carried on in the laboratory concurrently with the theory. Laboratory demonstrations are a poor substitute for actual contact with the instruments and with the problems encountered in instrumental analysis. Some students are inclined to have a natural fear of instruments and think that these instruments should not be touched, lest they be damaged. Occasionally, the instructor also shares this attitude and keeps an expensive instrument carefully locked up where it can only be admired from a distance. This is not a constructive attitude. Instruments are valuable only when effectively used. They prove their comparative worth only under actual experimental conditions. Unless the student has the opportunity to make measurements with an instrument, he remains relatively unaware of its potentialities in the field of research.

The choice of experiments to be included in this chapter was dependent upon several factors. In the first place, the basic experiments usually covered in a course in physical chemistry have been omitted. Second, an attempt has been made to select experiments that have a practical value because they deal with actual analyses which are frequently performed. Although, for the most part, these experiments have been tested for a period of five years at Rensselaer, they are not necessarily simple or completely foolproof. They have been selected in many instances from the current literature, and may occasionally present the student with the same sort of minor problems he will encounter when he becomes a practicing chemist. For this reason, the student is urged to read the references cited before

379

undertaking a particular laboratory experiment. He will then be well informed concerning the more important variables, and will be in a better position to judge the worth of a published method.

The experiments have been listed in four major subdivisions to correspond with the sequence of the chapters in this text. After the experiments, concise operating instructions have been given for a few of the most common instruments. An attempt has been made to keep the experiments general enough to comply with the wide variety of instruments available in academic laboratories. Suitable unknown or standard samples are available for many of these experiments and suggestions regarding their acquisition have been given in Appendix I.

The experiments can be finished in two semesters involving two 3-hour laboratory periods a week. For a one-semester course in instrumental analysis, approximately one-half the experiments can be completed. The experiments marked with an asterisk are to be recommended for the academic laboratory with the normal type of instrumental equipment.

Experiment

Absorption Spectroscopy

22.1 *	Spectrophotometric Determination of Manganese in Steel
22.2	Rapid Photometric Determination of Copper in Ferrous Alloys
22.3	Colorimetric Determination of Nickel in Steel
22.4 *	Ultraviolet-Absorption Spectrum of an Organic Compound
22.5 *	Quantitative Determination of Vitamin A in Cod Liver Oil
22.6 *	Qualitative and Quantitative Infrared Spectroscopy
22.7	Qualitative and Quantitative Raman Spectroscopy
22.8 *	Fluorometric Determination of Aluminum in Steel
22.9	Fluorometric Determination of Thiamine (Vitamin B_1)

Emission Spectroscopy

22.10 *	Qualitative Spectrographic Analysis of Brass
22.11 *	Quantitative Spectrographic Analysis of Aluminum Alloys
22.12 *	Determination of Calcium in Limestone with the Flame Photometer

Electrometric Methods

22.13	Determination of pH
22.14 *	Potentiometric Determination of a Sodium Carbonate–Bicarbonate Mixture
22.15 *	Potentiometric Determination of Chromium in Steel
22.16	Potentiometric Determination of Manganese in Steel

Miscellaneous Methods

Instrument Operating Instructions

Beckman Model-B Spectrophotometer
Beckman Model-DU Spectrophotometer
Klett-Summerson Filter Photometer
Duboscq Colorimeter
Klett Fluorimeter
Fisher Elecdropode

Suggested Desk List for Instrumental Analysis

Experiment 22.1   Spectrophotometric Determination of Manganese in Steel [1]

Instruments.   Available spectrophotometers and filter photometers.

Reagents.   *Acid mixture* (equal parts nitric acid, phosphoric acid, and water).

Solid potassium periodate (KIO_4).

Standard manganese solution (0.2 mg of manganese per ml). Dissolve 0.6153 gram of reagent-grade $MnSO_4 \cdot H_2O$ in 1 liter of water.

Procedure.   *Unknown samples.* Weigh three 0.500-gram samples of steel into 250-ml Pyrex volumetric flasks, add 50 ml of the acid mixture, and boil on a hot plate to remove oxides of nitrogen. Dilute to about 100 ml, add cautiously about ¼ gram of KIO_4, and boil 3 minutes to oxidize the manganese. (Three minutes are necessary for complete oxidation; longer boiling within reason does no harm.) Cool the solution to room temperature, dilute to the mark with water, mix well and measure.

Standards.   Weigh four 0.500-gram samples of ingot iron, dissolve in the acid mixture as above, and boil out oxides of nitrogen. To three of the samples add, respectively, with pipets or a buret 5, 15,

[1] H. H. Willard and L. H. Greathouse, *J. Am. Chem. Soc.*, 39, 2366 (1917).

and 25 ml of standard manganese solution, leaving one sample for a blank. Complete as above.

Measurements. *Spectrophotometers.* Measure the absorbance (or per cent transmittance) for the blank, 15-ml, and 25-ml standards from 360 to 660 mμ, taking readings every 20 mμ, except where the absorbance reaches a maximum. At this portion of the curve take readings every 5 mμ. Plot the absorbance (or per cent transmittance) against the wavelength on regular coordinate graph paper. Select the wavelength of maximum absorbance, and measure all the standards and the three unknowns at this wavelength. Plot a graph of absorbance versus concentration of manganese (milligrams per 250 ml). If per cent transmittance values have been obtained, plot this data on semilog paper. From the calibration graph, determine the manganese in the unknown samples and report as per cent manganese.

Filter photometers. Select the filter that is peaked at the wavelength of maximum absorbance. Measure the absorbance (or per cent transmittance) of the four standards and the three unknown samples. Prepare calibration graphs as described above, and determine the per cent manganese in the unknown samples.

Duboscq Colorimeter. Select the standard that is the closest visual match to the sample, and compare according to the directions for the instrument.

Experiment 22.2   Rapid Photometric Determination of Copper in Ferrous Alloys [2]

Instruments. Any available spectrophotometer or filter photometer and a pH meter.

Reagents. *α-Benzoinoxime,* 0.5% solution in 0.25 N sodium hydroxide.

10% sodium hydroxide (10 grams of sodium hydroxide in 100 ml of water).

Rochelle salt solution (300 grams sodium potassium tartrate in 500 ml of water).

Chloroform, reagent grade.

Standard copper solution (0.100 mg of copper per ml).

Dilute nitric acid (mix 1 part of concentrated nitric acid with 2 parts of water).

30% hydrogen peroxide.

[2] R. A. Dunleavy, S. E. Wiberley, and J. H. Harley, *Anal. Chem.,* 22, 170 (1950).

Procedure. Weigh three 0.500-gram samples into 150-ml beakers, and dissolve in 20 ml of dilute nitric acid. If necessary, add a drop or two of 30% hydrogen peroxide to dissolve any manganese dioxide, and boil off the oxides of nitrogen. If the sample does not dissolve readily in the dilute nitric acid, a few drops of hydrochloric acid may be added to dissolve the alloy completely. Cool slightly, and add 25 ml of Rochelle salt solution and 30 ml of 10% sodium hydroxide. Adjust the pH to the range 11.3 to 12.3 with 10% sodium hydroxide, and add 2 ml (pipet) of 0.5% α-benzoinoxime solution. Transfer to a 250-ml Squibb separatory funnel, add 40 ml of chloroform, and shake vigorously for three 30-second periods. Filter the chloroform through a small paper into a 50-ml volumetric flask, and rinse by running 5 ml of chloroform through the separatory funnel and the filter. Make up the extract to volume with chloroform, and measure the intensity of the color. (The maximum absorbance is at 440 mμ, and measurements with a spectrophotometer should be made at this wavelength. Measurements with a filter photometer should be made with a filter peaked at 440 mμ. Prepare a calibration graph by adding 2, 4, 6, and 8 ml, respectively, of the standard copper solution to 0.500-gram samples of steel containing no copper. Follow the same procedure as described for the unknown sample. From the calibration graph, determine the amount of copper in the unknown.

Experiment 22.3   Colorimetric Determination of Nickel * in Steel [3]

Instruments. Any available spectrophotometer or filter photometer.

Reagents. *Acid mixture* (133 ml of concentrated sulfuric acid, 167 ml of phosphoric acid diluted to 1 liter).

8 N nitric acid.

Tartaric acid solution (20 grams of tartaric acid in 100 ml of water).

Saturated bromine water.

Concentrated ammonium hydroxide.

---

* For steels containing copper or manganese in excess of 0.5% the method of M. D. Cooper, *Anal. Chem.*, 23, 875 (1951), should be used in place of the one outlined above for more accurate results.

[3] G. R. Makepeace and C. H. Craft, *Ind. Eng. Chem., Anal. Ed.*, 16, 375 (1944).

Dimethylglyoxime solution (1 gram of dimethylglyoxime dissolved in 100 ml of methyl alcohol).

6 N sodium hydroxide.

Standard nickel solution (0.100 mg of nickel per ml). Dissolve 1.000 gram of pure nickel in 15 ml of concentrated nitric acid, add 10 ml of concentrated sulfuric acid, fume, cool, and, after dissolving the salts formed with 50 ml of water, dilute to 1 liter. To 10.0 ml of this solution, add 10 ml of 1-to-1 sulfuric acid, and dilute to 1 liter in a volumetric flask.

Procedure. Weigh three 0.250-gram samples of nickel steel and three 0.250-gram samples of pure iron into 250-ml volumetric Pyrex flasks. Dissolve in 20 ml of the acid mixture. Cautiously add 10 ml of 8 N nitric acid, and boil to expel oxides of nitrogen. Cool, and dilute to the mark. Transfer by pipet to a 100-ml volumetric flask an aliquot of the diluted steel solutions according to the following table.

Suspected Nickel. Content, %	Aliquot, ml
0.01–0.50	50
0.50–1.00	25
1.00–1.50	10
1.50–5.0	2
Above 5.0	1

Transfer from the iron solutions the same aliquots to 100-ml volumetric flasks, and add 1, 2, and 3 ml of the standard nickel solution, respectively, to each flask.

Add to each flask, mixing after each addition, 5 ml of tartaric acid solution, 5 ml of bromine water, 10 ml of concentrated ammonium hydroxide, and 5 ml of alcoholic dimethylglyoxime solution. After 1 minute add 10 ml of 6 N sodium hydroxide, and dilute to the mark. After 5 minutes measure the absorbance or per cent transmittance at 490 mμ with a spectrophotometer or with a filter photometer containing a filter peaked at approximately the same wavelength.

Plot a calibration curve from the data obtained on the solutions containing known amounts of nickel, and determine the amount of nickel in the three unknowns. Report the per cent nickel in the unknown steel.

Experiment 22.4 Ultraviolet-Absorption Spectrum of an Organic Compound

Instrument. Spectrophotometer with ultraviolet accessories.

Procedure. Obtain a liquid † compound of either known or unknown structure. Measure the absorption spectrum of the compound versus water (or the organic solvent if used as a solution), starting at 400 mμ. Take readings every 20 mμ. If the absorbance exceeds 1.500, dilute (in appropriate steps) a known weight of the sample in a 10-ml volumetric flask with isoöctane (2,2,4-trimethylpentane) until the absorbance readings taken every 20 mμ do not exceed 1.500 for any wavelength above 225 mμ. Using the final selected dilution, measure the absorption spectrum every 2 mμ from 215 to 300 mμ and every 10 mμ from 300 to 400 mμ. If the sample is an unknown, compare the spectrum obtained with the American Petroleum Institute compilation, and report the probable structure of the compound.

Experiment 22.5 Quantitative Determination of Vitamin A in Cod Liver Oil [4-6]

Instrument. Spectrophotometer with ultraviolet accessories.

Reagents. *95% ethyl alcohol.*

USP Vitamin A Reference Standard (Vitamin A acetate in cottonseed oil) 1 capsule = 2500 USP units.

Procedure. Dissolve the contents of 1 capsule of the Vitamin A Reference Standard in ethyl alcohol in a 50-ml volumetric flask, and dilute to the mark (solution A). Prepare three standard solutions by adding 2, 5, and 10 ml, respectively, of solution A to 25-ml volumetric flasks and diluting to the mark with ethyl alcohol.

Measure the absorption spectrum of the solution containing the 5-ml aliquot of solution A from 225 to 400 mμ versus the ethyl alcohol. At the wavelength of maximum absorption (approximately 328 mμ) measure each of the other standard solutions.

Unknown sample. Weigh a 25-ml volumetric flask, add 2 to 3 drops (approximately 50 mg) of the unknown cod liver oil, and weigh the flask again to obtain the weight of the unknown sample

---

† If the sample is a solid, prepare a dilute solution of known concentration.

[4] F. P. Zscheile and R. L. Henry, *Ind. Eng. Chem., Anal. Ed.*, 16, 436 (1944).

[5] B. L. Oser, D. Melnick, M. Pader, R. Roth, and M. Oser, *ibid.*, 17, 559 (1945).

[6] G. R. Halpern, *ibid.*, 18, 621 (1946).

by difference. Dilute to the mark with 95% ethyl alcohol, and, after the sample is in solution, measure the absorbance at 328 mμ. Plot the absorbance of the standard 5 ml aliquot of solution A against the wavelength. Plot the calibration curve of concentration in USP units versus absorbance for the standard samples. From the calibration curve determine the USP units of vitamin A per gram for the unknown sample of cod liver oil.

Experiment 22.6 Qualitative and Quantitative Infrared Spectroscopy

Instrument. An infrared spectrometer.

Procedure. *Qualitative part.* Obtain a sample of a known or unknown compound from the instructor. If it is a liquid fill a sealed 0.10-mm absorption cell and measure the absorption spectrum from 650 to 4000 cm^{-1} with the instrument equipped with a rocksalt prism. In the region of the spectrum where the bands are too broad, repeat the measurements with the sample in a 0.025-mm cell. If the bands are still unresolved, place a single drop of the liquid between two rocksalt windows with no spacer, and again record this region of the spectrum.

If the sample is a solid, the spectrum may be obtained by dissolving it in an appropriate solvent and following the same procedure. Or it may be finely ground in an agate mortar and then mulled with mineral oil (Nujol) and measured as a suspension between two rocksalt windows.

If the spectrum has been obtained on a single-beam instrument, determine the frequency in cm^{-1} of the absorption bands or the wavelength in microns from a prism calibration curve. Cancel out any absorption bands caused by water vapor or carbon dioxide. If the sample was a solid, cancel out the bands caused by either Nujol or the solvent. From Fig. 5.9 tabulate as many frequency assignments as possible. Compare the spectrum of the compound with that reported in the literature (if available).

Quantitative part. From the infrared spectra of toluene and cyclohexane ‡ select a wavelength at which only toluene absorbs. Prepare a series of four standards containing 2, 4, 6, and 8% toluene in cyclohexane. At the wavelength selected, measure the absorbance of these standards in a 0.025-mm fixed cell with log paper in the recorder,

‡ Spectra numbers 308 and 368, respectively, in the American Petroleum Institute compilation.

using cyclohexane to set the 0 absorbance value. Plot a calibration curve of absorbance versus concentration. Measure the absorbance of the unknown sample, and from the calibration curve determine the per cent toluene in the unknown sample.

For a more difficult experiment the determination of o-, m-, and p-xylene in a mixture is suggested.[7] The wavelengths at which the mixture and standards should be measured are as follows:

o-xylene	13.48 microns
m-xylene	13.00 microns
p-xylene	12.59 microns

Carbon disulfide is a suitable solvent, and a suitable concentration range is from 0.1 to 5 grams of xylene per 100 ml of carbon disulfide.

Experiment 22.7   Qualitative and Quantitative Raman Spectroscopy

Instruments. Raman source, spectrograph, and densitometer or recording Raman unit.

Procedure. *Qualitative part.* Obtain a sample of a known or unknown compound from the instructor. Distil the sample into a Raman tube, and obtain the Raman spectrum. If the spectrum is recorded on a photographic plate, several exposures should be taken so that both the strong and weak lines can be obtained. With the Hilger Raman source unit, exposure times of 5, 15, and 30 minutes are usually satisfactory. The 4358-A mercury line is recommended for the exciting line with filter solutions of saturated potassium nitrite and Rhodamine 5 GDN extra.§ Eastman Kodak plates 103-O or 103-J are suitable for the photographic method. The plate should be developed for 3 minutes in D-19 developer, rinsed in a 5% acetic acid solution, and fixed for 10 minutes in acid fixer. If there is a large amount of continuous background on the plate, the sample should be heated on an oil bath with activated charcoal for 20 minutes. The temperature should be maintained at about 100° C or at least 20° C below the boiling point of the sample. Then it should be filtered and the Raman spectrum again obtained.

Using the traveling microscope and a prism calibration curve, measure the Raman shifts for the compound. Compare the values obtained with those reported in the literature (if available).

[7] G. Duyckaerts and G. Michel, *Méthodes physiques de chimie analytique,* Société Cooperative de l'AEES, Liége, Belgium.

§ Available from E. I. du Pont de Nemours and Company, Wilmington, Del.

Quantitative part. Determine the per cent toluene in cyclohexane, using any one of the methods described in Section 6.4.

Experiment 22.8   Fluorometric Determination of Aluminum in Steel [8]

Instruments. Any available fluorimeter.

Reagents. *2% 8-hydroxyquinoline* in 1 *N* acetic acid; 2 grams of 8-hydroxyquinoline, and 6 ml of glacial acetic acid in 100 ml of water.

Buffer solution. 20 grams of ammonium acetate and 7 ml of concentrated ammonium hydroxide dissolved in 100 ml of water.

Standard aluminum solution (2 μg of aluminum per ml). Prepare by volumetric dilution from a standard solution containing 1.000 mg of aluminum per ml. The solution containing 1.000 mg of aluminum per ml can be prepared by dissolving 17.6 grams of $Al_2(SO_4)_3 \cdot K_2SO_4 \cdot 24H_2O$ in 1 liter, and standardized by precipitation of the aluminum with ammonium hydroxide and ignition to Al_2O_3.

Quinine sulfate solution in 1 *N* sulfuric acid (1 μg of quinine sulfate per ml). Prepare by volumetric dilution from a solution containing 0.1000 gram of quinine sulfate per liter of 1 *N* sulfuric acid. This solution is used to set the fluorimeter sensitivity according to the instrument instructions.

Reagent grade chloroform.||

1 N sulfuric acid.

Spot test reagents. (*a*) 20% ammonium acetate. (*b*) hydroxylamine hydrochloride in water. (*c*) A saturated solution of *o*-phenanthroline in ethanol.

Procedure. In this method a sample of steel is dissolved and then electrolyzed in a mercury cathode cell to remove interfering elements. The *p*H is adjusted, the aluminum salt of 8-hydroxyquinoline is extracted into chloroform, and the fluorescence is measured. The amount of aluminum present is determined from a standard calibration curve.

Preparation of standard solutions. Add 50 ml of H_2O to each of four 250-ml separatory funnels and 2, 4, and 5 ml of standard aluminum solution (2 μg per ml), respectively, to three of the separatory funnels. Add 2 ml of 8-hydroxyquinoline solution and 2 ml of buffer solution to each, extract with two 20-ml portions of chloroform (shaking vigorously for at least 1 minute), and then filter each portion

---

[8] E. Goon et al., *Anal. Chem.*, 25, 608 (1953).

|| If the chloroform is reclaimed by distillation, 0.2% ethyl alcohol should be added as a preservative.

into 50-ml volumetric flasks.   Dilute to the mark with chloroform.

Solution of sample.   Weigh two 1-gram samples of steel to the nearest milligram.   Dissolve the samples in 400-ml Vycor beakers in an acid mix of 10 ml of water, 10 ml of concentrated nitric acid, and 20 ml of 72% perchloric acid.   Bring to fumes, cool, dilute to approximately 200 ml with water, and filter into a 250-ml volumetric Pyrex flask.   Dilute to the mark.   A blank sample with no steel but with the same amounts of reagents is similarly treated.

Electrolysis.¶   Pipet aliquots containing approximately 10 μg of aluminum into each of the two mercury cathode cells (Fig. 22.1) or suitable substitutes.   Adjust the volume to approximately 25 ml and the acidity to approximately 0.5 N with 1 N sulfuric acid.   Add a similar aliquot of the blank sample and the same amount of sulfuric acid to a 250-ml beaker and set aside.

Electrolyze approximately one hour, washing down the cell walls and split cover glasses several times with water during the electrolysis.   Determine whether all the iron has been removed by a spot test as follows: Remove a drop of the steel solution from the cell, and add to a white spot plate.   Add a drop of each of the spot test reagents in the order listed.   The resulting solution should be the same degree of pink as a similar blank test with only the reagents.   If not, continue the electrolysis until such a test results.

Extraction.   Drain the mercury out of the cell and filter the two samples with appropriate washing through a rapid filter paper into 250-ml beakers.   Add to these two samples and the blank sample, previously prepared, 2 ml of buffer solution and 2 ml of 8-hydroxyquinoline.   Using a pH meter equipped with glass and calomel electrodes, adjust the pH to 8.0 ± 1.5 with ammonium hydroxide added from a dropping bottle.   Wash the samples into three 250-ml separatory funnels, and extract as previously described.

Measurement.   Measure the fluorescence of the four standards, and subtract the value for the blank standard from each reading.   Plot a calibration curve of fluorimeter reading as ordinate versus micrograms of aluminum as the abscissa.   Measure the fluorescence of the unknown samples and the blank treated concurrently with the unknown samples.   Correct each reading for the blank, and determine the amount of aluminum present from the calibration curve.   From the original sample weight and the aliquot taken, calculate the per cent aluminum in the steel.

¶ For an excellent discussion of mercury-cathode electrolysis, see J. A. Maxwell and R. P. Graham, *Chem. Revs.*, *46*, 471 (1950).

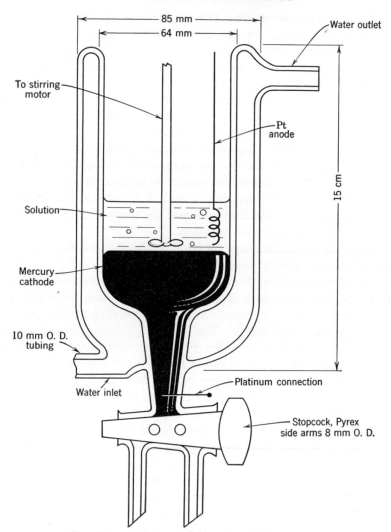

Fig. 22.1 Water-jacketed mercury-cathode cell

Experiment 22.9 Fluorometric Determination of Thiamine (Vitamin B₁) [9]

Instruments. Any available fluorimeter.

Reagents. *0.01 N hydrochloric acid.*

25% potassium chloride, 25 grams in 100 ml of water.

[9] R. Patrick and J. F. H. Wright, *Analyst, 74*, 303 (1949).

0.8% mercuric chloride, 8 grams in 1 liter of water.

Acetone, reagent grade.

0.04 N potassium hydroxide.

Quinine sulfate. 1 μg per ml. Dissolve 0.1000 gram of quinine sulfate in 1 liter of 1 N sulfuric acid. Pipet 100 ml of this solution into a 1-liter volumetric flask, and dilute to the mark with 1 N sulfuric acid. Repeat this procedure to obtain the solution containing 1 μg of quinine sulfate per ml. This solution is used to set the fluorimeter sensitivity according to the instrument instructions.

Standard thiamine solution. 2 μg of thiamine hydrochloride per ml. This solution should be prepared daily by dilution from one containing 0.1000 gram per ml of thiamine hydrochloride in 25% potassium chloride in 0.1 N hydrochloric acid.

Procedure. (Vitamin B_1 tablets.) Weigh a quantity (0.1 to 1.0 gram) of finely powdered sample, and shake with 0.01 N hydrochloric acid in a 1-liter volumetric flask. Make up to volume with 0.01 N hydrochloric acid, allowing the insoluble material, if any, to settle.

Pipet into a 50-ml volumetric flask an aliquot of the above solution so that the total amount of thiamine will be from 2 to 10 μg. If the total volume is less than 15 ml, dilute to approximately this volume with 25% potassium chloride solution.

Add 2 ml of 0.8% mercuric chloride from a buret (do not pipet), and mix well.

Add 8 ml of 0.04 N potassium hydroxide and mix well.*

Heat in a water bath at 40° C for 15 minutes. Cool and make up to volume with acetone.

Prepare a standard calibration curve by measuring the fluorescence of solutions containing 0, 2, 5, and 10 μg of pure thiamine, treated in the same manner.

Determine the weight of thiamine hydrochloride in the unknown.

Experiment 22.10 Qualitative Spectrographic Analysis of Brass

Instruments. Any available spectrograph.

Samples. R.U. powder, copper electrodes, and brass samples.

Procedure. Obtain the samples, two sample cups, two copper electrodes, and two pointed carbon electrodes. Use one cup for the

---

* It is important to shake well before and after the addition of potassium hydroxide.

R.U. powder, and the other for the brass. One pointed carbon is used for the R.U. powder and one for the brass. The electrodes are mounted in the holders (*use forceps*) and their position adjusted with the focusing light. The d-c arc is struck with an insulated carbon rod, and the exposures are made as follows:

Sample	Exposure Time, Seconds	Excitation
R.U.	60	D-c arc
Brass	20	D-c arc
Copper	20	Spark

The spectra are superimposed by means of a Hartmann diaphragm or by appropriate plate-racking technique. The plate should be processed by the normal procedure described in Section 8.10 and after drying should be stored in an envelope until read.

To determine the elements present in the brass, the lines appearing in the R.U. powder and sample spectra but not in the copper spectrum should be marked with a fine pen on the emulsion side of the plate. Then by comparing with a master R.U. plate or photograph, the lines may be marked according to element.

Three lines for one element are considered definite proof of its presence. Elements showing fewer than three lines should be reported along with the number of lines appearing.

Experiment 22.11   Quantitative Spectrographic Analysis of Aluminum Alloys

For this experiment two procedures are given. Procedure *A* involves the measurement of line heights with a traveling microscope and should only be followed if a densitometer is not available. Procedure *B* involves the measurement of line densities with a densitometer.

Instruments. *Procedure A.* A stigmatic spectrograph, a traveling microscope, and a log sector.

Procedure B. A spectograph and a densitometer.

Procedure. Obtain an unknown sample and a set of three standard aluminum samples, and determine the Si, Fe, Mg, Cu, Cr, and Mn as follows:

(*a*) *Excitation.* High-voltage spark.

Power (2 kva).

Maximum inductance (0.36 henry).

(These values apply to an ARL spark source unit.)

(*b*) *Exposure.* Slit width (50 microns).

Petrey stand with a pointed carbon electrode.

3 exposures per sample.

Prespark (10 seconds).

Spark (45 seconds) with log sector for *Procedure A.*

Spark (10 seconds) for *Procedure B.*

(*c*) *Development.* Follow the procedure outlined in Section 8.10.

(*d*) *Line measurement.* The following lines should be used:

Element	3S Alloy	52S Alloy
Al	3059.9	3059.9
Si	2506.9	2881.6
Fe	2743.2	2755.7
Mn	3228.1	2933.1
Cu	3274.0	3274.0
Mg	2790.8	2762.6

For Procedure A the line heights of the above lines should be measured with the traveling microscope.

For Procedure B the above lines should be measured with a densitometer.

(*e*) *Calculations. Procedure A.* From the measured line heights of the standard samples obtain the ratio of element to aluminum (3060-A line) for each reading. Prepare a working curve for each element, plotting the ratios as ordinate with the per cent element as abscissa on log-log paper. From the measured line heights of the unknown sample, obtain the ratio element to aluminum for each reading. Determine the per cent of each element in the unknown sample from the working curve.

Procedure B. With an emulsion calibration curve prepared by one of the methods outlined in Section 10.3, determine the intensity ratio of element to aluminum for each reading. From the average value of the three exposures for each standard, prepare a working curve for each element, plotting the ratios as ordinates and per cent element as abscissa on log-log paper. From the working curves, read off the per cent of each element, and report the average of the three exposures.

Experiment 22.12 Determination of Calcium in Limestone with the Flame Photometer

Instruments. Any flame photometer.

Reagents. *1:1 hydrochloric acid.*

Standard calcium solution. Dissolve 0.5000 gram of calcium carbonate in 10 ml of 1:1 hydrochloric acid, and dilute to 1 liter (1 ml = 0.40 mg of calcium).

Procedure.† Weigh two 1.000-gram samples of limestone in two platinum crucibles. Ignite for 30 minutes with a Meker burner. Dissolve the ignited residue in 10 ml of 1:1 hydrochloric acid, and dilute to 1 liter. Pipet a 25-ml aliquot from each sample, and dilute to 100 ml in a Pyrex volumetric flask.

To prepare four solutions of known calcium content, pipet 5, 10, 25, and 50 ml of standard calcium solution into 100-ml Pyrex volumetric flasks, and dilute to the mark.

Measure the four standards and the two unknown samples. Plot a calibration curve of the concentration of calcium in milligrams per liter (ppm) versus the flame photometer dial reading. Determine the per cent calcium in the unknown limestone.

Experiment 22.13 Determination of pH

Instruments. Available pH meters, LaMotte Roulette, Hellige comparator, and pH indicator papers.

Reagents. 0.1 M monopotassium citrate.

0.1 M hydrochloric acid.

0.1 M sodium hydroxide.

0.1 M monopotassium phosphate.

0.1 M boric acid in 0.1 M potassium chloride.

Indicators	pH Range
Methyl red	4.2–6.3
Bromthymol blue	6.0–7.6
Cresol red	7.2–8.8
Thymol blue	8.0–9.6

† For flame photometers equipped for lithium as an internal standard, a known concentration of lithium may be added and the intensity ratio of calcium to lithium measured. The recommended concentration is 50 ppm of lithium.

Procedure. Prepare 100 ml of buffers covering the pH range from 2.2 to 9.2 at intervals of one unit as follows:

Composition	pH
49.7 ml 0.1 M HCl + 50 ml 0.1 M citrate	2.2
17.2 ml 0.1 M HCl + 50 ml 0.1 M citrate	3.2
16.3 ml 0.1 M NaOH + 50 ml 0.1 M citrate	4.2
54.2 ml 0.1 M NaOH + 50 ml 0.1 M citrate	5.2
8.60 ml 0.1 M NaOH + 50 ml 0.1 M phosphate	6.2
35.00 ml 0.1 M NaOH + 50 ml 0.1 M phosphate	7.2
5.90 ml 0.1 M NaOH + 50 ml 0.1 M boric acid	8.2
26.70 ml 0.1 M NaOH + 50 ml 0.1 M boric acid	9.2

Dilute to 100 ml.

Measurements. Adjust the pH meters with a standard commercially available buffer solution. Measure, with the pH meters, the pH of each of the buffer solutions. Using the appropriate indicator, measure the pH of each of the buffer solutions on the LaMotte Roulette and the Hellige comparator.

Obtain an unknown solution. Determine the approximate pH with a pH indicator paper. Accurately measure the pH with the pH meters and with the Hellige comparator and the LaMotte Roulette.

Experiment 22.14   Potentiometric Determination of a Sodium Carbonate–Bicarbonate Mixture

Instruments. Any available pH meter equipped with a glass electrode and a calomel electrode.

Reagents. 0.1 N hydrochloric acid.

Sodium carbonate.

Procedure. *Standardization of HCl.* Weigh approximately 0.2 gram of reagent-grade anhydrous sodium carbonate to the nearest tenth of a milligram. Dissolve this sample in a 600-ml beaker with approximately 400 ml of distilled water, and titrate with 0.1 N hydrochloric acid, using 2-ml increments (except, where the pH is rapidly changing, use $\frac{1}{4}$-ml increments) until the pH is less than 2.0. Plot the date obtained, and determine the milliliters of hydrochloric acid required for the endpoint. Calculate the normality of hydrochloric acid.

Unknown determination. Weigh 2.0 grams of an unknown carbonate–bicarbonate mixture to the nearest milligram, and dissolve in a 1-liter volumetric flask. Pipet a 100-ml aliquot, and transfer to a 600-ml beaker. Dilute the sample to approximately 400 ml, and titrate in the same manner as described above. Plot the data obtained, and determine the milliliters of hydrochloric acid required for the two endpoints corresponding to the reactions.

$$Na_2CO_3 + HCl \rightarrow NaHCO_3 + NaCl$$

and $$NaHCO_3 + HCl \rightarrow H_2CO_3 + NaCl$$

From the milliliters of hydrochloric acid required for the two endpoints and the normality previously determined, calculate the percentages of sodium carbonate and sodium bicarbonate in the mixture.

Experiment 22.15　Potentiometric Determination of Chromium in Steel

Instrument. Any available oxidation-reduction titrator, such as the Beckman pH meter equipped with calomel and platinum electrodes.

Reagents. *10% ammonium persulfate solution* (freshly prepared).
1:4 sulfuric acid.
2.5% silver nitrate.
1:3 hydrochloric acid.
0.0500 N potassium dichromate.
0.05 N ferrous ammonium sulfate in 1 N sulfuric acid.

Procedure. Weigh six 2-gram samples of steel to the nearest milligram. Transfer to individual 600-ml beakers. Add 100 ml of 1:4 H_2SO_4 and 3 ml of concentrated HNO_3, and heat to boiling until solution is complete. Dilute to approximately 250 ml and add 10 ml of a 2.5% $AgNO_3$ solution and 20 ml of a freshly prepared 10% solution of ammonium persulfate. Heat to boiling, and, if no pink color develops on boiling, add additional ammonium persulfate solution. Complete oxidation is indicated by the formation of permanganic acid or manganese dioxide (a reddish-brown precipitate). When oxidation is complete, add 5 ml of 1:3 hydrochloric acid, and boil 5 minutes after the manganese dioxide or the color of permanganic acid has disappeared. (The hydrochloric acid reduces the MnO_4^- to Mn^{++} but does not reduce the chromium. A precipitate of silver chloride will also be formed.)

Standardization.‡ Pipet a 25-ml sample of potassium dichromate into a 600-ml beaker. Add 100 ml of 1:4 H_2SO_4, and dilute to ap-

‡ An alternative and slightly better procedure is to standardize the ferrous ammonium sulfate against a steel sample of known chromium content.

proximately 250 ml. Cool to 10–15° C in an ice-water bath. Adjust the balancing circuit of the titrimeter until the galvanometer or indicating tube is balanced. Titrate, and determine the endpoint when a permanent (approximately full-scale) deflection on the galvanometer is obtained. Calculate the normality of the ferrous ammonium sulfate.

Unknown. Cool the unknowns to 10–15° C in an ice-water bath, and titrate as above, measuring two samples on each titrimeter available. Calculate the per cent chromium in the steel.

Experiment 22.16 Potentiometric Determination of Manganese in Steel

Instruments. Any available oxidation-reduction titrator such as the Beckman pH meter equipped with calomel and platinum electrodes.

Reagents. *Acid mix,* 525 ml H_2O, 125 ml H_3PO_4, 100 ml H_2SO_4, 3 grams $AgNO_3$.

25% ammonium persulfate solution (freshly prepared).

Sodium arsenite solution (1 gram sodium arsenite per liter).

Procedure. Dissolve three 1.000-gram samples of steel or cast iron in 400-ml beakers, using 30 ml of acid mix for each sample. Heat gently to complete solution, and boil out oxides of nitrogen. Add 100 ml of hot water and 10 ml of ammonium persulfate solution. Bring to a boil, and boil exactly 1 minute. Cool to 15° C or below, and titrate with sodium arsenite solution. The arsenite should be added rapidly until the pink color almost disappears and then at a rate of about a drop per second until the endpoint is reached. Do not try to titrate drop by drop, as the large excess of persulfate will reoxidize the manganese if the titration is protracted.

Standards. Measure a standard sample containing 0.3 to 0.7% manganese with each set of samples. For exact work a sample containing within 0.1% of the manganese content of the unknown steel should be used, as the titer of the arsenite varies with the amount of manganese titrated.

Calculate the per cent manganese in the unknown sample.

Experiment 22.17 Analysis of Chloride–Iodide Mixture

Instrument. Beckman pH meter or Fisher type-S potentiometer with calomel and silver electrodes.

Reagent.   *0.1000 N silver nitrate.*

Procedure.   Weigh 1.5 grams to the nearest milligram of unknown mixture, and dilute to 500 ml.

Take a 100-ml aliquot in a 600-ml beaker, and dilute to about 300 ml with distilled water.   Titrate with 0.1 N silver nitrate, taking the potentiometer reading after each addition of 2 ml.   When the change in emf becomes greater than 20 mv per 2 ml addition, take readings every 0.4 ml.

Plot a graph of millivolts versus milliliters of 0.1 N silver nitrate. From the two breaks in the curve, determine the amount of chloride and iodide in the mixture.   Report as per cent chloride and per cent iodide.

Experiment 22.18   Conductimetric Titration of Vanillin in Vanilla Extract

Instruments.   Apparatus for conductimetric titrations (see Fig. 15.7).   The standard Wheatstone bridge is supplied with audio-frequency alternating current by an electronic oscillator.   The balance point may be read by a pair of headphones, adjusting the bridge to minimum sound in the phones, or by a cathode-ray oscilloscope, adjusting the bridge to minimum deviation from a linear trace on the tube, starting with a low gain on the oscilloscope and increasing the gain to a maximum value for the final balance point.

Reagents.   *0.1000 N hydrochloric acid.*   Standardized in experiment 22.14.

0.1 N sodium hydroxide.

Procedure.   Standardize 0.1 N sodium hydroxide versus 10 ml of standard 0.1000 N hydrochloric acid diluted to 500 ml.   Measure conductance at 2-ml increments to 20 ml.   Plot $1/R$ vs. milliliters added, determine the endpoint graphically, and determine the normality of the sodium hydroxide.

Pipet 50 ml of sample solution of vanilla extract, and dilute with water to about 500 ml.   Titrate with 0.1 N sodium hydroxide, measuring conductance from 0 to 10 ml at 1-ml increments and from 10 to 20 ml at 2-ml increments.   Plot the data.   Determine the endpoint, and calculate the grams of vanillin per liter of vanilla extract.

When the experiment is completed, the conductivity cell should be rinsed thoroughly and left immersed in distilled water.

Experiment 22.19   Polarographic Analysis of Magnesium Alloys [10]

Instruments. Any available polarograph.

Reagents. *1:1 hydrochloric acid.*

0.5 N sodium hydroxide.

0.2% bromphenol blue solution.

Standard stock solution. Dissolve 0.400 gram each of copper, cadmium, and zinc in 20 ml of 1:1 hydrochloric acid, and dilute to 1 liter with 2.0 N potassium chloride.

Procedure. *Standard solution.* Pipet a 25-ml portion of the standard stock solution into a 100-ml volumetric flask. Add indicator and 0.5 N sodium hydroxide until the solution is weakly acid. A standard prepared in this way will contain 2.00% of copper, cadmium, and zinc for a 0.500-gram sample.

Unknown sample. Dissolve a 0.500-gram sample with 20 ml of water and 8 ml of 1:1 hydrochloric acid in a 150-ml beaker. When solution is complete, add one drop of 30% H_2O_2, and boil 5 minutes to remove the excess. Transfer to a 100-ml volumetric flask, add 20 drops of bromphenol blue, and add 0.5 N sodium hydroxide until the solution is weakly acid. Dilute to the mark, and mix well.

Measurements. Obtain polarograms of the standard, and of the sample according to the instructions for the instrument. From the polarogram determine the elements present, and from the wave heights relative to the standard determine the percentage of each element that is present.

Note. The magnesium chloride acts as the supporting electrolyte, and the indicator as maximum suppressor.

Experiment 22.20   Amperometric Titration of Chloride in a Soluble Chloride

Instruments. Any manual polarograph or amperometric titrator.

Reagents. *0.0250 N AgNO₃.*

1 N KNO₃ (approx.).

0.1% gelatin.

0.1 N HNO₃ (approx.).

Procedure. Weigh 0.100 gram of an unknown soluble chloride sample. Dissolve the sample in 25 ml of 1 N potassium nitrate. Add

[10] C. H. Gull, *J. Soc. Chem. Ind. London,* **56,** 177 (1937).

a drop of indicator, 1 ml of 0.1% gelatin, and then a few drops of 0.1 N nitric acid to make the solution weakly acidic. Transfer to a 500-ml volumetric flask, and dilute to the mark with 1 N potassium nitrate. Bubble nitrogen through the solution for 10 minutes, and then titrate a 100-ml aliquot, using 1-ml increments of 0.025 N silver nitrate. After each addition of silver nitrate, stir by bubbling nitrogen through the solution, and, after shutting off the nitrogen, read the galvanometer. Take readings to 10 ml, and then plot the readings against the milliliters of silver nitrate added. Determine the endpoint graphically, and calculate the per cent chloride in the unknown sample. If time is available, run a duplicate determination.

Experiment 22.21   High-Frequency Titration of Fluoride

Instruments. A high-frequency titrator.
Reagents. *0.01 M thorium nitrate* (approx.).
Chlorphenol red indicator solution.
0.05 N HClO₄ (approx.).
Standard fluoride solution (1 ml = 50 μg of fluoride). Dissolve 0.110 gram dried sodium fluoride in water, and dilute to 1 liter. Store in a polyethylene bottle.

Procedure. Transfer 5 ml of the standard fluoride solution to the titration cell, and dilute to proper volume. Adjust the titrator according to instructions. Add 0.05-ml increments of 0.01 M thorium nitrate solution until 1 ml has been added. Plot the titrator response against volume of reagent, select the endpoint, and calculate the exact normality of the thorium nitrate.

Obtain a sample containing an unknown quantity of fluoride in alkaline solution. Transfer a 10-ml aliquot to the titration cell, add 1 drop of *p*-nitrophenol indicator, and make just barely acid with 0.5 N HClO₄. Dilute to proper volume, and titrate in the same manner as described for the standard.

Calculate the fluoride present as micrograms of fluoride per milliliter (parts per million).

Experiment 22.22   Qualitative Analysis by X-Ray Diffraction

Instruments. X-ray diffraction unit.
Procedure. Load the X-ray diffraction camera in the darkroom. Mount the unknown powder sample in the holder, and check the

alignment with a small fluorescent screen. Turn on the X-ray beam. The exposure time will vary from 2 to 10 hours, depending upon the nature of the radiation and the sample. The instructor should be consulted for this information. After the exposure, develop the film for 5 minutes in D-19 developer, and then keep in acid fixer for twice the time it requires the film to clear (approximately 15 minutes). Wash well and allow to dry.

Determine the d values (interplanar spacings), and, using the ASTM index, identify the unknown sample.

Experiment 22.23 Mass Spectrum of an Organic Compound

Instruments. A mass spectrometer.

Procedure. Introduce the sample into the mass spectrometer through an appropriate leak. Record the mass spectrum, using an ionizing potential of 70 volts. If the sample is an unknown, compare the mass spectrum obtained with the compilation published by S. M. Rock,[11] and if possible identify the compound.

Experiment 22.24 Characterization of an Isotope by Half-Life Determination and Absorption Measurements

Instruments. Beta-gamma counter, scaler with standard beta and gamma sources, planchets, sets of aluminum and of lead absorbers.

Procedure. Prepare the sample by pipetting 0.1 ml of the sample solution onto a filter-paper disk cut to fit the counter planchets. Dry the sample in an oven, and cool. Determine whether the sample is a beta emitter, a gamma emitter, or both, by counting the sample with and without a lead absorber of about 2500 mg per cm². Measure the counter background and its efficiency for beta and gamma standards, and count the sample for a total net count of over 5000 counts, or a maximum time of 30 minutes. The sample count should be repeated at daily intervals if possible to determine the half-life.

Plot logarithms of the net counts per minute against the time, draw the best visual curve, and estimate the half-life. From the type of radiation and the half-life, list the possible isotopes that could be present. From the number of d/m/ml of sample estimate the activity of the sample at the time of the initial count in terms of millicuries per liter.

[11] S. M. Rock, *Anal. Chem.*, 23, 261 (1951).

The isotope may be more completely characterized by determining its absorption characteristics. The counts per minute, using the various lead absorbers (for gamma) or aluminum absorbers (for beta), should be measured, and the logarithm of the relative count (net counts per minute divided by net counts per minute with no absorber) should be plotted against absorber thickness. For gamma radiation, the slope of this line is the absorption coefficient, and the value obtained may be checked against literature values for lead absorption of the isotopes with the proper half-life. Another method is to determine the half-thickness and estimate the energy from Fig. 21.7.

For beta radiation it is necessary to make a Feather plot of the results. For this plot, an absorption curve for an isotope of known range must be run as well as the unknown. The relative count for the standard corresponds to a fraction of its known range in the absorbing material. It is assumed that the same relative count for the sample corresponds to the same fraction of the sample range. From the sample absorption curve, the relative counts may be converted to fractions of the sample range. Thus, for each value of relative count, an apparent range may be calculated. If this apparent range is plotted against the corresponding value of fraction of range, it will approach a constant value (Fig. 21.10) as the fraction approaches unity. This constant value is accepted as the actual range of the beta activity. This range may be compared with literature values, or the maximum energy of the beta particle may be estimated by use of Fig. 21.11.

Note. The absorber thickness plotted must include the window thickness for the counter, the air space between the sample and the counter, and one-half the filter-paper thickness. These, and the aluminum thickness should be expressed as milligrams per square centimeter.

Beckman Model-B Spectrophotometer

Description of controls. *Sensitivity.* The gain selector switch, located on the extreme left of the front panel and designated *Sensitivity,* controls the amplification of the signal from the phototube.

The *Standby* position is employed when it is desired to nullify needle movement on the milliammeter scale but still leave the instrument on for immediate use.

The other *four* positions on the dial control a set of precision resistors in the electronic feedback network, which in turn controls the amplifier sensitivity. Position 1 represents the lowest gain position, and consequently requires the widest slits.

Regardless of the gain position used for setting the 100% transmittance point (0% absorbance) with the solvent in the light path, subsequent transmittance and absorbance readings may be made directly from the scale when the switch remains in the *same* gain position.

Dark Current. The dark-current control compensates for the dark current in the phototube and for the amplifier grid current and bias. This adjustment is always made with the shutter closed and consists of bringing the milliammeter needle to zero on the scale while the sensitivity multiplier is in the position to be used in measuring the sample.

Wavelength. The wavelength mechanism controls the relative position of the Féry prism with respect to the entrance and exit slits.

Slit. The dial designated *Slit* continuously controls the width of the entrance and exit slits and therefore the band width of the light striking the phototube.

Shutter. The *Shutter* control is located on the extreme right hand end of the front panel and has three positions: *Fltr, Shtr,* and *Open.* When the shutter knob is set at *Fltr,* a Corning 9863 filter prevents visible light from reaching the phototube. The *Fltr* position is used when measurements are to be made at wavelengths of 320 to 400 mμ. When the shutter control is set at *Shtr* a metal panel cuts off all light to the phototube. When set at *Open* light from the exit slit passes uninterrupted from the sample to the phototube. This position is used for all measurements between 400 and 1000 mμ.

Operation

1. If milliammeter needle is not at zero adjust *carefully* with meter zeroing screw.

2. Plug instrument into power line (115 alternating current, 60 cycle).

3. Turn sensitivity multiplier to *Standby* position and power supply toggle switch to *On.*

4. Allow instrument to warm up for 5 minutes.

5. Turn shutter control to *Shtr,* and turn sensitivity multiplier to desired position.

6. Insert cells containing distilled water and solutions to be measured in cell holder, and place in cell compartment. Lower compartment cover.

7. Move cell containing distilled water into light path.

8. Set wavelength to desired value with knob marked *Wavelength*.

9. Set slit control (*Slit*) almost closed to approximately 0.05, and adjust *Dark Current* to a zero reading on the milliammeter dial.

10. Turn shutter control to *Open* and adjust meter to 0% absorbance with slit control.

11. Move cells containing solutions to be measured into light path.

12. Read *absorbance* on meter scale for each solution.

13. Repeat steps 7 to 11 to obtain absorbance values at different wavelengths.

Beckman Model-DU Spectrophotometer

1. Turn the lamp switch *On*, set selector switch to *Check*, and turn shutter switch to *Off*.

2. Rotate wavelength knob until desired scale value is shown under hairline.

3. Select proper phototube. (The model DU is equipped with ultraviolet-sensitive and red-sensitive phototubes for the range 220 to 1000 mμ. The proper phototube to use is determined by the spectral range to be investigated. The red-sensitive phototube, required for use *above* 625 mμ (but usable to 400 mμ), is in position when the knob on the phototube housing is pushed in. The ultraviolet-sensitive phototube for use *below* 625 mμ is in position when the knob is pulled *out* as far as possible.)

4. Select proper filter. (A small knob on the front end near the cell compartment has three positions. When the knob is pushed in, measurements are made with the hydrogen lamp as a source, or with the tungsten lamp from 400 to 1000 mμ. When the knob is pulled out to the first stop a red-purple filter is inserted between the exit slit and the cell. This position is used from 320 to 400 mμ with the tungsten lamp. The third position is blank, and is available for inserting filters or lenses for special studies.)

5. Remove cell compartment cover, and put filled cells in place. Make sure that the cells and holder are seated properly, then replace the compartment cover, and place the solvent or "blank" in the light path.

6. Rotate dark-current knob to zero the meter needle. This adjustment must be repeated occasionally (for highest accuracy between each absorbance reading).

7. Turn shutter switch *On*. This switch must be turned gently; otherwise the phototube housing may be jarred, resulting in needle shift or unsteadiness.

8. Rotate slit knob to approximately zero the needle, to give the desired slit width.

9. Rotate the sensitivity knob to accurately zero the needle. For highest accuracy, this adjustment should be 1 to 3 turns from its clockwise limit and should be checked between each absorbance reading.

10. Operate the slider knob to place an unknown sample in the light beam.

11. Set selector switch to 1.0, and rotate absorbance knob to again zero the needle. Record the absorbance reading.

12. Place the next unknown sample in the light path, and zero the needle by rotating the absorbance knob. Again record the absorbance reading. Repeat step 12 to measure the absorbance of the third sample.

13. Subsequent readings at different wavelengths are obtained by repeating steps 1 to 11 with steps 3 to 5 being neglected except when changing samples, the filter, or the phototube.

Operation of Beckman Model DU in Ultraviolet Region

1. Replace the tungsten lamp with the hydrogen lamp.

2. Turn the switch on the power supply for the hydrogen lamp from off to on.

3. Turn the switch on the far right of the power supply five clicks clockwise.

4. Wait 2 minutes to allow tube filaments to warm up. Then push starter button on power supply to apply plate voltage.

5. Turn the switch on the far right counterclockwise five clicks and check to see if the hydrogen lamp is lit.

6. Obtain the spectrum in the same manner as outlined for the visible region.

Klett-Summerson Filter Photometer

Preliminary Adjustments

1. Be sure that the proper glass color filter is in place.

2. Set galvanometer short-circuiting switch (right side) to *On*.

3. Be sure that colorimeter lamp switch (on lamp housing) is off.

4. Set the galvanometer needle to coincide with the hairline of the galvanometer scale by adjusting the knob at the top of the galvanometer housing.

5. If rectangular cells are to be used, pull the shutter knob (left side) out, or, if test tubes are to be used, push the shutter knob in. This controls the incident light area in accordance with the cell size.

Zero Setting

6. Fill a clean cell with distilled water, and place in the cell compartment. Close the compartment cover.

7. Set the scale to zero by means of the large knob at the front of the instrument. Note that the scale is divided in arbitrary logarithmic units and corresponds loosely to an absorbance scale.

8. Turn on the colorimeter lamp, and allow the instrument to warm up for a few minutes.

9. Set the galvanometer needle to coincide with the hairline by means of the knob to the left of the cell compartment.

Readings on a Solution

10. Remove the cell, and replace the distilled water by the solution being tested.

11. Bring the galvanometer needle back to coincidence by adjusting the scale knob at the front of the instrument. Record the scale reading of the solution.

12. Further solutions may be tested by repeating steps 10 and 11.

Notes

(*a*) It may be necessary to make the preliminary adjustments each time the instrument is used, but usually it is in adjustment.

(*b*) The zero setting should be repeated for every series of solutions. For very accurate work, the setting should be checked before each unknown solution is measured.

(*c*) The cells supplied with this instrument are not necessarily matched, and so the same cell is usually taken for each series following a blank or zero adjustment.

(*d*) The pass bands of the filters are: blue 400–465 mμ, green 500–570 mμ, red 640–700 mμ.

(*e*) The cells should be filled to a height of at least 5 cm or the solution will not intercept all the light beam and erroneous readings will be obtained.

Duboscq Colorimeter

1. Select the standard that is the closest visual match to the unknown sample.

2. Clean both cups with distilled water, rinse with the standard selected, and fill both cups two thirds full of the standard solution.

3. Set the cups in place in the instrument, and replace the metal hood.

4. Turn the illuminator lamp on.

5. Set both scales to read 30.0, and adjust the slide at the rear of the illuminator until the halves of the split field are balanced.

6. Remove the right-hand cell, and fill two thirds full of the unknown sample.

7. With the left-hand (standard) scale still at 30.0 adjust the right-hand (sample) depth until the fields balance, and read the scale. Make five readings approaching balance from the high side and five readings approaching balance from the low side.

8. Average the ten readings, and from the reduced Beer's law equation ($c_1b_1 = c_2b_2$, where c is the concentration and b the depth measured) calculate the concentration of the unknown.

Klett Fluorimeter §

1. Set the switch on the transformer to value closest to line voltage. Plug the polarized cap of the fluorimeter lamp into the transformer, and turn the switch to light the lamp. The lamp should be lit for 5 minutes before taking a measurement.

2. Connect the galvanometer leads to the two binding posts on the galvanometer. (Never move a taut-suspension galvanometer unless the two galvanometer posts are connected by a short piece of wire— the short-circuiting link.) Plug the galvanometer light cord into the other receptable of the duplex receptable in the transformer housing. The spot of light shown in the window of the galvanometer should be near the center of the scale, and the dark hairline in the spot of

§ The type AH-4 mercury lamp is an intense high-pressure arc and should be always kept covered. Prolonged exposure to the arc is distinctly harmful to the human eye.

Use of the Bias Control. Under certain circumstances it is advantageous to apply a potential in opposition to that set up in the electrode system. One case is when a large excess of a very easily reducible metal is present in the determination of a less-reducible element. The potential is advanced to the point at which measurements are to be made, the galvanometer index brought to zero by the bias control, and the analysis carried out in the usual way.

It is important that the *Bias* control be returned to the *Off* position after use.

Suggested Desk List for Instrumental Analysis

1 thermometer, 110° C.
1 spatula, nickel.

Transfer Pipets

1 ea.: 1 ml, 2 ml, 3 ml, 5 ml, 10 ml, 25 ml, 50 ml, 100 ml.

Graduated Cylinders

1 ea.: 10 ml, 25 ml, 50 ml, 100 ml.

Volumetric Flasks (Pyrex)

1 1000 ml.
1 500 ml.
7 250 ml.
6 100 ml.
4   50 ml.
2   10 ml.

Beakers

4 150 ml.
4 250 ml.
6 400 ml.
2 800 ml.
3 400 ml Vycor.

1 filter stand.
4 separatory funnels, Squibb, 250 ml, T/S.
1 camel's-hair brush, 75 mm.
6 watch glasses, Speedyvap, 4½-inch.
6 stirring rods.
1 buret, 50 ml.
1 microburet, 10 ml.

Appendix A

Groups of Mercury Lines Useful for Wavelength Identification

George R. Harrison, Richard C. Lord, John R. Loofbourow, *Practical Spectroscopy*, Copyright 1948 by Prentice-Hall, New York. Reprinted by permission of the publisher

Group	Color	Wavelengths, A	Approximate Intensity
1	Red	6234.37	10
		6149.50	20
2	Yellow	5790.65–5789.66	50
		5769.59	50
3	Green	5460.74	100
4	Blue	4358.35–4347.50	20
5	Violet	4077.81	8
		4046.56	10
6	Ultraviolet	3663.28–3654.83–3650.15	70
7	Ultraviolet	3341.48	10
8	Ultraviolet	3131.83–3131.55–3125.66	40
9	Ultraviolet	3025.62–3021.50	30
10	Ultraviolet	2967.28	10
11	Ultraviolet	2893.60	10
12	Ultraviolet	2804.46	20
13	Ultraviolet	2752.84–2752.78	10
14	Ultraviolet	2652.04	8
15	Ultraviolet	2536.52	30
16	Ultraviolet	2482.72–2482.01	5
17	Ultraviolet	2399.74–2399.38–2378.33	3

Appendix B

Sensitive Arc Lines of 50 Elements

Reprinted by permission from the table prepared by J. W. Ryde
and H. G. Jenkins

Element	Wavelength	Intensity	Element	Wavelength	Intensity
Al	3961.54	7	Be (*Cont.*)	2650.94	0
	3944.03	5		2650.31	0
	3092.72	3		2494.87	0
	3082.16	3		2494.44	0
	2575.11	0		2348.62	5
	2567.99	0			
	2373.13	1	Bi	3067.73	5
	2367.06	0		2897.98	2
Sb	3267.48	2	B	2497.73	5
	3232.52	1		2496.78	4
	3029.80	0	Cd	5085.82	1
	2877.92	4		4799.91	1
	2769.94	1		3610.51	3
	2598.08	4		3467.66	2
	2528.53	4		3466.20	3
	2311.50	3		3403.65	2
As	2898.73	2		3261.05	5
	2860.46	3		2288.03	2
	2780.23	3	Ca	4455.88	25
	2745.00	2		4434.96	20
	2492.91	2		4425.44	15
	2456.52	2		4318.65	12
	2381.20	2		to	
	2370.77	2		4283.10	12
	2369.67	2		4226.73	50
	2349.84	4		3968.48	40
	2288.14	3		3933.67	40
Ba	5535.53	8	C	2478.53	2
	4934.09	5	Cs	4593.20	1
	4554.04	15		4555.36	3
Be	3321.35	2			
	3321.08	2	Cr	4289.72	2
	3131.06	2		4274.80	2
	3130.42	3		4254.34	2

Sensitive Arc Lines of 50 Elements (Continued)

Element	Wavelength	Intensity	Element	Wavelength	Intensity
Cr (*Cont.*)	3605.33	2	Fe (*Cont.*)	3475.46	2
	3593.48	2		3465.86	2
	3578.69	3		3440.61	2
				3047.61	1
Co	3453.51	3		3021.08	1
	3405.12	1		3020.65	2
	2407.26	0		2983.57	0
				2973.24	0
Cu	3273.96	15		2966.90	0
	3247.55	20		2742.41	1
				2719.04	1
F	CaF$_2$ band head at 5291			2631.05	0
				2613.84	1
Ga	4172.06	5		2527.44	0
	4033.01	5		2522.86	2
	2943.64	4		2488.15	2
	2874.24	4		2483.28	3
Ge	3039.08	2	La	4429.90	1
	2754.59	2		4333.80	1
	2709.61	2		4123.23	2
	2691.35	1		4086.71	2
	2651.60	1		3995.75	1
	2651.15	2		3949.10	4
	2592.55	1		3337.49	3
Au	2675.95	2	Pb	4057.83	10
	2427.98	2		3739.95	2
				3683.47	8
In	4511.31	6		3671.50	1
	4101.76	4		3639.58	6
	3258.56	2		3572.74	2
	3256.08	5		2873.32	4
	3039.35	2		2833.07	5
				2823.20	2
Ir	3513.67	1		2663.17	3
	3220.79	1		2614.20	4
	3133.31	1		2577.28	1
	2639.70	0		2476.39	2
	2543.98	0		2393.81	1
Fe	3749.49	1	Li	6707.86	20
	3748.26	1		6103.52	5
	3745.56	1		4602.99	2
	3734.87	2		3232.67	1
	3719.94	2			
	3647.85	1	Mg	5183.62	30
	3617.79	1		5172.68	25
	3581.20	2		5167.33	20
	3570.10	2		3838.29	25
	3565.38	1			
	3490.58	1			

Sensitive Arc Lines of 50 Elements (Continued)

Element	Wavelength	Intensity	Element	Wavelength	Intensity
Mg	3832.31	20	Os (*Cont.*)	2637.12	0
(*Cont.*)	3829.36	15		2488.55	2
	3096.92	30			
	3093.05	15	Pd	3634.68	1
	3091.09	10		3609.55	1
	2852.13	100		3516.95	2
	2802.71	30		3481.16	2
	2795.54	30		3460.75	2
				3421.23	3
Mn	4034.49	3		3404.59	4
	4033.07	3		3242.71	3
	4030.76	4			
	2798.27	3	P	2554.93	1
	2605.69	1		2553.28	2
	2593.73	1		2535.65	2
	2576.12	1		2534.01	1
Hg	2536.52	2	Pt	3064.71	2
Mo	3902.96	4		3042.62	1
	3864.12	5		2997.96	1
	3798.26	5		2929.79	1
	3447.13	1		2830.29	1
	3358.12	0		2719.02	1
	3208.88	1		2705.89	0
	3193.98	3		2702.40	1
	3170.34	3		2659.44	2
	3158.15	2		2650.86	1
	3132.60	3		2628.02	0
	3112.12	0	K	4047.22	5
Ni	3524.54	2		4044.16	5
	3515.06	0		3447.70	1
	3446.26	1		3446.72	1
	3414.77	2			
Nb	4123.85	1	Rh	4374.82	1
	4100.97	1		3692.35	1
	4079.73	2		3657.99	0
	4058.97	3		3596.19	0
	3358.38	2		3434.90	2
				3323.10	0
Os	4420.46	1	Ru	3728.02	2
	4260.85	1		3726.93	2
	3267.94	2		3661.35	1
	3262.30	1		3634.94	1
	3058.66	2		3596.17	0
	3030.70	1		3593.03	1
	3018.04	1		3498.95	4
	2909.08	3		3436.74	2
	2838.63	1		3428.63	1

Sensitive Arc Lines of 50 Elements (*Continued*)

Element	Wavelength	Intensity	Element	Wavelength	Intensity
Ru	3428.31	1	Tl (*Cont.*)	2918.33	1
(*Cont.*)	3417.35	0		2767.88	3
Rb	4215.58	4	Sn	3330.60	2
	4201.81	4		3262.33	4
				3175.05	3
Sc	4246.85	1		3034.12	3
	4023.72	2		3009.14	1
	4020.42	1		2863.32	4
	3911.89	2		2839.99	4
	3907.54	1		2706.50	3
	3642.81	0		2661.25	0
	3580.98	1		2546.55	1
	3572.57	1		2429.50	2
				2354.84	2
Si	3905.52	1	Ti	⌈4536.05	1
	2881.59	8		to	
	2528.52	4		⌊4533.25	1
	2524.12	4		3998.64	2
	2519.21	4		3989.76	1
	2516.12	5		3981.77	0
	2514.32	4		3958.21	1
	2506.90	4		3956.34	0
	2435.16	2		3653.50	1
Ag	3382.89	10		3642.68	1
	3280.67	10		3635.47	1
				3377.59	1
Na	5895.93	30		3372.80	2
	5889.97	30		3371.46	2
	5688.22	1		3370.44	1
	5682.68	0		3361.22	2
	3302.94	4		3354.64	1
	3302.34	4		3349.41	2
				3349.04	1
Sr	4607.34	10		3341.87	3
	4215.52	6		3322.94	0
	4077.71	10		3241.99	0
				3239.04	1
Ta	3318.85	1		3236.58	1
	3311.14	1		3234.52	1
	3103.25	0		3199.92	1
	2714.68	2			
	2656.60	1	W	4294.62	0
	2653.28	1		4008.76	1
	2647.49	1	V	4594.10	0
Tl	5350.47	7		4460.31	1
	3775.73	6		⌈4408.52	1
	3529.41	4		to	
	3519.21	6		⌊4379.24	2

Sensitive Arc Lines of 50 Elements (Continued)

Element	Wavelength	Intensity	Element	Wavelength	Intensity
V (*Cont.*)	4134.47	0	Y (*Cont.*)	3710.30	2
	4132.00	1		3633.13	0
	4128.07	2		3620.94	1
	4116.70	1		3327.88	1
	4111.79	2		3242.28	2
	4105.17	1		3216.68	1
	4099.80	1			
	3185.41	2	Zn	6362.35	20
	3183.99	2		4810.53	50
	3183.42	1		4722.16	50
	3110.71	0		4680.14	30
	3102.30	1		3345.93	30
	3066.37	1		3345.57	30
	3060.45	1		3302.91	25
	2908.81	1		3302.56	25
				3282.32	20
Y	4643.69	0			
	4374.95	1	Zr	3572.47	1
	4142.87	2		3496.21	2
	4102.38	3		3481.16	0
	3982.60	0		3438.23	2
	3774.33	2		3391.98	2

Appendix C

Buffer Solutions of Clark and Lubs

Prepared according to W. M. Clark, *The Determination of Hydrogen Ions*,
3rd Edition, Williams and Wilkins Co., Baltimore (1928)

The following volumes of standard solutions are mixed and diluted to 200 ml
to obtain the specified pH

pH	ml 0.2 M KH phthalate	ml 0.2 M HCl	ml 0.2 M NaOH	ml 0.2 M KH$_2$PO$_4$	ml 0.2 M H$_3$BO$_3$ + 0.2 M KCl
2.2	50.00	46.60			
2.4	50.00	39.60			
2.6	50.00	33.00			
2.8	50.00	26.50			
3.0	50.00	20.40			
3.2	50.00	14.80			
3.4	50.00	9.95			
3.6	50.00	6.00			
3.8	50.00	2.65			
4.0	50.00		0.40		
4.2	50.00		3.65		
4.4	50.00		7.35		
4.6	50.00		12.00		
4.8	50.00		17.50		
5.0	50.00		23.65		
5.2	50.00		29.75		
5.4	50.00		35.25		
5.6	50.00		39.70		
5.8	50.00		43.10		
6.0			5.64	50.00	
6.2			8.55	50.00	
6.4			12.60	50.00	
6.6			17.74	50.00	
6.8			23.60	50.00	
7.0			29.54	50.00	
7.2			34.90	50.00	
7.4			39.34	50.00	
7.6			42.74	50.00	
7.8			45.17	50.00	
8.0			4.00		50.00
8.2			5.90		50.00
8.4			8.55		50.00
8.6			12.00		50.00
8.8			16.40		50.00
9.0			21.40		50.00
9.2			26.70		50.00
9.4			32.00		50.00
9.6			36.85		50.00
9.8			40.80		50.00
10.0			43.90		50.00

Appendix D

Redox Potentials

Reprinted by permission from W. M. Latimer, *Oxidation Potentials*, Prentice-Hall, 2nd ed., New York (1952)

Reaction in Acid Solution	$E°$
$Li = Li^+ + e^-$	3.045
$K = K^+ + e^-$	2.925
$Ba = Ba^{++} + 2e^-$	2.90
$Sr = Sr^{++} + 2e^-$	2.89
$Ca = Ca^{++} + 2e^-$	2.87
$Na = Na^+ + e^-$	2.714
$Mg = Mg^{++} + 2e^-$	2.37
$Al = Al^{+++} + 3e^-$	1.66
$Zn = Zn^{++} + 2e^-$	0.763
$U^{+++} = U^{++++} + e^-$	0.61
$Fe = Fe^{++} + 2e^-$	0.440
$Cr^{++} = Cr^{+++} + e^-$	0.41
$Ti^{++} = Ti^{+++} + e^-$	ca 0.37
$Pb + SO_4^= = PbSO_4 + 2e^-$	0.356
$Tl = Tl^+ + e^-$	0.3363
$H_3PO_3 + H_2O = H_3PO_4 + 2H^+ + 2e^-$	0.276
$V^{++} = V^{+++} + e^-$	0.255
$S_2O_6^= + 2H_2O = 2SO_4^= + 4H^+ + 2e^-$	0.22
$Sn = Sn^{++} + 2e^-$	0.136
$Pb = Pb^{++} + 2e^-$	0.126
$HS_2O_4^- + 2H_2O = 2H_2SO_3 + H^+ + 2e^-$	0.08
$H_2 = 2H^+ + 2e^-$	0.00
$HCHO (aq) + H_2O = HCOOH (aq) + 2H^+ + 2e^-$	−0.056
$H_2S = S + 2H^+ + 2e^-$	−0.141
$Sn^{++} = Sn^{++++} + 2e^-$	−0.15
$Cu^+ = Cu^{++} + e^-$	−0.153
$H_2SO_3 + H_2O = SO_4^= + 4H^+ + 2e^-$	−0.17
$U^{++++} + 2H_2O = UO_2^{++} + 4H^+ + 2e^-$	−0.334
$Cu = Cu^{++} + 2e^-$	−0.337
$Fe(CN)_6^{---} - Fe(CN)_6^{=-} + e^-$	−0.36
$V^{+++} + H_2O = VO^{++} + 2H^+ + e^-$	−0.361
$HCN (aq) = \frac{1}{2}C_2N_2 + H^+ + e^-$	−0.37
$S_2O_3^= + 3H_2O = 2H_2SO_3 + 2H^+ + 4e^-$	−0.40
$Cu = Cu^+ + e^-$	−0.521
$3I^- = I_3^- + 2e^-$	−0.536
$H_2O_2 = O_2 + 2H^+ + 2e^-$	−0.682

Redox Potentials (*Continued*)

Reaction in Acid Solution $E°$

$$Fe^{++} = Fe^{+++} + e^- \qquad -0.771$$
$$2Hg = Hg_2^{++} + 2e^- \qquad -0.789$$
$$Ag = Ag^+ + e^- \qquad -0.7991$$
$$N_2O_4 + 2H_2O = 2NO_3^- + 4H^+ + 2e^- \qquad -0.80$$
$$Rh = Rh^{+++} + 3e^- \qquad ca \ -0.8$$
$$CuI = Cu^{++} + I^- + e^- \qquad -0.86$$
$$Hg_2^{++} = 2Hg^{++} + 2e^- \qquad -0.920$$
$$HNO_2 + H_2O = NO_3^- + 3H^+ + 2e^- \qquad -0.94$$
$$NO + 2H_2O = NO_3^- + 4H^+ + 4e^- \qquad -0.96$$
$$2Br^- = Br_2 \ (l) + 2e^- \qquad -1.0652$$
$$Cu(CN)_2^- = Cu^{++} + 2CN^- + e^- \qquad -1.12$$
$$\tfrac{1}{2}I_2 + 3H_2O = IO_3^- + 6H^+ + 5e^- \qquad -1.195$$
$$2H_2O = O_2 + 4H^+ + 4e^- \qquad -1.229$$
$$Mn^{++} + 2H_2O = MnO_2 + 4H^+ + 2e^- \qquad -1.23$$
$$Tl^+ = Tl^{+++} + 2e^- \qquad -1.25$$
$$2Cr^{+++} + 7H_2O = Cr_2O_7^= + 14H^+ + 6e^- \qquad -1.33$$
$$2Cl^- = Cl_2 + 2e^- \qquad -1.3595$$
$$Pb^{++} + 2H_2O = PbO_2 + 4H^+ + 2e^- \qquad -1.455$$
$$Au = Au^{+++} + 3e^- \qquad -1.50$$
$$Mn^{++} + 4H_2O = MnO_4^- + 8H^+ + 5e^- \qquad -1.51$$
$$\tfrac{1}{2}Br_2 + 3H_2O = BrO_3^- + 6H^+ + 5e^- \qquad -1.52$$
$$IO_3^- + 3H_2O = H_5IO_6 + H^+ + 2e^- \qquad -1.6$$
$$Ce^{+++} = Ce^{++++} + e^- \qquad -1.61$$
$$\tfrac{1}{2}Cl_2 + H_2O = HClO + H^+ + e^- \qquad -1.63$$
$$Au = Au^+ + e^- \qquad ca \ -1.68$$
$$MnO_2 + 2H_2O = MnO_4^- + 4H^+ + 3e^- \qquad -1.695$$
$$2H_2O = H_2O_2 + 2H^+ + 2e^- \qquad -1.77$$
$$Co^{++} = Co^{+++} + e^- \qquad -1.82$$
$$2SO_4^= = S_2O_8^= + 2e^- \qquad -2.01$$
$$2F^- = F_2 + 2e^- \qquad -2.65$$
$$2HF \ (aq) = F_2 + 2H^+ + 2e^- \qquad -3.06$$

Reaction in Basic Solution

$$SO_3^= + 2OH^- = SO_4^= + H_2O + 2e^- \qquad 0.93$$
$$S_2O_3^= + 6OH^- = 2SO_3^= + 3H_2O + 4e^- \qquad 0.58$$
$$S^= = S + 2e^- \qquad 0.48$$
$$HO_2^- + OH^- = O_2 + H_2O + 2e^- \qquad 0.076$$
$$NO_2^- + 2OH^- = NO_3^- + H_2O + 2e^- \qquad -0.01$$
$$2S_2O_3^= = S_4O_6^= + 2e^- \qquad -0.08$$
$$I^- + 6OH^- = IO_3^- + 3H_2O + 6e^- \qquad -0.26$$
$$4OH^- = O_2 + 2H_2O + 4e^- \qquad -0.401$$
$$MnO_2 + 4OH^- = MnO_4^= + 2H_2O + 2e^- \qquad -0.60$$
$$Br^- + 6OH^- = BrO_3^- + 3H_2O + 6e^- \qquad -0.61$$
$$N_2H_4 + 2OH^- = 2NH_2OH + 2e^- \qquad -0.73$$
$$3OH^- = HO_2^- + H_2O + 2e^- \qquad -0.88$$

Appendix E

Half-Wave Potentials of Metals

Courtesy E. H. Sargent and Co., 155–165 East Superior Street, Chicago, Ill.

All values in the following tables are volts referred to the normal calomel electrode.

Metal	Valence	Neutral or Acid	Alkali	NH₄OH NH₄Cl
Aluminum	3	−1.7		
Ammonium	1	−2.09		
Antimony	3	−0.2	−1.8	
Barium	2	−1.94		
Bismuth	3	−0.1		
Cadmium	2	−0.68	−0.80	−0.85
Calcium	2	−2.23		
Cesium	1	−2.1		
Chromium	2	−1.42	−2.0	−1.74
Chromium	3	−0.7		−1.46
Chromium	6		−0.36	−0.36
Cobalt	2	−1.23	−1.44	−1.32
Cobalt	3	−0.4		−0.4
Copper	2	−0.03		−0.27
Copper	1	−0.03		−0.54
Gallium	3	−1.23		
Gold	1		−1.2	
Gold	3		−0.55	
Hydrogen	1	−1.60		
Indium	3	−0.63	−1.2	
Iron	2	−1.33	−1.56	−1.52
Iron	3	−0.1(?)		
Lead	2	−0.46	−0.81	
Lithium	1	−2.31	−2.31	
Manganese	2	−1.53	−1.7	−1.69
Manganese	3		−1.3	
Manganese	4			
Manganese	6		−0.2	
Nickel	2	−1.09		−1.13
Potassium	1	−2.17	−2.17	
Radium	2	−1.88		
Rhenium	7	−1.2	−1.2	−1.2
Rubidium	1	−2.07	−2.07	
Selenium	4			−1.6
Sodium	1	−2.15	−2.15	
Strontium	2	−2.13	−2.13	
Tellurium	4		−0.7	−0.75
Thallium	1	−0.50	−0.50	−0.50

Half-Wave Potentials of Metals (Continued)

Metal	Valence	Neutral or Acid	Alkali	NH₄OH NH₄Cl
Tin	2	−0.47	−1.1	
Titanium	4	−0.98		
Uranium	4			
Uranium	6	−0.14	−0.9	
Vanadium	5			−1.23
Zinc	2	−1.06	−1.41	−1.38

Appendix F

Commonly Used Radioisotopes

Reprinted by permission from National Bureau of Standards Circular 499,
Nuclear Data

The values for energy and half-life given below are average values extracted
from NBS 499. Dubious values are indicated by a question mark. The
source of the isotope is abbreviated, fission product (*F*), reactor irradiation
(*R*), accelerator product (*A*), and natural (*N*).

Atomic Number	Symbol	Atomic Weight	Activity	Energy, Mev	Half-Life	Source
1	H	3	β	0.018	12.3y	R
4	Be	7	γ	0.48	54d	A
6	C	14	β	0.155	6000y	R
11	Na	24	β	1.39	14.9h	R
			γ	2.8, 1.4		
15	P	32	β	1.72	14.3d	R
16	S	35	β	0.167	88d	R
19	K	40	β	1.4	1.5×10^9y	N
			γ	1.5		
20	Ca	45	β	0.25	176d	R
24	Cr	51	γ	0.33, 0.25	26d	R
25	Mn	54	γ	0.84	310d	R
26	Fe	59	β	0.46, 0.26	46d	A
			γ	1.1, 1.3		
27	Co	60	β	0.31	5.2y	R
			γ	1.17, 1.33		
29	Cu	64	β	0.57 *	12.8h	R
			γ	1.34		
30	Zn	65	γ	1.1	250d	R
33	As	76	β	3.1, 2.6, 1.4	26h	R
			γ	0.57, 1.2		
35	Br	82	β	0.46	35h	R
			γ	0.55, 0.79, 1.4		
38	Sr	89	β	1.5	54d	F
		90	β	0.57	24y	F
40	Zr	95	β	0.40	65d	F
			γ	0.72		
42	Mo	99	β	0.3, 1.2	66h	R
			γ	0.14, 0.75		
47	Ag	110	β	0.09, 0.57	260d	R
			γ	0.66, 0.9, 1.4		

* $\beta + 0.65$.

Commonly Used Radioisotopes (*Continued*)

Atomic Number	Symbol	Atomic Weight	Activity	Energy, Mev	Half-Life	Source
48	Cd	115	β	1.67	44d	R
			γ	0.5		
50	Sn	113	γ	0.09	112d?	R
51	Sb	125	β	0.7, 0.3	2.7y?	R
			γ	0.17, 0.43, 0.61		
53	I	131	β	0.3, 0.60	8.0d	F
			γ	0.36, 0.64		
55	Cs	137	β	0.53	35y	F
			γ	0.67		
56	Ba	140	β	1.0, 0.46	12.7d	F
			γ	0.54		
58	Ce	141	β	0.42, 0.56	30d	F
			γ	0.16		
79	Au	198	β	0.97	2.7d	R
			γ	0.41		
80	Hg	203	β	0.21	48d?	R
			γ	0.28		
82	Pb	210	β	0.03	22y	N
			γ	0.007		
		212	β	0.33, 0.57	10.6h	N
			γ	0.24		
		214	β	0.7	27m	N
			γ	0.05		
83	Bi	210	β	1.17	5.0d	N
		212	α	6.0	60.5m	N
			β	2.25		
			γ	0.72, 0.8		
		214	β	1.65, 3.16	19.7m	N
			γ	0.60		
84	Po	210	α	5.3	140d	N
			γ	0.8		
		218	α	6.0	3.05m	N
86	Rn	220	α	6.3	54.5s	N
		222	α	5.5	3.825d	N
88	Ra	224	α	5.7	3.64d	N
			γ	0.25		
		226	α	4.8, 4.6	1600y	N
			γ	0.19		
90	Th	228	α	5.4	1.90y	N
			γ	0.09		
		232	α	4.1	1.39×10^{10}y	N
		234	β	0.2, 0.1	24.1d	N
			γ	0.09		
92	U	235	α	4.5	8.8×10^{8}y	N
		238	α	4.2	4.5×10^{9}y	N
94	Pu	239	α	5.15	2.4×10^{4}y	R

Appendix G

Dissociation Constants of Acids

Acid	K_1	K_2	K_3
Acetic	1.75×10^{-5}		
Barbituric	1.05×10^{-4}		
Benzoic	6.3×10^{-5}		
Boric	6.4×10^{-10}		
Bromacetic	1.38×10^{-3}		
Butyric	1.48×10^{-5}		
Carbonic	3.5×10^{-7}	4.4×10^{-11}	
Chloracetic	1.4×10^{-3}		
Citric	8.4×10^{-4}	1.8×10^{-5}	4×10^{-6}
Dichloracetic	5×10^{-2}		
Formic	1.76×10^{-4}		
Fumaric	1×10^{-3}	3×10^{-5}	
Hydroquinone	1.1×10^{-10}		
Lactic	1.38×10^{-4}		
Nitrous	4×10^{-4}		
Oxalic	6.5×10^{-2}	6.1×10^{-5}	
Phenol	1.3×10^{-10}		
Phosphoric	1.1×10^{-2}	7.5×10^{-8}	4.8×10^{-13}
Phthalic	1.26×10^{-3}	3.1×10^{-6}	
Picric	1.6×10^{-1}		
Salicylic	1.06×10^{-3}	1×10^{-13}	
Succinic	6.6×10^{-5}	2.8×10^{-6}	
Sulfanilic	6.2×10^{-4}		
Sulfuric		2×10^{-2}	

Dissociation Constants of Bases

Name	K	Name	K
Ammonium hydroxide	1.8×10^{-5}	Propylamine (norm.)	4.7×10^{-4}
Aniline	4.6×10^{-10}	Pyridine	2.3×10^{-9}
Diethylamine	1.26×10^{-3}	Quinine	2.2×10^{-7}
Dimethylamine	5.2×10^{-4}	Quinoline	1×10^{-9}
Dipropylamine	1.02×10^{-3}	m-Toluidine	5.5×10^{-10}
Ethylamine	5.6×10^{-4}	o-Toluidine	3.3×10^{-10}
Ethylenediamine	8.5×10^{-5}	p-Toluidine	2×10^{-9}
Isopropylamine	5.3×10^{-4}	Triethylamine	6.4×10^{-4}
Methylamine	5×10^{-4}	Trimethylamine	7.4×10^{-5}
α-Naphthylamine	9.9×10^{-11}	Urea	1.5×10^{-14}
β-Naphthylamine	2×10^{-10}		

Appendix H

Questions on Selected Topics

Absorption Spectroscopy

1. The field of absorption spectroscopy is often subdivided into ultraviolet, visible, and infrared regions. (*a*) Compare the types of substances that absorb in these three regions. (*b*) Mention the major experimental advantages and disadvantages of each region with regard to analytical possibilities. (*c*) Mention the major differences in instrumentation, i.e. (with respect to source, monochromator, optics, and receptor) needed to handle each region.

2. Show how Beer's law may be used in designing a filter photometer, and describe how the factors are treated in one of the instruments used in the laboratory.

3. Describe how you would select the proper filter to use in a colorimetric method (*a*) if a spectrophotometer is available, (*b*) if a spectrophotometer is not available.

4. Describe the essential differences between a filter photometer and a fluorimeter, and the phenomena of absorption and fluorescence.

5. How would you test for the following defects: (*a*) photocell fatigue (filter photometer), (*b*) misadjusted wavelength scale (spectrophotometer), (*c*) unmatched solution cells (either)?

6. The aluminum salt of 8-hydroxyquinoline in chloroform yields a yellow color as well as a green fluorescence. If you had to choose between a colorimetric method or a fluorimetric method for a particular determination of aluminum, which method would you select? Justify your choice with a factual discussion.

7. Infrared spectroscopy is employed for quantitative analysis more frequently than Raman spectroscopy. Why is this so? With what type of solutions would Raman spectroscopy offer distinct advantages?

8. The Raman spectrum, ultraviolet spectrum, and infrared spectrum of acetone are all available in the chemical literature. (*a*) Describe briefly how such spectra are obtained. (*b*) Sketch with typical coordinates these spectra (based on your experience, your outside reading and mostly your imagination). (*c*) Of what value are such spectra to the chemist?

9. Given the two organic compounds

$$
\begin{matrix}
& O & H_2 & & & & H_2 & H_2 & H_2 & H_2 \\
& \| & | & & & & | & | & | & | \\
(1) & CH_3-C-C-NO_2 & & \text{and} & (2) & CH_3-C-C-C-C-CH_3
\end{matrix}
$$

briefly discuss how you would determine (1) quantitatively in the presence of (2), using absorption spectroscopy, and justify your choice of procedure.

10. Two 1-gram samples of steel, one unknown and one containing 0.23% manganese were dissolved and treated to produce the permanganate color. The

following readings were obtained when the standard was set at a depth of 20.0 mm in one cell of a Duboscq colorimeter (To avoid differences between cells, both standard and unknown were measured in the same cell):

Standard —19.7, 21.3, 20.0, 21.7, 19.9, 21.6
Unknown—13.5, 14.3, 13.3, 14.4, 13.7, 14.6

What is the per cent manganese in the unknown?

11. The absorption characteristics of two glass filters are given in the table below. Plot the per cent transmittance for the individual filters and for the combination filter on a single graph. What is the wavelength of maximum transmission for the combination, and what is the per cent transmittance at this wavelength?

Wavelength	% Transmittance Blue Filter	% Transmittance Yellow Filter
320 mμ	0.0	0.0
340	6.0	0.0
360	37.0	19.0
380	65.0	32.3
400	78.0	6.2
420	80.0	3.7
440	79.5	18.4
460	72.7	40.7
480	45.8	51.5
500	20.5	58.1
520	4.9	83.3
540	1.2	85.8
560	2.2	86.3
580	0.5	86.8
600	0.1	87.8
620	0.1	87.8
640	0.0	88.0

12. The transmittance of a solution is 28.5% when measured in a 5.00-cm cell. What would be the transmittance in a 1.00-cm cell?

13. The following readings on the Klett fluorimeter were obtained for the determination of aluminum in steel (all samples in 50-ml volumes):

Samples	Reading
4γ Al	95
8γ Al	166
10γ Al	202
Unknown	84.6
Blank	22.3

Plot the net readings against quantity of aluminum on linear paper, determine the amount of aluminum present, and calculate the percentage aluminum in the steel if a 0.0250-gram sample of steel was used.

14. A Raman spectrum plate was run for the mercury source and for CCl_4. The data below shows the millimeter readings (from an arbitrary point) for the Hg and CCl_4 lines. Determine the CCl_4 wavelengths from a plot of the mercury wavelengths, calculate the frequency shifts, and compare with the values given in the text.

Reading, mm	Source	Wavelength, A
111.045	Hg	4046.56
108.945	Hg	4077.81
106.994	CCl_4	
97.124	CCl_4	
95.660	CCl_4	
94.702	CCl_4	
93.107	Hg	4347.50
92.558	Hg	4358.35
69.300	Hg	4916.04

Emission Spectroscopy

1. Three types of rotating sectors are often employed in front of the slit of a spectrograph. (a) Name these three sectors. (b) Show by a diagram the images they will yield on a photographic plate. (c) Explain the value and use of each type in emission spectroscopy.

2. Define the concept of homologous pairs, and describe its use in quantitative spectrographic analysis, in the preparation of both plate calibration curves and analytical working curves.

3. High-purity magnesium samples of the following composition have been submitted to you for analysis, lithium 5–10%, aluminum 2–4%.

(a) Describe in detail how you would establish a method for lithium using a flame photometer. Mention any variables that are likely to cause large errors in the determination and how you would control or compensate for them.

(b) Describe how you would separate the aluminum from the magnesium (a mercury cathode will not work), and then determine it fluorometrically. Briefly discuss what variables should be considered to keep errors at a minimum.

(c) Rods of these same samples are to be used as spectrographic standards for aluminum analysis. Discuss how you would establish a quantitative method using emission spectroscopy. Justify your choice of method of excitation, exposure, type of photographic plate, development of the photographic plate, and measurement of line height or line density used.

4. Outline a method for the detection of small amounts of hafnium in silicate rock. (Hafnium has a low volatility and is not in R.U. powder.)

5. Explain the effect of increasing the focal length of a grating spectrograph on dispersion, resolution, and photographic speed. What steps can be taken to reduce any deficiencies in these properties?

6. In a legal problem, it was necessary to determine whether an ink used on a certain document contained iron. The sample consists of scrapings from a few letters, perhaps 0.1 mg. The analysis must be done with one exposure, no more sample is available. How would you prepare the sample, what excitation would you use, how would you select the wavelength range, and what other spectra would you put on the plate?

7. Using the calibration-curve data given in the text, prepare an emulsion calibration curve. Using this curve, determine the percentage silicon in an aluminum alloy from the data below.

	Deflection	
% Silicon	Al 3060	Si 2514
0.39	76.1	70.7
0.58	73.8	27.5
0.81	72.5	16.9
1.01	80.7	11.5
Unknown	75.1	25.5

8. The following spectral lines are measured on a measuring microscope:

	Microscope
Wavelength, A	Reading, mm
2907.5	10.00
3050.1	46.14
3057.2	47.42
Unknown	28.35

Calculate the wavelength of the unknown line by the Hartmann formula.

Electrometric Methods

1. On the basis of the Nernst equation, explain what factors influence the potential break at the endpoint of a potentiometric redox titration.

2. What is the potential change in the half-cell reaction for the oxidation of divalent cerium to the tetravalent state for a tenfold change in concentration ratio?

3. Explain how a glass electrode may be used as an indicator electrode in one case and a reference electrode in another.

4. Sketch the curves obtained and label coordinates for each of the following: (a) a conductometric titration of a mixture of HCl and HOAc with NaOH, (b) a potentiometric titration of a mixture of U^3 and U^4 to U^6 using potassium dichromate, (c) an amperometric titration of a solution of $AgNO_3$ with a standard NaCl solution, (d) a potentiometric titration of a mixture of KOH and NaOH with HCl. State what electrodes (indicator and reference or other type) you could use for each of the titrations, and briefly compare their characteristics.

5. What indicator and what reference electrodes would you use to follow the titrations listed below: (a) H_3PO_4 with LiOH, (b) NaCNS with $AgNO_3$, (c) H_2O_2 with $KMnO_4$, (d) phenol with Br_2?

6. Distinguish between pH and the acidity as found by titration.

7. What does the buffer system weak-acid–salt have as an advantage over the system weak-base–salt?

8. Formic acid has a dissociation constant of about 10^{-4}. What would be the useful range of formic acid–sodium formate buffers?

9. Name four types of solutions that would give erroneous pH values with the indicator method, and state whether or not the electrometric method would be better.

10. If you had the following solutions for pH measurement, would you use an indicator or glass electrode method: (*a*) antifreeze solution (ethylene glycol and water), (*b*) drinking water, (*c*) strong brines, (*d*) dye baths, (*e*) bleaching solutions (chlorine water), (*f*) grape juice, (*g*) liquid glue, (*h*) gin, (*i*) 3% hydrogen peroxide?

11. The Ilkovic equation, $i = 607\ ncD^{1/2}\ m^{2/3}\ t^{1/6}$, contains many variables. Explain how it is possible for us to use the simple relationship $i = kc$ in our analyses.

12. Given an acid solution containing small amounts of Co^{++} and Fe^{++}. If the half-wave potentials of these two ions are -1.2 and -1.4 volts, draw the polarogram you would obtain as you varied the potential from 0 to -2.0 volts. Indicate on this polarogram the contribution of the residual current, diffusion current, and migration current. Explain, using this polarogram, how you would quantitatively determine the cobalt and iron.

13. Explain why a suitable amperometric titration may be more accurate than a polarographic analysis for the same element.

14. The half-wave potential for $CrO_4^=$ is -0.36 volt and for lead is -0.81 volt. An amperometric titration of lead with chromate may be carried out at a potential of -0.50 volt or -1.00 volt. Sketch roughly the shape of the titration curve in each case.

15. The mobilities of certain cations are related—$H>K>Ag>Na>Li$. Would you use HCl, KCl, NaCl, or LiCl in the conductometric titration of $AgNO_3$? Why? Explain briefly.

16. Calculate the equivalence potential for the reaction of dichromate with iodide in 0.1 N and 1.0 N acid solutions.

17. Fifty milliliters of 0.1 N Fe^{++} is titrated with 0.2 N Ce^{+++}. What is the potential difference in going from 1 drop (0.05 ml) before the equivalence point to 1 drop past the endpoint?

18. The following resistance values were measured in the conductometric titration of 50 ml of standard 0.0100 N NaOH and of 50 ml of an unknown aniline solution with approximately 0.1 N HCl. What is the concentration of the aniline solution in grams per liter?

Ml HCl	R NaOH	R Aniline
0	120	8500
1.0	137	7100
2.0	162	6200
3.0	190	5450
4.0	236	4850
5.0	310	3650
6.0	440	1460
7.0	365	940
8.0	200	680
9.0	140	530
10.0	104	440

19. The following reactions give the corresponding standard electrode potentials:

$$Ag = Ag^+ + e, \qquad E_0 = -0.799$$

$$Ag + I = AgI + e, \qquad E_0 = +0.151$$

Calculate the solubility product of AgI.

Miscellaneous Methods

1. What target elements should be used for the X-ray diffraction patterns of (a) long-chain fatty acids, (b) mixture of iron oxides, (c) lead–tin solder?

2. Compare X-ray and visible-region fluorescence with respect to (a) energy of incident radiation, (b) energy of emitted radiation, (c) physical nature of the process, (d) receptors used for measurement.

3. What are the advantages and disadvantages of monochromatic radiation in X-ray absorption measurements?

4. What is the cause of discrimination in a sector-type mass spectrometer, and how may this be corrected for?

5. What are the advantages of gamma emitters for radioactive-tracer studies?

6. What characteristics would you measure to distinguish between tracer amounts of Cu^{64}, Co^{60}, and Mn^{54}?

7. The radius of curvature for Ne^{20} in a 180° mass spectrometer is 12.0 cm. What would be the linear separation at the collector for Ne^{20} and Ne^{22}?

8. The wavelength of tungsten K_a X rays is 0.211 A. What percentage of this radiation would be transmitted by ⅛ inch of lead whose mass-absorption coefficient is 5.45 cm² per gram? Would the transmittance of copper K_a, whose wavelength is 1.54 A, be greater or less than for the tungsten radiation?

9. The minimum X-ray wavelength that can be produced by a given peak tube voltage may be approximated as

$$\lambda \ min = \frac{12,345}{voltage}$$

Calculate the voltages required to produce the copper K_a ($\lambda = 1.54$) and L_a ($\lambda = 13.3$) X rays. What would be the minimum wavelength for diagnostic X rays at 25-kv peak?

10. What are the relative velocities of an alpha particle and a beta particle having an energy of 4.0 Mev?

11. What is the energy of gamma radiation whose half-thickness is 1 cm of lead? What is the value of the absorption coefficient for this radiation?

12. Calculate the energy in Mev of photons at the extremes of visible region (400 mμ and 750 mμ).

Appendix I

Standard Samples and Unknown Samples for Laboratory Work

The analytical methods described in Chapter 22 are practical procedures used in industrial analysis. In some cases other methods may be more prevalent, but the ones described have been selected to reduce chemical manipulation time and to represent actual uses of the instruments. However, in some instances, commercially available samples are limited or nonexistent, and it is necessary for the instructor to prepare or to standardize samples.

The National Bureau of Standards furnishes standard samples at nominal cost for ferrous and nonferrous alloys, ores, and many other materials. However, it is specifically requested by the Bureau that these samples not be used for student unknowns. Thorn Smith, 1847 North Main Street, Royal Oak, Mich., supplies analyzed samples for student unknowns. These may be used in Experiments 22.1, 3, 14, 17, 18, 21, and 22.

Aluminum alloys for 22.13 are available from Aluminum Company of America Research Laboratories, New Kensington, Pa.

Pure vitamins B_1 and A may be purchased at drug supply houses for standards in 22.5 and 22.11, while commercial tablets or capsules may be used for unknowns. These must be analyzed, as the manufacturer is required only to state the minimum amount per tablet or capsule on the label.

The major problems in the experiments described are obtaining analyzed copper-bearing steels for 22.2 and aluminum-bearing steels for 22.10. Both of these may be solved by furnishing "spiked" steel solutions for student unknowns.

Index